Spectroscopic Properties of Rare Earths

Spectroscopic Properties
of Rare Earths

Brian G. Wybourne
Argonne National Laboratory
Argonne, Illinois

INTERSCIENCE PUBLISHERS
a division of
John Wiley & Sons, Inc.   New York · London · Sydney

CHEMISTRY

QC
454
$W9$

Library of Congress Catalog Card Number: 65–12697

PRINTED IN THE UNITED STATES OF AMERICA

Preface

In 1947, Yost, Russell, and Garner reviewed the basic properties of the rare earths in their book, *The Rare Earth Elements and Their Compounds.* From the time of their review the study of the properties of the rare earths has advanced tremendously. The preparation of isotopes of promethium has resulted in the completion of the first series of rare earth elements, the lanthanides, and isotopes of the entire actinide series have been produced to complete the second rare earth series.

Recent developments, especially in the field of solid-state physics, have placed added emphasis on the need to make quite detailed studies of the electronic properties of the rare earths both in the gaseous and solid states. Progress in the interpretation of these properties has been severely limited by the sheer complexity of the electronic structure of the rare earths. Theoretical techniques that have had great application in the interpretation of the spectroscopic properties of the simpler elements have proved very often to be quite inadequate for the rare earths.

In this book I have endeavored to give a rather detailed discussion of some of the problems associated with the interpretation of the spectroscopic properties of the rare earths. My aim has been to present the major theoretical results in a form that will be usable by experimentalists without requiring a specialized knowledge of the theory of tensor operators or of group theory. Consequently, no attempt has been made to give detailed derivations. The emphasis is on the application of the results of theoretical investigations to the interpretation of experimental data rather than on the theoretical techniques themselves.

I have chosen to discuss five specific topics in the interpretation of the spectroscopic properties of rare earths. The first four topics concern the properties of rare earth atoms and ions in the gaseous state.   Considerable emphasis is given in Chapter 2 to the energy levels of rare earth atoms and ions.   Chapter 3 deals with intensities in rare earth spectra.   This topic has received relatively little attention to date, but I am sure it will assume greater importance in the fields of atomic spectroscopy and astrophysics.   The Zeeman effect in the rare earths is discussed in Chapter 4, with particular emphasis being placed on the role of the different coupling schemes.   A rather extensive treatment of hyperfine structure and isotope shifts is given in Chapter 5.   In these five chapters I have tried to avoid limiting the presentation solely to the rare earths, realizing that many of the methods that have been developed for interpreting their properties have wide application in many other fields.   I hope that much of this material will be of value to those interested in the general fields of atomic spectroscopy, microwave spectroscopy, and solid-state physics.

Chapter 6 has been devoted to several topics in the field of rare earth crystal spectra.   Realizing that many working in this field have unfortunately not been exposed to courses in group theory, I have attempted to give a brief introduction.   The emphasis is on the electronic properties of rare earth ions in crystal fields.   I have not attempted to treat those properties that are associated with cooperative phenomena or lattice interactions; this would have taken me far away from the general approach of the rest of the book.

The emphasis throughout the text is on the phenomenological interpretation of spectroscopic properties rather than interpretation through *ab initio* calculations.   It is my conviction that it will be a considerable time until meaningful *ab initio* calculations will be possible for the rare earths, especially in the solid state.   In the meantime much valuable information can be gained from a phenomenological approach.

I have attempted to supply the reader with a fairly extensive bibliography of references to papers relevant to the general field of this book; nevertheless, I can make no claim to be free from overlooking the work of others. The subject has advanced to the stage where a complete bibliography is no longer feasible.

My interest in the electronic properties of the rare earths was stimulated by my early contact with A. G. McLellan and W. A. Runciman, from whom I gained a great deal.   I am grateful to Mrs. Suzanne Swift, who has patiently typed a somewhat difficult manuscript.   Finally, I owe a debt of gratitude to my wife, Jennifer, and my children, Ruth, Lucy, and Mark who have endured all the trials and tribulations of the author.

BRIAN G. WYBOURNE

November, 1964

Contents

Spectroscopic Properties of Rare Earths

CHAPTER 1

The Rare Earths

1-1 Electronic Structure

The rare earths are characterized by the progressive filling of the $4f$- or $5f$-shells of their electronic configurations. They occur as two groups, each of fourteen elements, known as the lanthanides and the actinides. The lanthanides, which are associated with the filling of the $4f$-shell, commence with the element cerium* ($Z = 58$) and end with the element lutecium ($Z = 71$), whereas the actinides, which are associated with the filling of the $5f$-shell, commence with thorium† ($Z = 90$) and end with the element lawrencium ($Z = 103$).

The neutral lanthanides possess the common feature of a xenon structure of electrons ($1s^2 2s^2 2p^6 3s^2 3p^6 3d^{10} 4s^2 4p^6 4d^{10} 5s^2 5p^6$) with two or three outer electrons ($6s^2$ or $5d6s^2$). Mayer[1]‡ and others[2,3] have shown that the energy and spatial extension of the $4f$-eigenfunction drops suddenly at the commencement of the lanthanides. Although Mayer calculates the binding energy of the $4f$-electron to be -0.95 eV for lanthanum ($Z = 57$), at neodymium ($Z = 60$) it has dropped to -5 eV. In lanthanum the $4f$-eigenfunction is still essentially located outside the

---

* Chemists frequently consider the lanthanides to commence with lanthanum on the basis of the similarities of its chemical properties to those of the other lanthanides, whereas spectroscopists usually omit lanthanum because of the absence of a $4f$-electron in its normal configuration.

† Frequently, actinium is included in the actinides. We shall regard the actinides as commencing with thorium by analogy with the lanthanides, although it should be noted that the normal configuration of the thorium atom does not contain $5f$-electron.

‡ References are listed at the end of the book.

xenon structure, whereas in neodymium the 4*f*-eigenfunction has contracted so that its maximum lies inside the $5s^2 5p^6$ closed shells of the xenon structure. At the commencement of the lanthanide series a deep potential well develops near the nucleus and the 4*f*-electrons are drawn from the outer shells of the atom into the interior. No such effect occurs for the eigenfunctions of *s*-, *p*-, or *d*-electrons. The *lanthanide contraction*, as it is usually called, arises from the imperfect shielding of one 4*f*-electron by another 4*f*-electron.[4] As we proceed through the lanthanide series, the nuclear charge, together with the number of 4*f*-electrons, increases by one at each step. Because of the imperfect screening of the 4*f*-electrons, with each increase the effective nuclear charge increases, causing a reduction of the entire $4f^N$-shell.

Spectroscopic data[5] have been shown to fully support the lanthanide contraction predicted by Mayer. Although in lanthanum the normal configuration ($5d6s^2$) does not contain a 4*f*-electron[6], in cerium a 4*f*-electron appears in the normal configuration ($4f5d6s^2$),[7] indicating the very rapid contraction of the 4*f*-eigenfunction with increasing atomic number.

The lanthanides may be ionized by the successive removal of electrons. The first stage of ionization, with the sole exception of lutecium, results from the removal of a 6*s*-electron. In the second stage of ionization, the removal of a further 6*s*-electron occurs, and at the third stage, all the 6*s*- and 5*d*-electrons, and frequently a 4*f*-electron, have been removed to leave, apart from the xenon structure, a $4f^N$ configuration where $N = 1$ for cerium and increases regularly to $N = 14$ for lutecium. In atomic spectroscopy[8] the stages of ionization are labeled by indicating the neutral (or un-ionized) atom, which gives rise to the *first* spectrum, by the Roman numeral I and by increasing numerals for the successive stages of ionization.*

The normal electronic configurations for the neutral lanthanides and their first three stages of ionization are given in Table 1-1. In designating the electronic configurations of the rare earths we shall follow the usual abbreviation of omitting the closed shells of the noble gas structure and indicate only the f^N-shell and the electrons outside the noble gas structure. Nearly all the normal configurations given in Table 1-1 have been either established or inferred from spectroscopic or magnetic data.

The actinides possess many features analogous to those of the lanthanides. The neutral actinides have the common feature of a radon

---

* Chemists usually assign Roman numerals according to the valence of the element rather than to the order of the spectrum. Thus trivalent cerium is written as Ce(III), whereas in describing the spectra of trivalent cerium spectroscopists write Ce IV.

structure $(1s^2 2s^2 2p^6 3s^2 3p^6 3d^{10} 4s^2 4p^6 4d^{10} 4f^{14} 5s^2 5p^6 5d^{10} 6s^2 6p^6)$ with two or three outer electrons ($7s^2$ or $6d7s^2$). The $5f$-eigenfunction exhibits a behavior very similar to that of the $4f$-eigenfunction of the lanthanides; its contraction, however, does not occur as rapidly, with the result that the normal configuration of thorium $(6d^2 7s^2)$ contains no $5f$-electron[9],* protactinium being the first actinide to contain a $5f$-electron in its normal configuration $(5f^2 6d7s^2)$.[10] After protactinium the $5f$-eigenfunction tends to contract so as to have its maximum inside the $6s^2 6p^6$ closed shells of the radon structure, although with a relatively greater spatial extension and lower binding energy than for the corresponding lanthanides.

TABLE 1-1   Normal configurations of lanthanide atoms and ions

Atomic No.	Lanthanide		I	II	III	IV
58	Ce	Cerium	$4f5d6s^2(^1G_4)$	$4f5d6s(^2G_{7/2})$	$4f^2(^3H_4)$	$4f(^2F_{5/2})$
59	Pr	Praseodymium	$4f^3 6s^2(^4I_{9/2})$	$4f^3 6s(^5I_4)$	$4f^3(^4I_{9/2})$	$4f^2(^3H_4)$
60	Nd	Neodymium	$4f^4 6s^2(^5I_4)$	$4f^4 6s(^6I_{7/2})$	$4f^4(^5I_4)$	$4f^3(^4I_{9/2})$
61	Pm	Promethium	$4f^5 6s^2(^6H_{5/2})$	$4f^5 6s(^7H_2)$	$4f^5(^6H_{5/2})$	$4f^4(^5I_4)$
62	Sm	Samarium	$4f^6 6s^2(^7F_0)$	$4f^6 6s(^8F_{1/2})$	$4f^6(^7F_0)$	$4f^5(^6H_{5/2})$
63	Eu	Europium	$4f^7 6s^2(^8S_{7/2})$	$4f^7 6s(^9S_4)$	$4f^7(^8S_{7/2})$	$4f^6(^7F_0)$
64	Gd	Gadolinium	$4f^7 5d6s^2(^9D_2)$	$4f^7 5d6s(^{10}D_{5/2})$	$4f^7 5d(^9D_2)$	$4f^7(^8S_{7/2})$
65	Tb	Terbium*	$4f^9 6s^2(^6H_{15/2})$	$4f^9 6s(^7H_8)$	$4f^9(^6H_{15/2})$	$4f^8(^7F_6)$
66	Dy	Dysprosium	$4f^{10} 6s^2(^5I_8)$	$4f^{10} 6s(^6I_{17/2})$	$4f^{10}(^5I_8)$	$4f^9(^6H_{15/2})$
67	Ho	Holmium	$4f^{11} 6s^2(^4I_{15/2})$	$4f^{11} 6s(^5I_8)$	$4f^{11}(^4I_{15/2})$	$4f^{10}(^5I_8)$
68	Er	Erbium	$4f^{12} 6s^2(^3H_6)$	$4f^{12} 6s(^4H_{13/2})$	$4f^{12}(^3H_6)$	$4f^{11}(^4I_{15/2})$
69	Tm	Thulium	$4f^{13} 6s^2(^2F_{7/2})$	$4f^{13} 6s(^3F_4)$	$4f^{13}(^2F_{7/2})$	$4f^{12}(^3H_6)$
70	Yb	Ytterbium	$4f^{14} 6s^2(^1S_0)$	$4f^{14} 6s(^2S_{1/2})$	$4f^{14}(^1S_0)$	$4f^{13}(^2F_{7/2})$
71	Lu	Lutecium	$4f^{14} 5d6s^2(^2D_{3/2})$	$4f^{14} 6s^2(^1S_0)$	$4f^{14} 6s^2(^2S_{1/2})$	$4f^{14}(^1S_0)$

* The ground states of Tb I and Tb II have not been unequivocally established.

The normal electronic configurations for the neutral actinides and several stages of ionization are given in Table 1-2. For the actinides, in contrast to the lanthanides, many of the normal configurations have not been firmly established. Configurations that have not been established and which cannot be inferred beyond reasonable doubt are underlined. These configurations must be considered as interpolations which, although most likely to be correct, will require further spectroscopic studies before they may be considered as firmly established.

The contraction of the f-eigenfunction in the rare earths is reflected in many of their properties. As a result of this contraction the f-shell behaves as an *inner* shell. The failure of the f-eigenfunction to penetrate

---

* Note, however, in triply ionized thorium[11] the normal configuration $(5f)$ does contain a $5f$-electron.

TABLE 1-2   Normal configurations of actinide atoms and ions

Atomic No.		Actinide	I	II
90	Th	Thorium	$6d^27s^2(^3F_2)$	$6d7s^2(^2D_{3/2})$
91	Pa	Protactinium	$5f^26d7s^2(^4K_{11/2})$	$5f^27s^2(^3H_4)$
92	U	Uranium	$5f^36d7s^2(^5L_6)$	$5f^37s^2(^4I_{9/2})$
93	Np	Neptunium	$5f^46d7s^2(^6L_{11/2})$	$5f^47s^2(^5I_4)$
94	Pu	Plutonium	$5f^67s^2(^7F_0)$	$5f^67s^2(^8F_{1/2})$
95	Am	Americium	$5f^77s^2(^8S_{7/2})$	$5f^77s^2(^9S_4)$
96	Cm	Curium	$5f^76d7s^2(^9D_2)$	$5f^76d7s(^{10}D_{5/2})$
97	Bk	Berkelium	$5f^86d7s^2(^8G_{15/2})$	$5f^86d7s(^9G_8)$
98	Cf	Californium	$5f^{10}7s^2(^5I_8)$	$5f^{10}7s(^6I_{17/2})$
99	E	Einsteinium	$5f^{11}7s^2(^4I_{15/2})$	$5f^{11}7s(^5I_8)$
100	Fm	Fermium	$5f^{12}7s^2(^3H_6)$	$5f^{12}7s(^4H_{13/2})$
101	Mv	Mendelevium	$5f^{13}7s^2(^2F_{7/2})$	$5f^{13}7s(^3F_4)$
102	No	Nobelium	$5f^{14}7s^2(^1S_0)$	$5f^{14}7s(^2S_{1/2})$
103	Lw	Lawrencium	$5f^{14}6d7s^2(^2D_{3/2})$	$5f^{14}7s^2(^1S_0)$

appreciably into the environment, together with the shielding of the f-electrons produced by the s^2p^6 closed shells, usually prevents any strong interaction of the f-electrons with their environment. Consequently, the surroundings of the lanthanide atoms or ions are of relatively little chemical significance, which is in marked contrast to the transition elements. There is little tendency for the 4f-electrons to participate in chemical bond formation.

Because of the greater spatial extension of the 5f-eigenfunction in the actinides (particularly for the earlier members of the series), the interaction of the 5f-electrons with the environment is greater than that for the corresponding lanthanides. The increased spatial extension of the 5f-eigenfunction has been made evident in electron spin resonance experiments. The electron spin resonance of UF_3 in a CaF_2 lattice shows hyperfine structure attributable to the interaction of the fluorine nuclei with the 5f-electrons of the U^{3+} ions.[12] This effect indicates that the 5f-orbitals overlap with those of the fluorine ions. No such effect is observed when the corresponding lanthanide ion, Nd^{3+}, is substituted into a CaF_2 lattice. In the early members of the actinide series some bond hybridization involving the overlapping of the 5f-orbitals with those of the bonding atoms is possible.[13] At the commencement of the series the energies of the 5f-, 6d-, 7s-, and 7p-orbitals are comparable, and there will be a spatial overlapping of these orbitals, with the result that bond hybridization may involve any or all of them. This overlapping makes it sometimes impossible to say which orbitals are being utilized in bonding

III	IV	V
$6d^2(^3F_2)$	$5f(^2F_{5/2})$	
$5f^26d(^4K_{11/2})$	$5f^2(^3H_4)$	$5f(^2F_{5/2})$
$5f^4(^5I_4)$	$5f^3(^4I_{9/2})$	$5f^2(^3H_4)$
$5f^5(^6H_{5/2})$	$5f^4(^5I_4)$	$5f^3(^4I_{9/2})$
$5f^6(^7F_0)$	$5f^5(^6H_{5/2}$	$5f^4(^5I_4)$
$5f^7(^8S_{7/2})$	$5f^6(^7F_0)$	$5f^5(^6H_{5/2})$
$5f^76d(^9D_2)$	$5f^7(^8S_{7/2})$	$5f^6(^7F_0)$
$5f^86d(^8G_{15/2})$	$5f^8(^7F_6)$	$5f^7(^8S_{7/2})$
$5f^{10}(^5I_8)$	$5f^9(^6H_{15/2})$	$5f^8(^7F_6)$
$5f^{11}(^4I_{15/2})$	$5f^{10}(^5I_8)$	$5f^9(^6H_{15/2})$
$5f^{12}(^3H_6)$	$5f^{11}(^4I_{15/2})$	$5f^{10}(^5I_8)$
$5f^{13}(^2F_{7/2})$	$5f^{12}(^3H_6)$	$5f^{11}(^4I_{15/2})$
$5f^{14}(^1S_0)$	$5f^{13}(^2F_{7/2})$	$5f^{12}(^3H_6)$
$5f^{14}7s(^2S_{1/2})$	$5f^{14}(^1S_0)$	$5f^{13}(^2F_{7/2})$

or whether the bonding is ionic or covalent. Considerations of bonding mechanisms become extremely important in discussions of the spectroscopic properties of the actinide complexes.[14-18]

The contraction of the f-eigenfunction is manifested in the regular *decrease* in the size of the lanthanide and actinide ions with *increasing* atomic number. There is also a regular decrease in the ionic radii with increasing ionization.

As a result of their lower binding energy, $5f$-electrons may be more readily removed from the actinides by oxidation than the $4f$-electrons of the corresponding lanthanides. This is reflected in the multiplicity of oxidation states displayed by many of the actinides in contrast to the very strong dominance of the $+3$ oxidation state in the lanthanides. Oxidation states other than $+3$ are known for several of the lanthanides, although these are always less stable than the $+3$ state.[19,20] The existence of the oxidation states of $+2$ and $+4$ can be partially correlated with the added stability associated with an empty, half-filled, or filled f-shell.[21] Thus cerium and terbium occur in the $+4$ state having the stable configurations $4f^0$ and $4f^7$ respectively, and europium and ytterbium occur in the $+2$ state with the stable configurations. The added stability of these configurations does not, however, explain the failure of americium to form divalent salts or the occurrence of the $+2$ state in samarium under some conditions. The energy of hydration in solution, or the energy of interaction of the ions with the lattice in solids, must also be considered. The importance of environmental effects in determining the stability of unusual oxidation states cannot be overemphasized; and the relatively recent successful preparation of all the remaining stable lanthanides in the divalent state under well-defined environmental conditions indicates the need for a greater study of the stabilization of rare earths in unusual oxidation states.[22-24]

Although the +3 oxidation state dominates the entire lanthanide series, it does not become the dominant state in the actinides until after uranium, whereupon the +3 state tends to become increasingly more stable. Curium, in marked contrast to its lanthanide analogue, gadolinium, is capable of forming compounds in the +4 state, but protactinium, unlike praseodymium, does not normally occur in the trivalent state in its compounds. The actinides are also radically different from the lanthanides in their ability to form stable compounds in quite high oxidation states. For example, the actinides from uranium through americium are all capable of occurring in the +6 oxidation state.

Although we have tended to emphasize the differences in the electronic structures of the lanthanides and actinides, and their consequences in determining their respective properties, the profound similarities of these two series of elements cannot be overlooked. Both series exhibit all the characteristic properties of an inner f-shell. In the triply ionized state the normal electronic configuration is the same for every actinide and its corresponding lanthanide analogue. In fact, the electronic structures of the two series are so similar that the theoretical procedures developed for understanding the electronic properties of the lanthanides may be transferred to the actinides almost without modification.

1-2   Rare Earth Spectra and Electronic Properties

Considerable information on the electronic structure of rare earth atoms and ions may be gained from studying their spectroscopic properties. The study of atomic beam resonances[25,26] has led to extremely precise measurements of the electronic properties of the ground states of rare earth atoms, and paramagnetic resonance techniques[27,28] have provided information on the ground states of rare earth ions in solids. The methods of optical spectroscopy give information about the energy-level structure of the normal configuration and many of the excited configurations.[29,30]*

A detailed analysis of the results of spectroscopic measurements can frequently be made only with considerable assistance from theoretical considerations of the properties of the configurations being studied. From a determination of the electronic structure of the gaseous rare earth

---

* Reference 29 contains an extensive review of the experimental data up to 1952.

atoms or ions, it should then be possible to consider the modifications that must be made to the theory in order to understand the properties of the atoms or ions in crystals. In the concluding chapter we shall consider the effects of crystal fields on the energy levels of the rare earth ions. One could undoubtedly start then to understand the fundamentals of the specific heats and magnetic susceptibilities of rare earth salts. In all the cases treated in this text we consider the interactions that affect a single rare earth atom or ion. Many times such a simple approach as this is not possible and considerable extensions to the theory will be required to treat phenomena in which the cooperative action of many ions or exchange interactions between ions must be considered.

CHAPTER 2

Energy Levels of Rare Earth Atoms and Ions

2-1 Principal Electronic Configurations

In this chapter we shall be primarily concerned with the energy-level structures of the principal electronic configurations encountered in the gaseous spectra of rare earth atoms and ions. In the neutral rare earth atoms there are two or three electrons outside the f^N core of the normal configuration, and hence in the *first* spectra of the rare earths very complex configurations can be expected. Thus in Pr I, in addition to the normal configuration $4f^36s^2$, the configurations $4f^36s6p$, $4f^35d6s$, and $4f^46s$ are all of spectroscopic interest.[29]   In Gd I, where the normal configuration is $4f^75d6s^2$, configurations of even greater complexity (for example, $4f^75d^26s$ and $4f^75d6s6p$) will be encountered.[31]

The spectra of the ionized rare earths normally involve substantially simpler configurations, especially when the atom has been ionized sufficiently to leave a normal configuration with not more than one nonequivalent electron outside the f^N core as is the case in all the doubly and triply ionized rare earths.   Thus in Pr III, where the normal configuration is $4f^3$, the configurations $4f^26s$, $4f^26p$, and $4f^25d$ are of spectroscopic importance.[32]

In general, we shall limit our treatment to configurations having not more than two electrons outside the f^N core. The results given can usually be extended to configurations of greater complexity without much difficulty, although usually the calculations become prohibitively large except when s-electrons are involved.   To study the energy-level structure of electron configurations we shall first examine the properties of the electrostatic interactions that separate the different terms and then the spin-orbit interactions which give rise to the fine structure of the terms.

2-2   The Central Field Approximation

For an N-electron atom with a nuclear charge Ze the nonrelativistic Hamiltonian may be written as[33,34]

$$H = -\frac{\hbar^2}{2m}\sum_{i=1}^{N}\nabla_i^2 - \sum_{i=1}^{N}\frac{Ze^2}{r_i} + \sum_{i<j}^{N}\frac{e^2}{r_{ij}} \tag{2-1}$$

if the nuclear mass is assumed to be infinite. The first term in the Hamiltonian is the sum of the kinetic energies of all the electrons, the second is the potential energy of all the electrons in the field of the nucleus and the last term is the repulsive Coulomb potential energy of the inter-actions between pairs of electrons. Exact solutions of Schrödinger's equation are not possible for systems with more than one electron. The most common approximation used for solving Schrödinger's equation for complex atoms is the *central field approximation*.[33-36] In this approximation each electron is assumed to move *independently* in the field of the nucleus and a central field made up of the *spherically* averaged potential fields of each of the other electrons. Hence each electron may be said to move in a *spherically symmetric* potential $-U(r_i)/e$. The Hamiltonian H_{cf} for the central field then becomes

$$H_{cf} = \sum_{i=1}^{N}\left[\frac{-\hbar^2}{2m}\nabla_i^2 + U(r_i)\right]. \tag{2-2}$$

The difference $H - H_{cf}$ may now be treated as a perturbation potential

$$H - H_{cf} = V = \sum_{i=1}^{N}\left[-\frac{Ze^2}{r_i} - U(r_i)\right] + \sum_{i<j}^{N}\frac{e^2}{r_{ij}}. \tag{2-3}$$

Schrödinger's equation for the central field,

$$\sum_{i=1}^{N}\left[\frac{-\hbar^2}{2m}\nabla_i^2 + U(r_i)\right]\Psi = E_{cf}\Psi, \tag{2-4}$$

can be separated by choosing a solution such that

$$\Psi = \sum_{i=1}^{N}\varphi_i(a^i) \quad\text{and}\quad E_{cf} = \sum_{i=1}^{N}E_i. \tag{2-5}$$

Each electron moving in the central field $U(r_i)$ will then satisfy equations of the type

$$\left[\frac{-\hbar^2}{2m}\nabla^2 + U(r)\right]\varphi(a^i) = E(a^i)\varphi(a^i), \tag{2-6}$$

where (a^i) represents a set of quantum numbers (nlm_l) which specify the state of motion of the single electron in the central field. Equation 2-6 differs from Schrödinger's equation for the hydrogen atom only in the replacement of the Coulomb potential energy $-e^2/r$ by the central field potential energy function $U(r)$. A further separation of the variables is made possible by introducing polar coordinates (θ, ϕ, r) and separating the one-electron eigenfunctions into their *radial* and *angular* parts. The resulting normalized solutions for the *bound* states can then be written as

$$\varphi(a^i) = r^{-1}R_{nl}(r)Y_{lm_l}(\theta, \phi). \tag{2-7}$$

The radial function $R_{nl}(r)$ depends on the central field potential energy function $U(r)$, whereas the spherical harmonics Y_{lm_l} are defined by[33]

$$Y_{lm_l}(\theta, \phi) = (-1)^m \left[\frac{(2l + 1)(l - |m|)!}{4\pi(l + |m|)!}\right]^{1/2} P_l^m (\cos \theta)\, e^{im\phi} \tag{2-8}$$

and

$$P_l^m(w) = \frac{(1 - w^2)^{m/2}}{2^l\, l!} \frac{d^{m+l}}{dw^{m+l}} (w^2 - 1)^l. \tag{2-9}$$

The angular part of the one-electron eigenfunction is identical to that of the hydrogenic eigenfunction and is capable of *exact* numerical evaluation, which is in contrast to the radial part which can be evaluated only approximately and is dependent on the form of the central field.

Thus far the *spin* variables in the one-electron eigenfunction have not been considered. The one-electron quantum number m_s may take on the values $\pm\frac{1}{2}$, corresponding to the two possible spin orientations along the z-axis. By introducing a spin coordinate σ, which may equal $\pm\frac{1}{2}$, and a spin function $\delta(m_s, \sigma)$ satisfying the orthonormality relation

$$\sum_\sigma \delta(m_s, \sigma)\delta(m_s', \sigma) = \delta(m_s, m_s'),$$

the one-electron eigenfunctions defined in Eq. 2-7 become

$$\varphi(nlm_lm_s) = \delta(m_s, \sigma)r^{-1} R_{nl}(r)Y_{lm_l}(\theta, \phi). \tag{2-10}$$

The solutions of Eq. 2-4, with the inclusion of spin, may now be written as

$$\Psi = \sum_{i=1}^{N} \varphi(\alpha^i), \tag{2-11}$$

where α^i represents the quantum numbers (nlm_lm_s) of the ith electron. Clearly, this solution of Eq. 2-4 is not unique since other solutions may be obtained by permutations of the coordinates of any of the N-electrons. To satisfy the Pauli exclusion principle we must choose a linear combination of these solutions such that the resulting wave functions are always *antisymmetric* with respect to the simultaneous permutation of the *spin* and *spatial* coordinates of any pair of electrons. The resulting anti-symmetrical solution of the central field wave equation may then be written as

$$\Psi = \frac{1}{\sqrt{N!}} \sum_p^N (-1)^p P \varphi_1(\alpha^1) \varphi_2(\alpha^2) \dots \varphi_N(\alpha^N), \qquad (2\text{-}12)$$

where P represents a permutation of the electrons and p is the parity of the permutation with the summation extending over all the permutations of the N-electron coordinates. This equation may be equivalently written in determinantal form as

$$\Psi = \frac{1}{\sqrt{N!}} \begin{vmatrix} \varphi_1(\alpha^1) & \varphi_2(\alpha^1) & \dots & \varphi_N(\alpha^1) \\ \varphi_1(\alpha^2) & \varphi_2(\alpha^2) & \dots & \varphi_N(\alpha^2) \\ \cdot & \cdot & \cdot & \cdot \\ \varphi_1(\alpha^N) & \varphi_2(\alpha^N) & \dots & \varphi_N(\alpha^N) \end{vmatrix}. \qquad (2\text{-}13)$$

The eigenvalues of Schrödinger's equation for the central field, Eq. 2-4, each correspond to the energy of a particular electronic configuration which is defined in terms of the quantum numbers $(n_1 l_1)(n_2 l_2) \dots (n_N l_N)$.

Having solved the central field problem and obtained a set of properly antisymmetrized zero-order wave functions, we may then use these wave functions to calculate the matrix elements of additional perturbations in which we may be interested, always obtaining our results in terms of radial integrals times their angular parts. The angular parts may be calculated exactly by group-theoretical and tensorial methods and the radial integrals evaluated by solution of the radial wave equation or left as parameters to be determined experimentally.

2-3 Classification of States

The calculation of the matrix elements of the perturbation Hamiltonian is facilitated by defining a complete set of basis states in some well-defined coupling scheme. Normally the approximation is made to consider only the set of states of the particular configuration under study. This amounts to neglecting the interactions between different configurations and may not always be a valid approximation. The particular coupling scheme used is usually chosen to be as near as possible to the physical coupling of the configuration studied. Sometimes none of the well-defined coupling schemes will even closely approximate to the physical coupling; however, the matrix elements of the perturbation Hamiltonian may still be calculated in terms of the basis states of some well-defined coupling scheme and a *transformation* made to the actual coupling scheme.

A coupling scheme frequently used is that of Russell-Saunders (LS coupling). In this coupling scheme the orbital angular momenta of the electrons are vectorially coupled to give a resultant total orbital angular momentum L and the spins are coupled to give a total spin S. These resultant angular momenta are then coupled to give a total angular momentum J. In this scheme the numbers L and S are said to define a *term* of the configuration. In some configurations there will be more than one term having the same L and S values, and additional quantum numbers τ must be introduced to distinguish these terms.* A particular basis *state* of a configuration will be labeled by specifying its $\tau SLJM$ quantum numbers and will be written as $\Psi(\tau SLJM)$. The matrix elements will usually be written in the form $(\tau SLJM \,|H_p|\, \tau'S'L'J'M')$, where H_p is the term in the perturbation Hamiltonian under study.

Difficulties arise when a unique labeling scheme for the states of the f^N configurations is desired. Frequently, several states having the same LS quantum numbers occur and additional quantum numbers must be found to permit a separation of these recurring states.

Racah[37,38] has shown how the states of any f^N configuration may be given a systematic classification using group theory. His method endeavors to classify the complete set of states of the f^N configuration by their properties under certain groups of transformations. The properties of these groups are then used to simplify the calculation of the matrix elements of the tensor operators that correspond to the interactions being studied. We can describe the way a particular state transforms under the operations of a group by using the irreducible representations of the group as labels. These irreducible representations then play the role of quantum numbers.†

The classification of the states of the f^N configuration commences by enumerating the irreducible representations of the group U_7 of all the unitary transformations in the seven-dimensional space spanned by the orbital states of a single f-electron ($m_l = -3, \ldots 0 \ldots +3$). These representations may be characterized by the partition of N into seven integral parts, which at the same time characterize some of the irreducible representations of the permutation group of order $N!$. The classification of the states obtained in this way is entirely equivalent to the usual classification obtained by specifying the total spin S of the state. If U_7 is restricted to its subgroup R_3, the three-dimensional rotational group,

---

* We note here that in determining the possible LS terms of a configuration we need only consider the couplings of those electrons not in closed shells since the angular momenta of the electrons in the closed shells will always sum to zero.[33]

† A detailed account of the group-theoretical method and its application to the f^N configuration has been given by Judd.[39]

the representations corresponding to the partition N break down into the irreducible representations D_L of R_3.   The irreducible representations D_L serve to classify the states according to the total orbital quantum number L.   The classification obtained at this stage is equivalent to the usual enumeration of the Russell-Saunders states; as yet we do not know how many times a given LS term appears in the configuration nor do we know how to separate the different terms possessing identical LS labels.

The states may be further classified according to the irreducible representations of the seven-dimensional rotational group R_7.   The irreducible representations of R_7 are characterized by the partition of N into three integers $W \equiv (w_1, w_2, w_3)$ such that $2 \geq w_1 \geq w_2 \geq w_3 \geq 0$. When R_7 is restricted to its subgroup G_2, the representations of R_7 break down into the irreducible representations of G_2, which can be characterized by the partition of N into two integers $U \equiv (u_1, u_2)$ such that $2 \geq u_1 \geq u_2 \geq 0$.   Using these additional quantum numbers as labels, we may obtain a complete separation of all the states of the f^N configurations with the exception of certain of those states with $U \equiv (31)$ and $U \equiv (40)$ where some doubly occurring LS states remain unseparated.*   These states may be separated in an arbitrary manner and an additional label τ introduced to distinguish these pairs of states.   Thus the states of the f^N configuration may be completely specified by writing the basis states as

$$| f^N \tau WUSL \rangle. \tag{2-14}$$

According to the Pauli equivalence theorem the classification of the states of the f^{14-N} configuration will be identical with those of the f^N configuration, and hence we need only enumerate the states for $N \leq 7$.

2-4   The Seniority Number

It is sometimes convenient to introduce another quantum number, the *seniority number*, v to classify the states,[37,40,41]   Here the states are classified according to the eigenvalues of the seniority operator

$$\mathbf{Q} = \sum_{i<j}^{N} \mathbf{q}_{ij}, \tag{2-15}$$

where $\mathbf{q}_{ij}$ is a scalar operator defined by the relation

$$(l^2 LM | \mathbf{q}_{ij} | l^2 LM) = (2l + 1)\delta(L, 0). \tag{2-16}$$

It may be shown that for every term of the l^N configuration with a non-vanishing $\mathbf{Q}$ a state of the same symmetry type occurs in l^{N-2}, and we

---

* A unique classification of *all* the states of f^N could be obtained using the four-dimensional rotational group R_4; however, this classification scheme is inferior for calculating matrix elements.

assign to each state a seniority number according to the value of N for which the term first appeared. The eigenvalues of the seniority operator Q depend only on N and v and are given by

$$Q(N, v) = \frac{(N - v)(4l + 4 - N - v)}{4}.$$ (2-17)

The seniority number is essentially equivalent to W as far as labeling the states. If we define a and b so that

$$w_1 = \cdots = w_a = 2, \qquad w_{a+1} = \cdots = w_{a+b} = 1, \qquad w_{a+b+1} = 0,$$

then v and W are related by

$$a = \frac{v}{2} - S, \qquad b = \min(2S, 2l + 1 - v).$$

In this notation the basis states of the f^N configuration will be written as $|f^N \tau v USL)$. The $\tau v WUSL$ classification of all the states of f^N for $N \leq 7$ is given in Table 2-1.

Having given a systematic classification of the states of the f^N configuration, it is a simple task to label the states formed by adding one or more nonequivalent electrons to the f^N core. Thus the states of the $f^N l$ configuration will be completely specified by writing them as

$$|f^N(\tau WUS_1 L_1)l; SL)$$ (2-18)

and those of the $f^N ll'$ configuration as

$$|f^N(\tau WUS_1 L_1), (ll')S_2 L_2; SL).$$ (2-19)

In writing out the states of the f^N core, we shall frequently write $f^N(\tau S_1 L_1)$ rather than indicating the complete set of group labels.

2-5 Coefficients of Fractional Parentage

In making calculations of the electronic properties of systems containing three or more *equivalent* electrons, frequent use is made of the concept of *fractional parentage*,[37-41] whereby any state $\Psi(l^N \tau SL)$ may be expanded in terms of products of the states of the first $(N - 1)$ electrons with those of the Nth electron as follows:

$$\Psi(l^N \tau SL) = \sum_{\bar{\tau}\bar{S}\bar{L}} \phi(l^{N-1}(\bar{\tau}\bar{S}\bar{L})l; SL) \cdot (l^{N-1}(\bar{\tau}\bar{S}\bar{L})l; SL|\}l^N \tau SL),$$

(2-20)

where the summation extends over all states $\bar{\psi}(l^{N-1}(\bar{\tau}\bar{S}\bar{L}))$ of the complete set for the l^{N-1} configuration. The barred states $\bar{\tau}\bar{S}\bar{L}$ of the l^{N-1}

TABLE 2-1   Classification of the states of the f^N configurations

N	v	W	U	SL
1	1	(100)	(10)	^2F
2	2	(110)	(10)	^3F
			(11)	^3PH
	2	(200)	(20)	^1DGI
	0	(000)	(00)	^1S
3	3	(111)	(00)	^4S
			(10)	^4F
			(20)	^4DGI
	3	(210)	(11)	^2PH
			(20)	^2DGI
			(21)	^2DFGHKL
	1	(100)	(10)	^2F
4	4	(111)	(00)	^5S
			(10)	^5F
			(20)	^5DGI
	4	(211)	(10)	^3F
			(11)	^3PH
			(20)	^3DGI
			(21)	^3DFGHKL
			(30)	$^3PFGHIKM$
	2	(110)	(10)	^3F
			(11)	^3PH
	4	(220)	(20)	^1DGI
			(21)	^1DFGHKL
			(22)	$^1SDGHILN$
	2	(200)	(20)	^1DGI
	0	(000)	(00)	^1S
5	5	(110)	(10)	^6F
			(11)	^6PH
	5	(211)	(10)	^4F
			(11)	^4PH
			(20)	^4DGI
			(21)	^4DFGHKL
			(30)	$^4PFGHIKM$
	3	(111)	(00)	^4S
			(10)	^4F
			(20)	^4DGI
	5	(221)	(10)	^2F
			(11)	^2PH
			(20)	^2DGI
			(21)	^2DFGHKL
			(30)	$^2PFGHIKM$
			(31)	$^2PDFFGHHIIKKLMNO$
	3	(210)	(11)	^2PH
			(20)	^2DGI
			(21)	^2DFGHKL
	1	(100)	(10)	^2F
6	6	(100)	(10)	^7F
	6	(210)	(11)	^5PH
			(20)	^5DGI
			(21)	^5DFGHKL
	4	(111)	(00)	^5S
			(10)	^5F
			(20)	^5DGI

N	v	W	U	SL
	6	(221)	(10)	^3F
			(11)	^3PH
			(20)	^3DGI
			(21)	^3DFGHKL
			(30)	$^3PFGHIKM$
			(31)	$^3PDFFGHHIIKKLMNO$
	4	(211)	(10)	^3F
			(11)	^3PH
			(20)	^3DGI
			(21)	^3DFGHKL
			(30)	$^3PFGHIKM$
	2	(110)	(10)	^3F
			(11)	^3PH
	6	(222)	(00)	^1S
			(10)	^1F
			(20)	^1DGI
			(30)	$^1PFGHIKM$
			(40)	$^1SDFGGHIIKLLMNQ$
	4	(220)	(20)	^1DGI
			(21)	^1DFGHKL
			(22)	$^1SDGHILN$
	2	(200)	(20)	^1DGI
	0	(000)	(00)	^1S
7	7	(000)	(00)	^8S
	7	(200)	(20)	^6DGI
	5	(110)	(10)	^6F
			(11)	^6PH
	7	(220)	(20)	^4DGI
			(21)	^4DFGHKL
			(22)	$^4SDGHILN$
	5	(211)	(10)	^4F
			(11)	^4PH
			(20)	^4DGI
			(21)	^4DFGHKL
			(30)	$^4PFGHIKM$
	3	(111)	(00)	^4S
			(10)	^4F
			(20)	^4DGI
	7	(222)	(00)	^2S
			(10)	^2F
			(20)	^2DGI
			(30)	$^2PFGHIKM$
			(40)	$^2SDFGGHIIKLLMNQ$
	5	(221)	(10)	^2F
			(11)	^2PH
			(20)	^2DGI
			(21)	^2DFGHKL
			(30)	$^2PFGHIKM$
			(31)	$^2PDFFGHHIIKKLMNO$
	3	(210)	(11)	^2PH
			(20)	^2DGI
			(21)	^2DFGHKL
	1	(100)	(10)	^2F

configuration are known as the *parents* of the state τSL of the l^N configuration, and the coefficients of the expansion, $(l^{N-1}(\bar\tau \overline{SL})l; SL|\}l^N\tau SL)$, commonly abbreviated to $(\bar\psi|\}\psi)$, are known as the *coefficients of fractional parentage* (c.f.p). The c.f.p. describe how the state ψ is built up from its possible parents $\bar\psi$ and can be looked upon as defining the state. They are chosen to yield the properly antisymmetrized eigenfunctions of the l^N configuration and are zero for all the forbidden states of the configuration. They are normalized and satisfy the relationship

$$\sum_{\bar\tau\overline{SL}} (l^N\tau SL\{|l^{N-1}(\bar\tau\overline{SL})l; SL)(l^{N-1}(\bar\tau\overline{SL})l; SL|\}l^N\tau'SL) = \delta(\tau, \tau').$$

Judd[39] has discussed the calculation of c.f.p in considerable detail.

The c.f.p. for the f^N configuration may be factorized into three parts,[37-39] namely,

$$(f^N\tau vWUSL\{|f^{N-1}(\bar\tau\bar v\overline{WUSL})f; SL) = (WU|\overline{WU} + f)(U\tau L|\overline{U}\bar\tau\overline{L} + f)$$
$$\times (f^NvSL\{|f^{N-1}\bar v\overline{SL} + f).$$
$$(2\text{-}21)$$

The magnitude of the last factor may be calculated from Eqs. 52a and 52b of Racah[37] and the phase determined from his Eq. 56. Racah[37] has given tables of the first two factors from which the c.f.p. for all the states of the f^2 to f^4 configurations may be evaluated, as well as those for the two highest multiplicities of f^5 to f^7.* Nielson and Koster[43] have calculated and tabulated the c.f.p. for all the states of the f^N configurations ($N \le 7$) giving the coefficients in their unfactorized form. Thus the calculation of the c.f.p. may be considered complete and the reader need never calculate them.

Tables of c.f.p. are usually given only up to the half-filled shell (for example, f^7). The c.f.p. for the states of the more than half-filled shell may be found from the tables by using the relationship[37]

$$(l^{4l+2-N}\tau SL\{|l^{4l+1-N}(\bar\tau\overline{SL})l; SL) = (-1)^{S+L+S+L-l-s}$$
$$\times \left[\frac{(N+1)(2\bar S+1)(2\bar L+1)}{(4l+2-N)(2S+1)(2L+1)}\right]^{1/2} (l^{N+1}\bar\tau\overline{SL}\{|l^N(\tau SL)l; SL). \quad (2\text{-}22)$$

For the states of the l^{2l+2} configuration (for example, f^8) this equation must be preceded by a factor $(-1)^{(\bar v-1)/2}$, where v is the parental seniority

---

* A similar tabulation is contained in Reference 39. The author[42] has given an extension to these tables; however, it should be noted that, although these tables are consistent among themselves, they do not use the same separation for the doubly occurring states with $U \equiv (31)$ as was used by Racah[37] in computing his tables of electrostatic interaction coefficients.

of the state.   In practice, we rarely need to make use of Eq. 2-22 because we can usually obtain the matrix elements of the l^{4l+2-N} configuration from those calculated for the l^N configuration.

2-6 Matrix Elements of Operators

Calculation of the energy levels of an atom or ion normally proceeds by first figuring the matrix elements of the electrostatic perturbation potential V defined in Eq. 2-3 as

$$V = \sum_{i=1}^{N} \left[-\frac{Ze^2}{r_i} - U(r_i) \right] + \sum_{i<j}^{N} \frac{e^2}{r_{ij}}. \qquad (2\text{-}3)$$

The first term is purely radial and contributes energy shifts that are the same for all the levels belonging to a given configuration without affecting the energy-level structure of the configuration.   The repulsive Coulomb interaction of the electrons, $\sum_{i<j} \frac{e^2}{r_{ij}}$, will be different for different states of the same configuration.   The summations in Eq. 2-3 are over the coordinates of all the electrons.   However, we may show[33-36] that the term energies of a configuration which contains closed shells are the same, apart from a constant energy shift of all the terms, as those of the configuration in which the closed shells have been omitted.   Thus in considering the energy-level structure of a configuration, we shall restrict the summation in Eq. 2-3 to those electrons in incomplete shells.   Hence in calculating the energy-level structure of a configuration, produced by the repulsive Coulomb interaction, we must calculate matrix elements of the type

$$\left(\tau SLJM \left| \sum_{i<j} \frac{e^2}{r_{ij}} \right| \tau'S'L'J'M' \right). \qquad (2\text{-}23)$$

Since the electrostatic Hamiltonian commutes with the angular momentum operators corresponding to $\mathbf{L}^2$, $\mathbf{S}^2$, $\mathbf{J}$, and $\mathbf{M}$, the matrix elements will be diagonal in L and S (although not in τ) and independent of J and M. Calculation of the matrix elements of Eq. 2-23 commences by first expanding the interaction between each pair of electrons in Legendre polynomials of the cosine of the angle w_{ij} between the vectors from the nucleus to the two electrons as follows:[33]

$$\frac{e^2}{r_{ij}} = e^2 \sum_{k} \frac{r_<^k}{r_>^{k+1}} P_k(\cos w_{ij}), \qquad (2\text{-}24)$$

where $r_<$ indicates the distance from the nucleus (the point of origin) to the nearer electron and $r_>$ the distance from the nucleus to the further away electron.   Using the spherical harmonic addition theorem,[33] we may write

$$P_k(\cos w_{ij}) = \frac{4\pi}{2k+1} \sum_q Y_{kq}^*(\theta_i, \phi_i)\, Y_{kq}(\theta_j, \phi_j)$$

$$= \sum_q (-1)^q (\mathbf{C}_{-q}^{(k)})_i (\mathbf{C}_q^{(k)})_j$$

$$= (\mathbf{C}_i^{(k)} \cdot \mathbf{C}_j^{(k)}), \tag{2-25}$$

where the $\mathbf{C}_q^{(k)}$ are defined by

$$\mathbf{C}_q^{(k)} = \left(\frac{4\pi}{2k+1}\right)^{1/2} Y_{kq}. \tag{2-26}$$

Thus Eq. 2-23 becomes

$$\sum_k e^2 \left(\tau SL \left| \sum_{i<j} \frac{r_<^k}{r_>^{k+1}} (\mathbf{C}_i^{(k)} \cdot \mathbf{C}_j^{(k)}) \right| \tau' SL \right). \tag{2-27}$$

The further evaluation of the matrix elements can be made either by use of the determinantal methods of Slater,[35] or the tensor operator methods of Racah.[40]   The use of determinantal methods have been discussed in detail by several writers.[33-35,39]   In this method each state $|\tau SLJM\rangle$ is expanded as a linear combination of the determinantal product states appearing in Eq. 2-13.   The linear combination is chosen to diagonalize the angular momentum operators corresponding to L^2, S^2, M_L, and M_S.   This requirement, together with orthogonality considerations, results in correctly antisymmetrized $\tau SLJM$ eigenfunctions.   The matrix elements of the operators corresponding to the interactions being considered are then evaluated in the nlm_lm_s scheme of the one-electron eigenfunctions of Eq. 2-10 in the manner described by Condon and Shortley.[33]   In practice, this method is unreasonably cumbersome for calculating the electronic properties of configurations of the complexity encountered in rare earth spectra.   Besides, these methods do not lead to general formulas for calculating the matrix elements of the many types of interactions we shall be considering.

To overcome the shortcomings of the determinantal method Racah[37,40,41] has developed the powerful tensor operator methods of calculating matrix elements which are a continuation of the original treatment of Condon and Shortley.[33]   It is to these methods we must now turn.   Judd[39] has made an extensive review of the application of these methods to f^N configurations and hence we shall consider only the main results of the theory.*

---

* The reader will also find the books of Edmonds,[44] and Fano and Racah[45] of considerable interest.

An irreducible tensor operator of rank k is defined by Racah[40] as an operator $\mathbf{T}^{(k)}$ whose $2k + 1$ components $\mathbf{T}^{(k)}_q$ ($q = -k, -k + 1, \ldots, k$) satisfy the same commutation rule with respect to the angular momentum J as the spherical harmonic operators Y_{kq}, that is,

$$[(J_x \pm iJ_y), \mathbf{T}^{(k)}_q] = [(k \mp q)(k \pm q + 1)]^{1/2}\mathbf{T}^{(k)}_{q \pm 1}$$

and $$[J_z, \mathbf{T}^{(k)}_q] = q\mathbf{T}^{(k)}_q. \tag{2-28}$$

For $k = 1$ we have

$$\mathbf{T}^{(1)}_{\pm 1} = \frac{\mp 1}{\sqrt{2}}(\mathbf{T}_x \pm i\mathbf{T}_y), \qquad \mathbf{T}^{(1)}_0 = \mathbf{T}_z. \tag{2-29}$$

Thus we see that $\mathbf{J}$ is a tensor operator of rank 1 with components $\pm J_\mp/(2)^{1/2}$, J_z. We note also that the $\mathbf{C}^{(k)}$'s appearing in Eq. 2-27 are, in fact, tensor operators and the evaluation of the matrix elements would be made possible if we could find a procedure for evaluating the matrix elements of tensor operators.

The m dependence of the matrix elements of $\mathbf{T}^{(k)}_q$ in the jm scheme is given by the Wigner-Eckart theorem as

$$(\alpha jm|\mathbf{T}^{(k)}_q|\alpha'j'm') = (-1)^{j-m}(\alpha j||\mathbf{T}^{(k)}||\alpha'j')\begin{pmatrix} j & k & j' \\ -m & q & m' \end{pmatrix}. \tag{2-30}$$

The last factor is a 3-j symbol which is related to the Clebsch-Gordon coefficients of Condon and Shortley[33] by the expression*

$$\begin{pmatrix} j_1 & j_2 & j_3 \\ m_1 & m_2 & m_3 \end{pmatrix} = (-1)^{j_1 - j_2 - m_3}([j_3])^{-1/2}(j_1m_1j_2m_2|j_1j_2j_3 - m_3).$$

The 3-j symbols have symmetry properties such that an *even* permutation of the columns leaves it invariant, whereas an *odd* permutation multiplies it by $(-1)^{j_1 + j_2 + j_3}$ as does a reversal of the signs of the indices $m_1, m_2,$ and m_3. The 3-j symbol is zero unless $m_1 + m_2 + m_3 = 0$ and the triangular conditions

$$j_1 + j_2 - j_3 \geq 0; \qquad j_1 - j_2 + j_3 \geq 0; \qquad -j_1 + j_2 + j_3 \geq 0 \tag{2-31}$$

are satisfied.† From these restrictions for nonzero symbols we see that Eq. 2-30 has nonzero matrix elements only if

$$j + j' \geq k \geq |j - j'| \qquad \text{and} \qquad m - m' = q.$$

---

* Throughout this book we shall make use of the abbreviation $[a, b, c, \ldots] = (2a + 1)(2b + 1)(2c + 1) \ldots$.

† An extensive tabulation of the numerical values of the 3-j and 6-j symbols together with a general review of their properties has been given by Rotenberg et al.[46] Sharp[47] and Yutsis et al.[48] have given extensive reviews of the algebra of the n-j symbols.

The matrix element on the right-hand side of Eq. 2-30 is called a *reduced matrix element* and is indicated by double rules around the tensor operator. We shall find it necessary at times to evaluate these reduced matrix elements. This may usually be done in a quite straightforward manner. For example, consider the reduced matrix element $(\alpha j||\mathbf{J}^{(1)}||\alpha' j')$. This can be evaluated by noting that[33]

$$(\alpha j m|\mathbf{J}_z|\alpha' j' m') = m \; \delta(\alpha, \alpha')\delta(j, j')\delta(m, m'). \tag{2-32}$$

Choosing $m = m' = \frac{1}{2}$ and $q = 0$, we may introduce Eq. 2-32 into Eq. 2-30 to obtain

$$(\alpha j \tfrac{1}{2}|\mathbf{J}^{(1)}_0|\alpha' j' \tfrac{1}{2}) = \tfrac{1}{2}\delta(\alpha, \alpha')\delta(j, j') = (-1)^{j-1/2}\begin{pmatrix} j & 1 & j \\ -\tfrac{1}{2} & 0 & \tfrac{1}{2} \end{pmatrix}(\alpha j||\mathbf{J}^{(1)}||\alpha j). \tag{2-33}$$

The 3-j symbol can be expressed explicitly in terms of its arguments[46] and the result

$$(\alpha j||\mathbf{J}^{(1)}||\alpha' j') = [j(j + 1)(2j + 1)]^{1/2}\delta(\alpha, \alpha')\delta(j, j') \tag{2-34}$$

obtained. In an exactly similar manner it may be shown that

$$(l||\mathbf{l}||l') = [l(l + 1)(2l + 1)]^{1/2}\delta(l, l'), \tag{2-35}$$

and

$$(s||\mathbf{s}||s') = [s(s + 1)(2s + 1)]^{1/2}\delta(s, s'). \tag{2-36}$$

With somewhat more difficulty it may be shown[39] that

$$(l||\mathbf{C}^{(k)}||l') = (-1)^l [(2l + 1)(2l' + 1)]^{1/2}\begin{pmatrix} l & k & l' \\ 0 & 0 & 0 \end{pmatrix}. \tag{2-37}$$

In addition to 3-j symbols we shall frequently encounter 6-j and 9-j symbols.[46] The 6-j symbol is associated with transformations between coupling schemes of three angular momenta and is defined as[46]

$$\begin{Bmatrix} j_1 & j_2 & j_{12} \\ j_3 & J & j_{23} \end{Bmatrix} = (-1)^{j_1 + j_2 + j_3 + J}([j_{12}, j_{23}])^{-1/2}$$

$$\times ((j_1 j_2)j_{12}, j_3; J|j_1, (j_2 j_3)j_{23}; J). \tag{2-38}$$

The 6-j symbol is invariant with respect to any permutation of its columns or interchange of the upper and lower arguments of any two columns and is nonzero only if the triangular conditions of Eq. 2-30 are satisfied by the four triads $(j_1 j_{23} J)$, $(j_{12} j_3 J)$, $(j_1 j_2 j_{12})$, and $(j_2 j_3 j_{23})$.

The 9-j symbol is associated with the transformations between coupling schemes of four angular momenta and is defined by the relation

$$
\begin{Bmatrix} j_1 & j_2 & j_{12} \\ j_3 & j_4 & j_{34} \\ j_{13} & j_{24} & J \end{Bmatrix} = ([j_{12}, j_{34}, j_{13}, j_{24}])^{-1/2}
$$

$$
((j_1 j_2)j_{12}, (j_3 j_4)j_{34}; J \,|\, (j_1 j_3)j_{13}, (j_2 j_4)j_{24}; J) \quad (2\text{-}39)
$$

$$
= \sum_t (-1)^{2t}([t])
$$

$$
\times \begin{Bmatrix} j_1 & j_2 & j_{12} \\ j_{34} & J & t \end{Bmatrix} \begin{Bmatrix} j_3 & j_4 & j_{34} \\ j_2 & t & j_{24} \end{Bmatrix} \begin{Bmatrix} j_{13} & j_{24} & J \\ t & j_1 & j_3 \end{Bmatrix}. \quad (2\text{-}40)
$$

An *even* permutation of rows or columns, or a *transposition* of rows and columns, leaves the 9-j symbol unchanged but an *odd* permutation multiplies the symbol by $(-1)^r$, where r is the sum of its nine arguments. If one of the arguments is zero, it reduces to a 6-j symbol, namely,

$$
\begin{Bmatrix} a & b & c \\ d & e & f \\ g & h & 0 \end{Bmatrix} = (-1)^{b+c+d+g}([c, g])^{-1/2} \begin{Bmatrix} a & b & c \\ e & d & g \end{Bmatrix} \delta(c, f)\delta(g, h). \quad (2\text{-}41)
$$

We may now examine the properties of commuting tensor operators $\mathbf{T}^{(k_1)}$ and $\mathbf{U}^{(k_2)}$ that operate on *different* parts of a system, for example, $\mathbf{T}^{(k_1)}$ operating on the coordinates of a particle 1 and $\mathbf{U}^{(k_2)}$ operating on those of a particle 2 as do the $\mathbf{C}^{(k)}$'s in Eq. 2-27. Consider a tensor operator $\mathbf{X}_Q^{(K)}$ which satisfies the commutation relationships of Eq. 2-28 and is itself the product of the tensor operators $\mathbf{T}^{(k_1)}$ and $\mathbf{U}^{(k_2)}$ such that

$$
\mathbf{X}_Q^{(K)} = [\mathbf{T}^{(k_1)} \times \mathbf{U}^{(k_2)}]_Q^{(K)}. \quad (2\text{-}42)
$$

Then we are required to evaluate the matrix element

$$
(\alpha j_1 j_2 jm | \mathbf{X}_Q^{(K)} | \alpha' j_1' j_2' j' m'), \quad (2\text{-}43)
$$

where the quantum numbers j_1, j_2, and jm refer to the parts 1, 2, and the total system, respectively and α refers to any additional quantum numbers required to specify the states. Applying the result of Eq. 2-30, we obtain the m-dependence of Eq. 2-43 as

$$
= (-1)^{j-m} \begin{pmatrix} j & K & j' \\ -m & Q & m' \end{pmatrix} (\alpha j_1 j_2 j || \mathbf{X}^{(K)} || \alpha' j_1' j_2' j'). \quad (2\text{-}44)
$$

The reduced matrix element on the right-hand side can then be written in terms of the reduced matrix elements of $\mathbf{T}^{(k_1)}$ and $\mathbf{U}^{(k_2)}$ to yield[39]

$$
(\alpha j_1 j_2 j||\mathbf{X}^{(K)}||\alpha' j_1' j_2' j') = \sum_{\alpha''} (\alpha j_1||\mathbf{T}^{(k_1)}||\alpha'' j_1')(\alpha'' j_2||\mathbf{U}^{(k_2)}||\alpha' j_2')
$$
$$
\times ([j, j', K])^{1/2} \begin{Bmatrix} j_1 & j_1' & k_1 \\ j_2 & j_2' & k_2 \\ j & j' & K \end{Bmatrix}. \qquad (2\text{-}45)
$$

The *scalar product* $(\mathbf{T}^{(k)} \cdot \mathbf{U}^{(k)})$ is defined by

$$
(\mathbf{T}^{(k)} \cdot \mathbf{U}^{(k)}) = \sum_q (-1)^q \mathbf{T}_q^{(k)} \mathbf{U}_{-q}^{(k)}. \qquad (2\text{-}46)
$$

The matrix elements of the scalar product in the $\alpha j_1 j_2 jm$ scheme may be found by putting $K = 0$ and $k_1 = k_2 = k$ in Eq. 2-45 and noting that

$$
(\mathbf{T}^{(k)} \cdot \mathbf{U}^{(k)}) = (-1)^k ([k])^{1/2} [T^{(k)} \times U^{(k)}]^{(0)}
$$

to give

$$
(\alpha j_1 j_2 jm|(\mathbf{T}^{(k)} \cdot \mathbf{U}^{(k)})|\alpha' j_1' j_2' j'm') = \delta(j, j')\delta(\alpha, \alpha')(-1)^{j_1' + j_2 + j}
$$
$$
\times \begin{Bmatrix} j_1 & j_1' & k \\ j_2' & j_2 & j \end{Bmatrix} \sum_{\alpha''} (\alpha j_1||\mathbf{T}^{(k)}||\alpha'' j_1')(\alpha'' j_2||\mathbf{U}^{(k)}||\alpha' j_2'). \qquad (2\text{-}47)
$$

To obtain the reduced matrix element of $\mathbf{T}^{(k)}$ operating only on part 1 in the $\alpha j_1 j_2 j$ scheme we put $k_2 = 0$ and $\mathbf{U}^{(k)} = 1$ in Eq. 2-45 and find

$$
(\alpha j_1 j_2 j||\mathbf{T}^{(k)}||\alpha' j_1' j_2' j') = \delta(j_2, j_2')(-1)^{j_1 + j_2 + j' + k}([j, j'])^{1/2}
$$
$$
\times (\alpha j_1||\mathbf{T}^{(k)}||\alpha' j_1') \begin{Bmatrix} j & j' & k \\ j_1' & j_1 & j_2 \end{Bmatrix}, \qquad (2\text{-}48)
$$

and for $\mathbf{U}^{(k)}$ operating only on part 2 we may similarly show that

$$
(\alpha j_1 j_2 j||\mathbf{U}^{(k)}||\alpha' j_1' j_2' j') = \delta(j_1, j_1')(-1)^{j_1 + j_2' + j + k}([j, j'])^{1/2}
$$
$$
\times (\alpha j_2||\mathbf{U}^{(k)}||\alpha' j_2') \begin{Bmatrix} j & j' & k \\ j_2' & j_2 & j_1 \end{Bmatrix}. \qquad (2\text{-}49)
$$

In these cases the matrix elements of the tensor operators are diagonal in *all* the quantum numbers of the parts of the system that are not operated on.

2-7   Electrostatic Interaction for Two Electrons

Having stated the principal results of the theory of tensor operators, we may consider further the evaluation of the matrix elements of electrostatic interactions. We shall first look at the simple problem of two-electron configurations and then examine the extensions to more complex configurations.

Using Eq. 2-12, we may write the antisymmetrized eigenfunction for two electrons whose angular momenta are LS coupled as

$$(n_a l_a, n_b l_b; SL| = (2)^{-1/2}[(n_{a1}l_{a1}, n_{b2}l_{b2}; SL| - (n_{a2}l_{a2}, n_{b1}l_{b1}; SL|], \quad (2\text{-}50)$$

where the indices 1 and 2 refer to the coordinates of the first and second electron respectively and we have suppressed the spin-angular momenta of the individual electrons for brevity. The second eigenstate of Eq. 2-50 differs from the first by an *odd* permutation of the electron coordinates relative to the quantum numbers $n_a s_a l_a$ and $n_b s_b l_b$. On recoupling the angular momenta of the second eigenstate, we may write Eq. 2-50 as

$$(n_a l_a, n_b l_b; SL| = (2)^{-1/2}[(n_{a1}l_{a1}, n_{b2}l_{b2}; SL|$$
$$- (-1)^{s_a + s_b + l_a + l_b + S + L}(n_{b1}l_{b1}, n_{a2}l_{a2}; SL|]. \quad (2\text{-}51)$$

The antisymmetrized eigenfunction of a second two-electron configuration $(n_c l_c, n_d l_d)$ may be written in LS coupling as

$$|n_c l_c, n_d l_d; SL) = (2)^{-1/2}[|n_{c1}l_{c1}, n_{d2}l_{d2}; SL)$$
$$- (-1)^{s_c + s_d + l_c + l_d + S + L}|n_{d1}l_{d1}, n_{c2}l_{c2}; SL)]. \quad (2\text{-}52)$$

The matrix elements of electrostatic interaction *between* the two configurations can, after simplifying the phases, be written as

$$(n_a l_a, n_b l_b; SL \left| \frac{e^2}{r_{12}} \right| n_c l_c, n_d l_d; SL)$$

$$= \tfrac{1}{2}\Big[(n_a l_a, n_b l_b; SL \left| \frac{e^2}{r_{12}} \right| n_c l_c, n_d l_d; SL)$$

$$+ (n_b l_b, n_a l_a; SL \left| \frac{e^2}{r_{12}} \right| n_d l_d, n_c l_c; SL)$$

$$+ (-1)^{l_a + l_b + S + L}(n_a l_a, n_b l_b; SL \left| \frac{e^2}{r_{12}} \right| n_d l_d, n_c l_c; SL)$$

$$+ (-1)^{l_a + l_b + S + L}(n_b l_b, n_a l_a; SL \left| \frac{e^2}{r_{12}} \right| n_c l_c, n_d l_d; SL)\Big]. \quad (2\text{-}53)$$

Because of the symmetry of e^2/r_{12}, the right-hand side of Eq. 2-53 reduces to

$$(n_a l_a, n_b l_b; SL \left| \frac{e^2}{r_{12}} \right| n_c l_c, n_d l_d; SL) + (-1)^{l_a + l_b + S + L}$$

$$\times (n_a l_a, n_b l_b; SL \left| \frac{e^2}{r_{12}} \right| n_d l_d, n_c l_c; SL).$$

With the aid of Eq. 2-27 it is now possible to write Eq. 2-53 in tensorial form as

$$(n_a l_a, n_b l_b; SL \left| \frac{e^2}{r_{12}} \right| n_c l_c, n_d l_d; SL)$$

$$= e^2 \sum_k \left[(n_a l_a, n_b l_b; SL \left| \frac{r_<^k}{r_>^{k+1}} (\mathbf{C}_1^{(k)} \cdot \mathbf{C}_2^{(k)}) \right| n_c l_c, n_d l_d; SL) + (-1)^{l_a + l_b + S + L} \right.$$

$$\left. \times (n_a l_a, n_b l_b; SL \left| \frac{r_<^k}{r_>^{k+1}} (\mathbf{C}_1^{(k)} \cdot \mathbf{C}_2^{(k)}) \right| n_d l_d, n_c l_c; SL) \right], \quad (2\text{-}54)$$

$$= \sum_k \left[f_k(l_a, l_b; l_c, l_d) R^k(n_a l_a, n_b l_b; n_c l_c, n_d l_d) \right.$$

$$\left. + g_k(l_a, l_b; l_d, l_c) R^k(n_a l_a, n_b l_b; n_d l_d, n_c l_c) \right], \quad (2\text{-}55)$$

where the f_k and g_k represent the *angular* parts of the matrix elements of Eq. 2-54 and the R^k's, the *Slater radial integrals*, which arise from the *radial* parts of the one-electron eigenfunctions. The angular factors may be evaluated by application of Eq. 2-47 to yield

$$f_k(l_a, l_b; l_c, l_d) = (-1)^{l_b + l_c + L} (l_a || \mathbf{C}_1^{(k)} || l_c)(l_b || \mathbf{C}_2^{(k)} || l_d) \begin{Bmatrix} l_a & l_c & k \\ l_d & l_b & L \end{Bmatrix}, \quad (2\text{-}56)$$

and

$$g_k(l_a, l_b; l_d, l_c) = (-1)^S (l_a || \mathbf{C}_1^{(k)} || l_d)(l_b || \mathbf{C}_2^{(k)} || l_c) \begin{Bmatrix} l_a & l_d & k \\ l_c & l_b & L \end{Bmatrix}. \quad (2\text{-}57)$$

The reduced matrix elements are evaluated using Eq. 2-37.

The Slater radial integrals R^k are defined by[33]

$$R^k(n_a l_a, n_b l_b; n_c l_c, n_d l_d)$$

$$= e^2 \int_0^\infty \int_0^\infty \frac{r_<^k}{r_>^{k+1}} R_{n_a l_a}(r_1) R_{n_b l_b}(r_2) R_{n_c l_c}(r_1) R_{n_d l_d}(r_2) \, dr_1 \, dr_2. \quad (2\text{-}58)$$

We note that although the radial integrals depend on the principal quantum numbers n of the electrons, the angular parts of the matrix elements do not.

When $n_a l_a = n_c l_c$ and $n_b l_b = n_d l_d$, Eq. 2-54 becomes

$$(n_a l_a, n_b l_b; SL \left| \frac{e^2}{r_{12}} \right| n_a l_a, n_b l_b; SL)$$

$$= \sum_k \left[f_k(l_a, l_b) F^k(n_a l_a, n_b l_b) + g_k(l_a, l_b) G^k(n_a l_a, n_b l_b) \right], \quad (2\text{-}59)$$

where

$$f_k(l_a, l_b) = (-1)^{l_a + l_b + L}(l_a||\mathbf{C}_1^{(k)}||l_a)(l_b||\mathbf{C}_2^{(k)}||l_b)\begin{Bmatrix} l_a & l_a & k \\ l_b & l_b & L \end{Bmatrix} \quad (2\text{-}60)$$

and

$$g_k(l_a, l_b) = (-1)^S(l_a||\mathbf{C}^{(k)}||l_b)^2\begin{Bmatrix} l_a & l_b & k \\ l_a & l_b & L \end{Bmatrix}, \quad (2\text{-}61)$$

whereas

$$F^k(n_a l_a, n_b l_b) = R^k(n_a l_a, n_b l_b; n_c l_c, n_d l_d) \quad (2\text{-}62)$$

and

$$G^k(n_a l_a, n_b l_b) = R^k(n_a l_a, n_b l_b; n_d l_d, n_c l_c). \quad (2\text{-}63)$$

The F^k's are known as *direct integrals* and the G^k's as *exchange integrals*. The F^k's are necessarily a *positive* and *decreasing* function of k. Racah[40] has shown that the G^k's are *positive* and that $G^k/([k])$ is necessarily a *decreasing* function of k. To avoid large denominators appearing in the matrix element calculations, Condon and Shortley[33] have redefined the radial F^k and G^k integrals in terms of the reduced radial integrals F_k and G_k, which are related by the expression

$$F_k = \frac{F^k}{D_k} \quad \text{and} \quad G_k = \frac{G^k}{D_k}, \quad (2\text{-}64)$$

where the D_k's are the denominators given in their tables* 1^6 and 2^6.

When $n_a l_a = n_b l_b = nl$, we no longer use Eq. 2-50 as the antisymmetric eigenfunction; rather we shall write

$$(nl, nl; SL| = ((nl)^2; SL|, \quad (2\text{-}65)$$

where only states with $L + S$ even are allowed. The electrostatic interaction *between* the configuration $(nl)^2$ and $(n_c l_c, n_d l_d)$ will be given by

$$(nl, nl; SL \left| \frac{e^2}{r_{12}} \right| n_c l_c, n_d l_d; SL)$$

$$= \sum_k (2)^{1/2}(nl, nl; SL \left| e^2 \frac{r_<^k}{r_>^{k+1}} (\mathbf{C}_1^{(k)} \cdot \mathbf{C}_2^{(k)}) \right| n_c l_c, n_d l_d; SL)$$

$$= \sum_k f_k(l, l; l_c, l_b)R^k(nl, nl; n_c l_c, n_d l_d), \quad (2\text{-}66)$$

where

$$f_k(l, l; l_c, l_d) = (-1)^{l + l_c + L}(2)^{1/2}(l||\mathbf{C}_1^{(k)}||l_c)(l||\mathbf{C}_2^{(k)}||l_d)\begin{Bmatrix} l & l_c & k \\ l_d & l & L \end{Bmatrix}. \quad (2\text{-}67)$$

---

* The reader using these tables is warned that the numbers 1524·6 and 7361·64 are given in *decimal* form and do not imply 1524 × 6 and 7361 × 64. Failure to note this rather obvious point has led to errors in the past.

If $n_a l_a = n_b l_b = nl$ and $n_c l_c = n_d l_d = n'l'$, then we may write the electrostatic interaction *between* the configurations as

$$\left((nl)^2; SL \left| \frac{e^2}{r_{12}} \right| (n'l')^2; SL \right) = \sum_k f_k(l, l; l', l') R^k(nl, nl; n'l', n'l'), \quad (2\text{-}68)$$

where

$$f_k(l, l; l', l') = (-1)^{l+l'+L} (l \| \mathbf{C}^{(k)} \| l')^2 \begin{Bmatrix} l & l' & k \\ l' & l & L \end{Bmatrix}. \quad (2\text{-}69)$$

We might note that in this case

$$R^k(nl, nl; n'l', n'l') = G^k(nl, n'l').$$

Finally, if all the electrons are equivalent, the matrix elements are of the form

$$\left((nl)^2; SL \left| \frac{e^2}{r_{12}} \right| (nl)^2; SL \right) = \sum_k f_k(l, l) F^k(nl, nl), \quad (2\text{-}70)$$

where

$$f_k(l, l) = (-1)^L (l \| \mathbf{C}^{(k)} \| l)^2 \begin{Bmatrix} l & l & k \\ l & l & L \end{Bmatrix}. \quad (2\text{-}71)$$

Thus we have obtained general formulas for the evaluation of the electrostatic interaction matrix elements *within* and *between* all possible two-electron configurations. We must now consider the extension of these results to the more complex configurations of Sec. 2-1.

2-8 One- and Two-Electron Operators

In many of the systems that we shall encounter there will be more than two equivalent electrons. In these cases it is desirable to make use of methods based on the concept of fractional parentage. In atomic systems there are only two types of electron operators that need to be considered: those operators that operate on the coordinates of a *single* electron at a time (type **F** operators) and those that operate on the coordinates of a *pair* of electrons at a time (type **G** operators). A knowledge of the properties of type **F** and type **G** operators allows us to reduce the calculation of the matrix elements of any operator to those of one- or two-electron systems.

The type **F** operator is defined by

$$\mathbf{F} = \sum_{i=1}^{N} \mathbf{f}_i, \quad (2\text{-}72)$$

where $\mathbf{f}_i$ is a single-particle operator operating on the coordinates of the ith particle. The matrix element of $\mathbf{F}$ between a state $(\psi|$ and a state $|\psi')$ of the l^N configuration will be just

$$(l^N\psi|\mathbf{F}|l^N\psi') = N(\psi|\mathbf{f}_N|\psi'), \qquad (2\text{-}73)$$

where $\mathbf{f}_N$ is a single-particle operator operating on the coordinate of the Nth electron. Using Eq. 2-20 we may write Eq. 2-73 as

$$(l^N\psi|\mathbf{F}|l^N\psi') = N\sum_{\bar\psi} (\psi\{|\bar\psi)(\bar\psi, l_N; \psi|\mathbf{f}_N|\bar\psi; l_N; \psi')(\bar\psi|\}\psi'). \qquad (2\text{-}74)$$

The matrix element on the right-hand side of Eq. 2-74 can then be evaluated using the tensor operator methods outlined in Sec. 2-6.

The matrix elements of a type $\mathbf{F}$ operator between a state $(\psi|$ of l^N and a state $|\psi_1, s'l'; \psi')$ of $l^{N-1}l'$ is given by

$$(l^N\psi|\mathbf{F}|l^{N-1}\psi_1, sl'; \psi') = N^{1/2}(\psi\{|\psi_1)(\psi_1, l_N; \psi|\mathbf{f}_N|\psi_1, l_N'; \psi'). \qquad (2\text{-}75)$$

It will be noted that the matrix elements of $\mathbf{F}$ between two states will vanish if the states differ in the coordinates of more than one electron.

The type $\mathbf{G}$ operators are defined by

$$\mathbf{G} = \sum_{i<j}^{N} \mathbf{g}_{ij}, \qquad (2\text{-}76)$$

where g_{ij} is a two-particle operator operating on the coordinates of the ith and jth particles. The Coulomb interaction operator, $\displaystyle\sum_{i<j} (\mathbf{C}_i^{(k)} \cdot \mathbf{C}_j^{(k)})$, is a typical example of a type $\mathbf{G}$ operator. The matrix elements of $\mathbf{G}$ between two states vanish if the states differ in the coordinates of more than two electrons. Racah[41] has discussed the calculation of the matrix elements of type $\mathbf{G}$ operators using two particle coefficients of fractional parentage. In practice, it is not necessary to calculate these matrix elements using Racah's method because it is always possible to use the properties of the one-particle coefficients of fractional parentage together with appropriate recouplings of the angular momenta to reduce their calculation to those of two-electron systems; this method avoids the complexities of the two-particle coefficients of fractional parentage.* It has been discussed by several writers.[49–54] A practical example is presented in Sec. 2-10.

---

* Nevertheless the formulas of Racah involving two-particle coefficients of fractional parentage are sometimes of great analytical value (see Ref. 49).

2-9 Electrostatic Interactions in f^N Configurations

The matrix elements of electrostatic interaction within the f^N configurations have been calculated in their entirety by using the methods of Racah.[37] The matrix elements are normally written as a linear combination of Slater radial integrals,

$$E = \sum_{k=0}^{6} f_k F^k(nf, nf) = \sum_{k=0}^{6} f^k F_k(nf, nf), \qquad (2\text{-}77)$$

where k is even and the f_k's are the coefficients of the linear combination and represent the *angular* part of the interaction. For two electrons, f_k is the expectation value of the scalar product $(\mathbf{C}_1^{(k)} \cdot \mathbf{C}_2^{(k)})$ as in Eq. 2-71. Although this operator is a scalar with respect to R_3, it does not have the transformation properties of the groups R_7 and G_2 that are used to classify the states.   By taking linear combinations of these operators it is possible to construct new operators which have simple transformation properties with respect to R_7 and G_2.[37]   The matrix elements may then be written as

$$E = \sum_{k=0}^{3} e_k E^k, \qquad (2\text{-}78)$$

where the e_k's are the angular parts of the new operators which are related to the f^k's of Eq. 2-77 by the expressions

$$
\begin{aligned}
e_0 &= f^0 = N(N-1), \\
e_1 &= \frac{9f^0}{7} + \frac{f^2}{42} + \frac{f^4}{77} + \frac{f^6}{462}, \\
e_2 &= \frac{143f^2}{42} - \frac{130f^4}{77} + \frac{35f^6}{462}, \\
e_3 &= \frac{11f^2}{42} + \frac{4f^4}{77} - \frac{7f^6}{462},
\end{aligned}
\qquad (2\text{-}79)
$$

whereas the E^k's are the linear combinations of the F_k's,

$$
\begin{aligned}
E^0 &= F_0 - 10F_2 - 33F_4 - 286F_6, \\
E^1 &= \frac{70F_2 + 231F_4 + 2002F_6}{9}, \\
E^2 &= \frac{F_2 - 3F_4 + 7F_6}{9}, \\
E^3 &= \frac{5F_2 + 6F_4 - 91F_6}{3}.
\end{aligned}
\qquad (2\text{-}80)
$$

It is frequently necessary to derive the F_k integrals from known values of the E^{k}'s. Solving Eq. 2-80, we obtain them as

$$F_0 = \frac{7E^0 + 9E^1}{7},$$

$$F_2 = \frac{E^1 + 143E^2 + 11E^3}{42},$$

$$F_4 = \frac{E^1 - 130E^2 + 4E^3}{77},$$

$$F_6 = \frac{E^1 + 35E^2 - 7E^3}{462}.$$

The coefficients e_k $(k > 0)$ for the f^{14-N} configuration are the same as those for the conjugate f^N configuration. The coefficients of E^0 depend only on N, and hence the contribution $e_0 E^0$ to the energy matrix has the effect of shifting the center of gravity of the entire f^N configuration without contributing to the structure of the configuration.

The electrostatic energy matrices, although diagonal in S and L, are not diagonal in the $\tau v W U$ quantum numbers. Consequently, the electrostatic matrices will have ranks equal to the number of states of a given SL that occurs in the configuration. Needless to say, the quantum numbers $\tau v W U$ will not be "good" quantum numbers when the energy matrices are diagonalized. They serve only to label the basis states of the configurations and as a mathematical aid in making computations.

In the particular case of the half-filled shell (f^7) each of the matrices is, in general, reducible into two smaller matrices. The eigenfunctions of the states of the half-filled shell may be constructed either from the one-electron eigenfunctions of seven f-electrons $\Psi_L(f^7 \alpha SL)$ or from seven f-electron "holes" $\Psi_R(f^7 \alpha SL)$. The eigenfunctions constructed in these two ways will differ from one another by not more than a phase and are, in fact, related by the expression[41]

$$\Psi_R(f^7 \alpha SL) = (-1)^{(v-1)/2} \Psi_L(f^7 \alpha SL). \tag{2-81}$$

Thus the states of the f^7 configuration may be divided into two classes, those whose eigenfunctions change sign on exchange of electrons for "holes" and those whose eigenfunctions do not change sign. States having seniority $v = 7$ and 3 belong to the former class (I), whereas those with seniority numbers $v = 5$ and 1 belong to the latter class (II). Racah[40,41] was able to show that the matrix elements of electrostatic interaction are zero for interactions between members of different class, and hence the energy matrix for states of a given SL will reduce into two matrices, one containing only states of class I and another containing only states of class II.

A complete tabulation of the electrostatic energy matrices for all the f^N configurations has been made by Nielson and Koster.[43]

2-10   Electrostatic Interactions in $l^N l'$ Type Configurations

The calculation of the matrix elements of electrostatic interactions within configurations of the type $l^N l'$ may be divided into two parts: (1) evaluation of the matrix elements within the l^N core and (2) evaluation of the matrix elements of the interactions of the added electron with the l^N core.

The matrix elements of the electrostatic interactions within the l^N core are the same as those for the l^N configuration since the matrix elements of the l^N core will be diagonal in all the quantum numbers of the electrons outside the core.

For the interactions between the core and the added electron the matrix elements will be of the form

$$\sum_k (l^N \alpha_1 S_1 L_1, sl'; SL \, |e^2 \, \frac{r_<^k}{r_>^{k+1}} \sum_{i<j} (\mathbf{C}_i^{(k)} \cdot \mathbf{C}_j^{(k)})| \, l^N \alpha_1' S_1' L_1', sl'; SL). \quad (2\text{-}82)$$

By using Eq. (2-20), each state of the l^N core may be expanded in terms of the states of l^{N-1}. Abbreviating the coefficients of fractional parentage to $(\bar{\psi}_1\{|\psi)$ and $(\bar{\psi}|\}\psi_1')$, we may write Eq. (2-82) as

$$= N \sum_k \sum_{\bar{\psi}} (\psi_1\{|\psi)(\bar{\psi}|\}\psi_1')(l^{N-1}\bar{\alpha}\bar{S}\bar{L}sl_N S_1 L_1, sl'; SL \left| \frac{r_<^k}{r_>^{k+1}} \, (\mathbf{C}_N^{(k)} \cdot \mathbf{C}_{N+1}^{(k)}) \right.$$
$$\times \left| l^{N-1}\bar{\alpha}\bar{S}\bar{L}sl_N S_1' L_1', sl'; SL). \quad (2\text{-}83) \right.$$

This operation has the effect of detaching the Nth electron of l^N. We now perform a recoupling of the spin and orbital momenta of both the bra and the ket of the matrix element in Eq. 2-83 to bring sl_N and sl' into association. These recouplings may be readily made using Eq. 2-38. A typical recoupling for the bra will be of the form

$$((\bar{L}l)L_1, l'; L|\bar{L}, (ll')\lambda; L) = (-1)^{\bar{L}+l+l'+L}([L_1, \lambda])^{1/2} \begin{Bmatrix} \bar{L} & l & L_1 \\ l' & L & \lambda \end{Bmatrix}. \quad (2\text{-}84)$$

On making the recouplings, the matrix element in Eq. 2-83 becomes

$$= \sum_{\substack{\sigma, \lambda \\ \sigma', \lambda'}} ([S_1, L_1, S_1', L_1', \sigma, \lambda, \sigma', \lambda'])^{1/2} \begin{Bmatrix} s & S & S_1 \\ \bar{S} & s & \sigma \end{Bmatrix} \begin{Bmatrix} s & S & S_1' \\ \bar{S} & s & \sigma' \end{Bmatrix} \begin{Bmatrix} l' & L & L_1 \\ \bar{L} & l & \lambda \end{Bmatrix}$$
$$\times \begin{Bmatrix} l' & L & L_1' \\ \bar{L} & l & \lambda' \end{Bmatrix} (l^{N-1}\bar{\alpha}\bar{S}\bar{L}, (sl, sl')\sigma\lambda; SL \left| e^2 \, \frac{r_<^k}{r_>^{k+1}} \, (\mathbf{C}_N^{(k)} \cdot \mathbf{C}_{N+1}^{(k)}) \right.$$
$$\times \left| l^{N-1}\bar{\alpha}\bar{S}\bar{L}, (sl, sl')\sigma'\lambda'; SL). \quad (2\text{-}85) \right.$$

Since $(\mathbf{C}_N^{(k)} \cdot \mathbf{C}_{N+1}^{(k)})$ is a scalar, the matrix element in Eq. 2-85 must be diagonal in σ and λ. The matrix element thus reduces to

$$\left((sl, sl')\sigma\lambda \left| e^2 \frac{r_<^k}{r_>^{k+1}} (\mathbf{C}_N^{(k)} \cdot \mathbf{C}_{N+1}^{(k)}) \right| (sl, sl')\sigma\lambda \right). \tag{2-86}$$

By performing a recoupling we have now managed to reduce the problem to that of just two electrons. The matrix element in Eq. 2-86 is of the same form as Eq. 2-59, and we obtain Eq. 2-86 as

$$= f_k'(l, l')F^k(nl, n'l') + g_k'(l, l')G^k(nl, n', l'), \tag{2-87}$$

where

$$f_k'(l, l') = (-1)^\lambda([l, l']) \begin{pmatrix} l' & k & l' \\ 0 & 0 & 0 \end{pmatrix} \begin{pmatrix} l & k & l \\ 0 & 0 & 0 \end{pmatrix} \begin{Bmatrix} l & l & k \\ l' & l' & \lambda \end{Bmatrix} \tag{2-88}$$

and

$$g_k'(l, l') = (-1)^\sigma([l, l']) \begin{pmatrix} l & k & l' \\ 0 & 0 & 0 \end{pmatrix}^2 \begin{Bmatrix} l & l' & k \\ l & l' & \lambda \end{Bmatrix}. \tag{2-89}$$

By using these results, Eq. 2-85 becomes

$$= ([l, l'])([S_1, L_1, S_1', L_1'])^{1/2} \sum_{\sigma, \lambda} ([\sigma, \lambda]) \begin{Bmatrix} s & S & S_1 \\ \bar{S} & s & \sigma \end{Bmatrix} \begin{Bmatrix} s & S & S_1' \\ \bar{S} & s & \sigma \end{Bmatrix}$$

$$\times \begin{Bmatrix} l' & L & L_1 \\ \bar{L} & l & \lambda \end{Bmatrix} \begin{Bmatrix} l' & L & L_1' \\ \bar{L} & l & \lambda \end{Bmatrix} \left[(-1)^\lambda \begin{pmatrix} l' & k & l' \\ 0 & 0 & 0 \end{pmatrix} \begin{pmatrix} l & k & l \\ 0 & 0 & 0 \end{pmatrix} \right.$$

$$\times \begin{Bmatrix} l & l & k \\ l' & l' & \lambda \end{Bmatrix} F^k(nl, n'l') + (-1)^\sigma \begin{pmatrix} l & k & l' \\ 0 & 0 & 0 \end{pmatrix}^2$$

$$\left. \times \begin{Bmatrix} l & l' & k \\ l & l' & \lambda \end{Bmatrix} G^k(nl, n'l') \right]. \tag{2-90}$$

The sum over σ for the coefficient of F^k may be performed using the identity[39]

$$\sum_\sigma ([\sigma]) \begin{Bmatrix} s & S & S_1 \\ \bar{S} & s & \sigma \end{Bmatrix} \begin{Bmatrix} s & S & S_1' \\ \bar{S} & s & \sigma \end{Bmatrix} = \delta(S_1, S_1'),$$

and the sum over λ may be found using the Biedenharn-Elliott sum rule[39]

$$\sum_\lambda (-1)^\lambda([\lambda]) \begin{Bmatrix} l & l & k \\ l' & l' & \lambda \end{Bmatrix} \begin{Bmatrix} l & L & L_1' \\ \bar{L} & l' & \lambda \end{Bmatrix} \begin{Bmatrix} l & L & L_1 \\ \bar{L} & l' & \lambda \end{Bmatrix} = (-1)^{L+L_1+L_1'+L+k}$$

$$\times \begin{Bmatrix} L_1 & L_1' & k \\ l & l & \bar{L} \end{Bmatrix} \begin{Bmatrix} L_1 & L_1' & k \\ l' & l' & L \end{Bmatrix}.$$

Summing over σ and λ the coefficients of $F^k(nl, n'l')$ become

$$f_k(l, l') = \delta(S_1, S_1')(-1)^{L+l+L_1'}([l, l']) \begin{pmatrix} l' & k & l' \\ 0 & 0 & 0 \end{pmatrix} \begin{pmatrix} l & k & l \\ 0 & 0 & 0 \end{pmatrix}$$

$$\times \begin{Bmatrix} l' & k & l' \\ L_1 & L & L_1' \end{Bmatrix} N([L_1, L_1'])^{1/2} \sum_{\bar\psi} (\psi_1\{|\bar\psi)(\bar\psi|\}\psi_1')(-1)^{L+L_1+l+k}$$

$$\times \begin{Bmatrix} L_1 & l & \bar{L} \\ l & L_1' & k \end{Bmatrix}. \quad (2\text{-}91)$$

If we define a unit tensor $\mathbf{u}^{(k)}$ such that

$$(nl||\mathbf{u}^{(k)}||n'l') = \delta(n, n')\delta(l, l'),$$

then the matrix elements of the tensor $\mathbf{U}^{(k)}$, which is the sum of the unit tensors $\mathbf{u}^{(k)}$ of the l^N core, will be given by

$$(\psi_1||\mathbf{U}^{(k)}||\psi_1') = N([L_1, L_1'])^{1/2} \sum_{\bar\psi} (\psi_1\{|\bar\psi)(\bar\psi|\}\psi_1')(-1)^{L+L_1+l+k}$$

$$\times \begin{Bmatrix} L_1 & l & \bar{L} \\ l & L_1' & k \end{Bmatrix}. \quad (2\text{-}92)$$

This result follows directly from application of Eqs. 2-49 and 2-74. Using Eq. 2-92 in Eq. 2-91 yields the result

$$f_k(l, l') = \delta(S_1, S_1')(-1)^{L_1'+L+l}([l, l']) \begin{pmatrix} l' & k & l' \\ 0 & 0 & 0 \end{pmatrix} \begin{pmatrix} l & k & l \\ 0 & 0 & 0 \end{pmatrix}$$

$$\times \begin{Bmatrix} l' & k & l' \\ L_1 & L & L_1' \end{Bmatrix} (\psi_1||\mathbf{U}^{(k)}||\psi_1'). \quad (2\text{-}93)$$

The sum over σ for the coefficient of $G^k(nl, n'l')$ is made by use of the identity[39]

$$\sum_\sigma (-1)^\sigma([\sigma]) \begin{Bmatrix} s & \bar{S} & S_1 \\ S & s & \sigma \end{Bmatrix} \begin{Bmatrix} s & \bar{S} & S_1' \\ S & s & \sigma \end{Bmatrix} = (-1)^{S_1+S_1'} \begin{Bmatrix} s & \bar{S} & S_1 \\ s & S & S_1' \end{Bmatrix},$$

and application of Eq. 2-40 gives the sum over λ as

$$\sum_\lambda (-1)^{2\lambda}([\lambda]) \begin{Bmatrix} \bar{L} & l & L_1 \\ l' & L & \lambda \end{Bmatrix} \begin{Bmatrix} l & k & l' \\ l & \lambda & l' \end{Bmatrix} \begin{Bmatrix} L_1' & l' & L \\ \lambda & \bar{L} & l \end{Bmatrix} = \begin{Bmatrix} \bar{L} & l & L_1' \\ l & k & l' \\ L_1 & l' & L \end{Bmatrix}.$$

Summing over σ and λ the coefficients of $G^k(nl, n'l')$ become

$$g_k(l, l') = N([l, l'])([S_1, L_1, S_1', L_1'])^{1/2}(-1)^{S_1 + S_1'}\begin{pmatrix} l' & k & l \\ 0 & 0 & 0 \end{pmatrix}^2$$

$$\times \sum_{\bar{\psi}} (\psi_1\{|\bar{\psi})(\bar{\psi}|\}\psi_1') \begin{Bmatrix} s & \bar{S} & S_1' \\ s & S & S_1 \end{Bmatrix} \begin{Bmatrix} \bar{L} & l & L_1' \\ l & k & l' \\ L_1 & l' & L \end{Bmatrix}. \quad (2\text{-}94)$$

Thus the total electrostatic interaction between the l^N core and the added electron $n'l'$ will be

$$\sum_k [f_k(l, l')F^k(nl, n'l') + g_k(l, l')G^k(nl, n'l')], \quad (2\text{-}95)$$

where the f_k and g_k are as given in Eqs. 2-93 and 2-94 respectively. These results were first given by Judd.[53]

We have dealt at some length with the derivation of the matrix elements of electrostatic interaction between an l^N core and an added $n'l'$ electron. The method outlined is quite general and can be used whenever type **G** operators are encountered. We first apply Eq. 2-83, which has the effect of separating from the l^N core a single l-electron. We next make a recoupling of the angular momenta and then operate on the coordinates of the two isolated electrons. Wybourne[51]* has discussed the problem of calculating the matrix elements of electrostatic interactions between two nonequivalent electrons and a core of equivalent electrons. The resulting formulas are somewhat more complicated than those just given because of the more extensive recoupling of the angular momentum. In principle, we can consider the coupling of any number of groups of equivalent electrons as has been examined by Innes and Ufford.[54]

Equations 2-93 and 2-94 undergo considerable simplification when the added electron has $l' = 0$. We may then write the interaction H_s of an s-electron with the l^N core as simply

$$(nl^N\psi_1, n's; S_1 \pm \tfrac{1}{2}L_1|H_s|nl^N\psi_1', n's; S_1 \pm \tfrac{1}{2}L_1)$$

$$= \delta(\psi_1, \psi_1')\left[NF^0(nl, n's) \mp G^l(nl, n's) \frac{2S_1 + 1 \pm (N - 1)}{2(2l + 1)}\right]. \quad (2\text{-}96)$$

The terms involving N are constant for all the states of the configuration and may be incorporated in the energy matrix as an additive constant. Apart from this additive constant, the electrostatic energy matrix of the $l^{4l + 2 - N}s$ configuration will be identical to that of the $l^N s$ configuration.

---

* The quantity k appearing in the phases of Eqs. 11 to 13 of this paper should be replaced by unity.

The relationship of the electrostatic energy matrices of the $l^N l'$ configuration to those of the conjugate $l^{4l+2-N} l'$ configuration is not as simple when $l' \neq 0$. Racah[40] has shown that the matrix elements of a tensor operator $\mathbf{T}^{(xy)}$ operating within the l^N configuration are simply related to those of the conjugate configuration, namely,

$$(l^N \psi_1 || \mathbf{T}^{(xy)} || l^N \psi_1') = -(-1)^{x+y} (l^{4l+2-N} \psi_1 || \mathbf{T}^{(xy)\dagger} || l^{4l+2-N} \psi_1'). \quad (2\text{-}97)$$

It follows that the coefficients $f_k(l, l')$ for the $l^{4l+2-N} l'$-configuration will be just the negatives of those found for the $l^N l'$ configuration. The behavior of the coefficients $g_k(l, l')$ under the operation of conjugation is of much greater complexity. For the $l^{4l+2-N} l'$ configuration the coefficients of fractional parentage appearing in Eq. 2-94 may be correlated with those of the l^{N+1} configuration using Eq. 2-22. Thus for the $l^{4l+2-N} l'$ configuration the $g_k(l, l')$'s will be given by

$$g_k(l, l') = (-1)^{N+L_1+L_1'} (N+1)([l, l']) \begin{pmatrix} l & k & l' \\ 0 & 0 & 0 \end{pmatrix}^2 \sum_{\bar{\psi}} (\bar{\psi}\{|\psi_1)(\psi_1'|\}\bar{\psi})([\bar{S}, \bar{L}])$$

$$\times \begin{Bmatrix} s & \bar{S} & S_1' \\ s & S & S_1 \end{Bmatrix} \begin{Bmatrix} \bar{L} & l & L_1' \\ l & k & l' \\ L_1 & l' & L \end{Bmatrix}, \quad (2\text{-}98)$$

where $\bar{\psi} = l^{N+1}(\bar{\alpha}\bar{S}\bar{L})$, $\psi_1' = l^N(\alpha_1 S_1 L_1)$, and $\psi_1' = l^N(\alpha_1' S_1' L_1')$. While this formula allows us to use the tables of coefficients of fractional parentage for $N \leq 2l + 1$, it does not lead to any general relationships of the matrix elements with those of the conjugate configuration. Some special cases for states of maximum multiplicity have, however, been given by Judd.[53]

The coefficients of the G^k's as given in Eq. 2-94 may be written in an alternative form that more readily demonstrates their behavior under conjugation.

$$g_k(l, l') = ([l, l']) \begin{pmatrix} l' & k & l \\ 0 & 0 & 0 \end{pmatrix}^2 \sum_x ([x]) \begin{Bmatrix} l & l & x \\ l' & l' & k \end{Bmatrix}$$

$$\times [(l^N \psi_1, sl'; SL||(\mathbf{U}^{(x)} \cdot \mathbf{u}^{(x)})||l^N \psi_1', sl'; SL) - 4(-1)^x (l^N \psi_1, sl'; SL \\ ||(\mathbf{V}^{(1x)} \cdot \mathbf{v}^{(1x)})||l^N \psi_1', sl'; SL)]/2, \quad (2\text{-}99)$$

where the tensors $\mathbf{U}^{(x)}$ and $\mathbf{V}^{(1x)}$ operate on the states of the l^N core and $\mathbf{u}^{(x)}$ and $\mathbf{v}^{(1x)}$ operate on the added electron. The double tensors $\mathbf{V}^{(1x)}$ are defined as

$$\mathbf{V}^{(1x)} = \sum_i (\mathbf{su}^{(x)})_i. \quad (2\text{-}100)$$

For the l^N configuration,

$$(l^N\psi_1||\mathbf{V}^{(1x)}||l^N\psi'_1) = N[s(s+1)(2s+1)[S_1, L_1, S_1', L_1']]^{1/2}$$

$$\times \sum_{\bar\psi} (\psi_1\{|\bar\psi)(\bar\psi|\}\psi_1') \begin{Bmatrix} S_1 & S_1' & 1 \\ s & s & \bar S \end{Bmatrix} \begin{Bmatrix} L_1 & L_1' & x \\ l & l & \bar L \end{Bmatrix} (-1)^{\bar S + \bar L + S_1 + L_1 + l + s + x + 1}$$

$$(2\text{-}101)$$

a result that follows directly from Eqs. 2-49 and 2-74.

The result of Eq. 2-99 may be found from Eq. 2-94. The 6-j symbol in the spins is expanded, after interchanging the second and third columns, to give

$$\begin{Bmatrix} s & S_1' & S \\ s & S_1 & \bar S \end{Bmatrix} = \sum_y ([y])(-1)^{y+S+s} \begin{Bmatrix} S_1 & S_1' & y \\ s & s & S \end{Bmatrix} \begin{Bmatrix} S_1 & S_1' & y \\ s & s & \bar S \end{Bmatrix},$$

where y is limited to the values 0 and 1. The rows and columns of the 9-j symbol are first rearranged and then expanded in terms of three 6-j symbols using Eq. 2-40 to yield

$$\begin{Bmatrix} \bar L & l & L_1' \\ l & k & l' \\ L_1 & l' & L \end{Bmatrix} = (-1)^{L+L_1+L_1'+L+k} \sum_x ([x])(-1)^{2x} \begin{Bmatrix} L_1 & L_1' & x \\ l' & l' & L \end{Bmatrix}$$

$$\times \begin{Bmatrix} L_1 & L_1' & x \\ l & l & \bar L \end{Bmatrix} \begin{Bmatrix} l & l & x \\ l' & l' & k \end{Bmatrix}.$$

These two results may then be substituted into Eq. 2-94 and the summations over $\bar\psi$ performed using Eqs. 2-92 and 2-101. The final result is then achieved by writing the tensors as a scalar product using Eq. 2-47. An alternative, and in some ways more direct, derivation of Eq. 2-99 has been indicated by Racah[40] and Arima et al.[55]

The behavior of $g_k(l, l')$ under conjugation now becomes clear when the tensors of Eq. 2-99 are examined in the light of Eq. 2-97. The rank x may take on both odd and even integral values. For even values the matrix elements of $\mathbf{U}^{(x)}$ will change their sign, although not their magnitude, under conjugation, whereas those of $\mathbf{V}^{(1x)}$ will remain unchanged. For odd values of x the reverse situation will hold. Thus apart from a few very special cases[53] no general relationships between the $g_k(l, l')$ coefficients of the $l^N l'$ and $l^{4l+2-N} l'$ configurations are to be expected.

2-11 Spin-Orbit Interaction

The effect of the electrostatic interaction between pairs of electrons is to remove the degeneracy of the different LS terms of the configurations.

Diagonalization of the electrostatic energy matrices leads to a set of energy levels, each being characterized by the quantum numbers L and S. These quantum numbers will remain "good" quantum numbers, whereas in most cases the $\tau v W U$ quantum numbers will not. As a result several energy levels may possess the same LS quantum numbers but contain different admixtures of the basis states in which the matrices were constructed. For light elements a pure electrostatic calculation of the energy levels may suffice for making assignments of quantum numbers to the observed energy-level schemes. For heavy elements such as the lanthanides, and even more so for the actinides, this treatment is entirely inadequate.

To calculate the energy levels of the electrons of a rare earth atom or ion with any reliability we must include, besides the electrostatic interactions, the magnetic interactions. These will include *spin-orbit*, *spin-spin*, *spin-other-orbit*, and similar interactions. Spin-orbit interaction is by far the predominant interaction. To include the effects of spin-orbit interaction we must add a term[33]

$$H_{s-o} = \sum_{i=1}^{N} \xi(r_i)(\mathbf{s}_i \cdot \mathbf{l}_i) \tag{2-102}$$

to the perturbation Hamiltonian of Eq. 2-3. Here r_i is the radial coordinate, $\mathbf{s}_i$ the spin, $\mathbf{l}_i$ the orbital angular momentum of the ith electron, and

$$\xi(r_i) = \frac{\hbar^2}{2m^2c^2r_i} \frac{dU(r_i)}{dr_i}. \tag{2-103}$$

The spin-orbit interaction is diagonal in the one-electron orbital quantum number l, although not in the principal quantum number n. Since the configurations of different n are usually widely separated in energy, interaction between configurations by way of the spin-orbit interaction need rarely be considered. H_{s-o} commutes with $\mathbf{J}^2$ and $\mathbf{M}$ but not with $\mathbf{L}^2$ or $\mathbf{S}^2$, and hence its matrix elements are diagonal in J and independent of M. They are not, however, diagonal in L and S, with the result that the spin-orbit interaction will couple states whose L and/or S differ by not more than one unit. When spin-orbit interaction is appreciable (as is true for all the heavy elements), states of different L and S will be mixed and the LS coupling of the electrons is said to be broken.

In the presence of strong spin-orbit interaction it is usual to perform an *intermediate coupling* calculation. Here the matrix elements of the electrostatic and spin-orbit interactions are calculated in a well-defined coupling scheme (usually the LS scheme). These matrix elements are then arranged in energy matrices, one for each value of J, with rank (which may be very large) equal to the number of states having the same J occurring in the configuration. The elements of the resulting matrices will now be expressible as a linear combination of the Slater radial integrals and the spin-orbit radial integrals. Particular values of these integrals, appropriate to the configuration being studied, are chosen and the matrix elements then put into numerical form and the matrices diagonalized[42] to yield a set of eigenvalues and their corresponding eigenvectors. A theoretical energy-level scheme may then be constructed. The eigenvectors will indicate the different admixtures of the basis states of the well-defined coupling scheme used in constructing the matrices. With the diagonalization of these matrices the largest perturbations will have been included. We may choose to label each energy level by the well-defined quantum numbers of the predominant basis states indicated by the components of its eigenvector.[56] In some cases an unambiguous nomenclature will not be possible, and the energy level under question can be indicated only by giving its energy, J, and the admixtures of the basis states from which it was formed.[57]

The wave function $\phi(\mathscr{S}\mathscr{L}JM)$* describing the resulting energy states can now be written in terms of the basis states (in the present case LS states) as

$$\phi(\mathscr{S}\mathscr{L}JM) = \sum_{\alpha SL} x(\alpha SLJ)\Psi(\alpha SLJM), \qquad (2\text{-}104)$$

where $x(\alpha SLJ)$ is the component of the eigenvector pertaining to the unperturbed state $\Psi(\alpha SLJM)$ and $\mathscr{S}\mathscr{L}$ serves to label the state.

The effects of an additional small perturbation H_s may be of interest (for example, in studies of hyperfine structure) for just a few levels. Rather than construct very large matrices for all the matrix elements of H_s, we may use the wave functions obtained by diagonalizing the combined electrostatic and spin-orbit interactions as "zero-order" perturbation wave functions and treat the additional interactions as first-order perturbations, noting that

$$(\phi(\mathscr{S}\mathscr{L}JM)|H_s|\phi(\mathscr{S}'\mathscr{L}'J'M')) = \sum_{\alpha SL} \sum_{\alpha'S'L'} x(\alpha SLJ)x(\alpha'S'L'J')$$
$$\times (\Psi(\alpha SLJM)|H_s|\Psi(\alpha'S'L'J'M')). \quad (2\text{-}105)$$

The matrix elements of spin-orbit interaction in an l^N configuration may be obtained readily by noting that the spin-orbit operator is of type

---

* We use script $\mathscr{S}$ and $\mathscr{L}$ to distinguish these numbers from the well-defined S and L quantum numbers of the basis states.

F. The *J*-dependence of the matrix elements is found by application of Eq. (2-47) to be

$$\left(l^N \alpha SLJM \middle| \zeta_{nl} \sum_{i=1}^{N} (\mathbf{s}_i \cdot \mathbf{l}_i) \middle| l^N \alpha' S'L'JM\right) = \zeta_{nl}(-1)^{J+L+S'} \begin{Bmatrix} L & L' & 1 \\ S' & S & J \end{Bmatrix}$$

$$\times \left(l^N \alpha SL \middle| \sum_{i=1}^{N} (\mathbf{s}_i \cdot \mathbf{l}_i) \middle| l^N \alpha' S'L'\right), \quad (2\text{-}106)$$

where ζ_{nl} is the spin-orbit radial integral which is a constant for the states of a given configuration and is defined as[33]

$$\zeta_{nl} = \int_0^{\infty} R_{nl}^2 \xi(r) \, dr. \quad (2\text{-}107)$$

For $S = S'$ and $L = L'$ the 6-*j* symbol may be written in its detailed form[46] to give the diagonal matrix elements as[58]

$$= \zeta_{nl} \frac{\lambda}{2} [J(J+1) - L(L+1) - S(S+1)], \quad (2\text{-}108)$$

where λ is a constant for a given *SL* state. This equation leads to the familiar Lande interval rule that in any Russell-Saunders multiplet the interval between neighboring levels is proportional to the higher *J* of the pair. Departures from the Lande interval rule in multiplets give a measure of the breakdown of Russell-Saunders coupling. For states of maximum multiplicity $\lambda = \pm\frac{1}{2}S$, the sign being taken as positive for $N \leq 2l + 1$ and negative for $N \geq 2l + 1$.

The matrix element on the right-hand side of Eq. 2-106 may be evaluated using first Eq. 2-74 and then applying Eqs. 2-35 and 2-49 to obtain

$$\left(l^N \alpha SL \middle| \sum_{i=1}^{N} (\mathbf{s}_i \cdot \mathbf{l}_i) \middle| l^N \alpha' S'L'\right) = [l(l+1)(2l+1)]^{1/2}$$

$$\times (l^N \alpha SL||\mathbf{V}^{(11)}||l^N \alpha' S'L'). \quad (2\text{-}109)$$

The matrix elements of $\mathbf{V}^{(11)}$ may be found from Eq. 2-101. Nielson and Koster[43] have calculated and tabulated the complete $\mathbf{V}^{(11)}$ matrices for all f^N configurations. They have also generated the complete spin-orbit matrices for these configurations and placed them on magnetic tape for general usage. Judd and Loudon[59] have given the complete spin-orbit matrices for the f^3 configuration and Crozier and Runciman[60] have given those for the f^4 configuration. Spedding[61] has calculated the f^2 spin-orbit matrices, although it should be noted that his matrix elements should be divided by two to bring them into agreement with Eq. 2-106.

Group-theoretical selection rules for the matrix elements of spin-orbit interaction have been discussed by McLellan.[62] Wybourne[63*] and Judd[64]

---

* The paper by Judd contains an important erratum to Wybourne's paper.

have examined some of the general properties of spin-orbit interaction matrix elements. The matrix elements for the l^{4l+2-N} configuration are of the same magnitude but opposite sign as those of the conjugate l^N configuration*. For the particular case of the half-filled shell the matrix elements connecting states of the *same* class vanish, and as a result the diagonal elements are zero; hence the fine structure of the LS terms can arise only through the spin-orbit interaction between states of *different* class.

The matrix elements of spin-orbit interaction for the $l^N l'$ configuration may be calculated in an LS basis using the formula

$$(nl^N\psi_1, n'sl'; SLJM|H_{s-o}|nl^N\psi_1', n'sl'; S'L'JM)$$

$$= (-1)^{S'+L+J+S_1+L_1+l'+s}\begin{Bmatrix} L & L' & 1 \\ S' & S & J \end{Bmatrix}([S, L, S', L'])^{1/2}$$

$$\times \left[[l(l + 1)(2l + 1)]^{1/2}(-1)^{L'+S'}\begin{Bmatrix} S & S' & 1 \\ S_1' & S_1 & s \end{Bmatrix}\begin{Bmatrix} L & L' & 1 \\ L_1' & L_1 & l \end{Bmatrix} \right.$$

$$\times (l^N\psi_1||V^{(11)}||l^N\psi_1')\zeta_{nl} + (-1)^{L+S}[l'(l' + 1)(2l' + 1)]^{1/2}\delta(\psi_1, \psi_1')$$

$$\times \left. \begin{Bmatrix} S & S' & 1 \\ s & s & S_1 \end{Bmatrix}\begin{Bmatrix} L & L' & 1 \\ l' & l' & L_1 \end{Bmatrix}(sl'||v^{(11)}||sl')\zeta_{nl'} \right]. \tag{2-110}$$

This equation follows directly from use of Eqs. 2-47 to 2-49. Except in a few simple cases, the calculation of spin-orbit matrices for $l^N l'$ configurations is a long and laborious task and as such is most suited to machine computation. Formulas for configurations with more than one electron outside the l^N-core may be readily found, but again their application is practical only on a computer. For example, in the f^7 configuration the largest matrix ($J = \frac{7}{2}$) is of rank 50. Addition of a single d-electron to form $f^7 d$ leads to matrices up to rank 426, and the addition of a p-electron to form $f^7 dp$ results in matrices up to rank 2443. Finally, if an s-electron were added to form the $f^7 dps$-configuration, which has supposedly been observed in Gd I spectra,[31] we would be faced with matrices up to rank 4829!

2-12   Calculation of Energy Levels

Having constructed the energy matrices of a particular configuration, it is necessary to determine the magnitudes of the radial integrals for the electrostatic and spin-orbit interactions so that the elements of the matrices may be put into numerical form ready for diagonalization. Two

---

* *N.B.* Under conjugation it is the phase of the *angular* part of the matrix element that changes; the spin-orbit radial integral ζ_{nl}, as defined in Eq. 2-107, is a necessarily *positive* function.

approaches are possible; they may be either evaluated from the radial eigenfunctions or treated as adjustable parameters. In the absence of reliable wave functions it has been a tradition of theoretical spectroscopy to treat the radial integrals as parameters. It might be noted at this point that even if accurate wave functions were known, configuration interaction would preclude a good calculation.

In general, the number of parameters is very much less than that of levels, and they may be chosen to minimize the root-mean-square deviation between the theoretical and experimental energy-level schemes,[65,66] The *mean error Δ* of such a calculation is usually defined by

$$\Delta = \sqrt{\sum_i \Delta_i^2/(n - m)}, \qquad (2\text{-}111)$$

where Δ_i are the differences between the observed and calculated levels, n is the number of known levels, and m is the number of free parameters. This definition assumes that the Δ_i are independent. In atomic energy-level calculations, however, the differences are usually the systematic errors of the theoretical approximation rather than the random errors of measurement.

The derivation of the parameters by a least-squares method naturally requires that the assignments of some levels of the configuration being studied be known. Usually, the parameters are chosen to fit the few known levels, and the resulting energy-level scheme is used to make further level assignments, after which the parameters may be refined. The size of the mean error will tend to indicate the correctness of the theoretical description of the energy-level structure of the atom or ion being studied, although it must be emphasized that the smallness of the mean error alone does not guarantee the correctness of the description. The fitting of energy levels cannot be regarded as a purely statistical problem. It is not enough to be able to just fit energy levels. A correct theoretical description should also yield eigenfunctions that can be used to calculate other physical observables with a comparable precision.

It is clear that it would be of considerable assistance if a preliminary estimate of the parameters could be made prior to making detailed calculations. Sometimes there are too few known levels to fix the parameters for an initial calculation. A useful starting *approximation**

---

* This approximation does not imply that the f-orbitals are in fact hydrogenic. Calculations show that the actual radial eigenfunctions are quite unlike hydrogenic eigenfunctions. The hydrogenic approximation happens to yield ratios of the Slater integrals F_k that are close to those of the rare earths, and the approximation ends there. Eigenfunctions quite unlike those of a hydrogenic atom can be found to yield almost the same ratios. The ratios of the Slater integrals turn out to be peculiarly insensitive to the precise shape of the eigenfunction.

for the f^N configurations is to assume the radial eigenfunction to be hydrogenic.[67] The ratios of the Slater radial integrals, F_4/F_2 and F_6/F_2, may then be calculated exactly for a hydrogenic eigenfunction to give for 4f-electrons,

$$\frac{F_4}{F_2} = \frac{41}{297} = 0.13805 \quad \text{and} \quad \frac{F_6}{F_2} = \frac{175}{11,583} = 0.01511,$$

and for 5f-electrons,

$$\frac{F_4}{F_2} = \frac{23,255}{163,559} = 0.14218 \quad \text{and} \quad \frac{F_6}{F_2} = \frac{102,725}{6,378,801}$$
$$= 0.01610.$$

From these ratios the parameters E^k may be evaluated in terms of the single radial integral F_2. The resulting values of E^k for 4f-electrons are

$$E^0 = -18.87F_2, \quad E^1 = 14.6818F_2, \quad E^2 = 0.07685F_2, \quad E^3 = 1.4845F_2,$$

and for 5f-electrons,

$$E^0 = -19.48F_2, \quad E^1 = 15.0094F_2, \quad E^2 = 0.07624F_2, \quad E^3 = 1.4625F_2.$$

Within this approximation the elements of the energy matrices for the f^N configuration may be expressed in terms of just two radial integrals, F_2 and ζ_{nf}.

Initial estimates of the various spin-orbit coupling constants can be made by studying the energy-level separations of the levels of one-electron type configurations. In configurations of the type l or l^{4l+1} there are only two SLJ states, $^2l_{2l+1}$ and $^2l_{2l-1}$. If we can assume that the separation of these two states arises solely from the spin-orbit interaction, then

T A B L E 2-2   Spin-orbit coupling constants ζ_{nl} for several one-electron-type configurations

Ion	Configuration	Energy Separation (cm^{-1})	ζ_{nl} (cm^{-1})
Ce IV[69]	$4f^1$	2,253	643.7
	$5d^1$	2,489	995.6
	$6p^1$	4,707	3138.0
Yb IV[70]	$4f^{13}$	10,090	2882.8
Tm I[9]	$4f^{13}6s^2$	8,771	2506.0
Th II[71–72]	$5f7s^2$	6,712	1917.7
	$6d7s^2$	3,888	1555.2
Th IV[11]	$5f^1$	4,325	1235.7
	$6d^1$	5,293	2117.2
	$7p^1$	12,817	8544.6

the energy difference of the states may be found by application of Eq. 2-108 to be just $(2l + 1)\zeta_{nl}/2$.* The values deduced from several configurations are tabulated in Table 2-2. We note from this tabulation that there is a considerable increase in ζ_{nl} with increasing atomic number and that ζ_{nl} is considerably greater in the actinides than in the corresponding lanthanides. In general, for a given rare earth the spin-orbit coupling constant increases with increasing ionization.

2-13 Energy Levels of f^N Configurations

A study of the energy levels of f^N type configurations leads to information concerning the interactions between f-electrons and the nature of the couplings of the f-electrons among themselves. A detailed understanding of the energy-level structure of the f^N configurations is an essential prerequisite to an understanding of the properties of the more complex $f^N l$ and $f^N l l'$ configurations. Fortunately, spectroscopic studies have led to the establishment of energy levels for several f^N configurations.

All the energy levels of the ^5I multiplet† of Nd I $(4f^4 6s^2)$ and of the ^7F multiplet of Sm I $(4f^6 6s^2)$ have been determined experimentally by Schuurmans[76] and Albertson[77] respectively. The spin-orbit splittings for these multiplets may be readily calculated in terms of the spin-orbit coupling constants of the atoms using Eq. 2-108. A first estimate of the magnitude of the spin-orbit coupling constants may then be found by requiring that they reproduce the $(^5I_8 - {}^5I_4)$ and $(^7F_6 - {}^7F_0)$ separations. This requirement yields

$$\zeta_{4f}(\text{Nd I}) = 776.7 \text{ cm}^{-1} \quad \text{and} \quad \zeta_{4f}(\text{Sm I}) = 1148.8 \text{ cm}^{-1}.$$

From these values the energies of the remaining levels of the multiplet may be calculated to give the energies of Table 2-3. An inspection of this table shows that the calculated energy levels differ from their experimentally determined values by as much as 350 cm^{-1}. This rather large discrepancy suggests that the assumption of pure LS coupling, which has neglected the off-diagonal spin-orbit matrix elements, is inadequate.[78]

To improve these results the off-diagonal matrix elements must be included. This means that the electrostatic plus spin-orbit interaction

---

* Kessler[68] has found that there is appreciable electrostatic interaction between the $5f7s^2$ and $5f6d7s$ configurations of Th II, with the result that the ζ_{5f} value obtained using Eq. 2-108 is overestimated. When configuration interaction is included, ζ_{5f} is reduced to approximately 1195 cm^{-1}.

† Later work by Hassan and Klinkenberg[73-75] has confirmed these levels of Nd I. Their earlier work[73,74] had indicated the possible existence of a $^5G_3$ level at 5287.80 cm^{-1}. It now appears doubtful that this level can be identified with the $4f^4 6s^2$ configuration.[75]

matrices must be diagonalized or a second—(or even higher) order perturbation calculation performed. In general, it is simplest to diagonalize the matrices on a high-speed computer to give an "exact" solution by including all the electrostatic and spin-orbit interactions within the configuration.

TABLE 2-3 Calculation of the ground-multiplet splittings in Nd I and Sm I for LS and intermediate coupling

	Nd I				Sm I		
	Expt.	*LS*	*Int.*		*Expt.*	*LS*	*Int.*
$^5I_4$	0	0	0	$^7F_0$	0	0	0
$^5I_5$	1128.04	970.88	1126.81	$^7F_1$	292.58	191.45	291.39
$^5I_6$	2366.58	2135.92	2367.22	$^7F_2$	811.92	574.40	812.13
$^5I_7$	3681.65	3495.15	3684.01	$^7F_3$	1489.55	1148.8	1490.28
$^5I_8$	5048.54	5048.55	5049.34	$^7F_4$	2273.09	1914.7	2274.81
				$^7F_5$	3125.46	2872.0	3126.72
				$^7F_6$	4020.66	4020.8	4020.67

If $4f$-hydrogenic ratios are used for the Slater integrals, the matrix elements of the $4f^4$ and $4f^6$ energy matrices* may be expressed in terms of the radial integrals F_2 and ζ_{4f}. When the matrices of these configurations are diagonalized for several values of F_2 and ζ_{4f}, the parameters that yield energy levels closest to the experimental energy levels are found to be[79]

$$\text{Nd I} \quad F_2 = 292.26 \text{ cm}^{-1}, \quad \text{Sm I} \quad F_2 = 335.63 \text{ cm}^{-1},$$
$$\zeta_{4f} = 777.41 \text{ cm}^{-1}, \quad \quad \quad \zeta_{4f} = 1062.27 \text{ cm}^{-1}.$$

The resulting energy levels are included in Table 2-3. The remaining discrepancies are now approximately 2 cm^{-1}. The agreement of the theory with the experimental results is quite startling and might be thought to validate this simple approach to a seemingly highly complex problem. Close agreement between theory and experiment, however, does not necessarily demonstrate the correctness of the theory. Before drawing any conclusions from these results an examination of the approximations of the theory must be made.

In making these calculations the following have been assumed.

---

* The $6s^2$ closed shell has no effect on the relative spacings of the levels and hence configurations of the type $l^N s^2$ may be given the same theoretical treatment as l^N configurations.

1. The $4f$-radial eigenfunction may be approximated by a $4f$-hydrogenic eigenfunction in so far as the *ratios* of the Slater radial integrals are concerned.

2. The f^N configuration may be treated as an isolated configuration not interacting with other configurations, that is, *configuration interaction* is ignored.

3. The remaining interactions such as spin-spin and spin-other-orbit may be neglected.

We shall postpone discussion of these last two assumptions until Secs. 2-17 and 2-19.

The first assumption has the advantage of reducing the number of electrostatic radial integrals to be determined from three to just one. In fixing F_2 and ζ_{4f}, experimental data involving only the *ground multiplet* have been used. In pure LS coupling, the structure of the ground multiplet is determined solely by the spin-orbit interaction within the multiplet. In the lanthanides, the levels of the ground multiplets are usually greater than 90% pure LS states and the perturbations of the levels by higher-energy levels of the configuration are relatively weak. Thus, although the splittings of the ground multiplet are a very sensitive function of the spin-orbit coupling constant, they are relatively insensitive to the choice of the Slater integrals. Had we chosen to use $5f$-hydrogenic ratios for the Slater integrals in calculating the levels of the ground multiplets of Nd I and Sm I, almost identical results would have been obtained except for the value of F_2. Any set of integrals that predicted the positions of the upper levels with only moderate accuracy could be expected to yield quite precise energy levels and eigenfunctions for the ground multiplet. The same set of Slater integrals will not necessarily give accurate energy levels for other than the ground multiplet.

It is very important to always bear in mind that in atomic spectra a precise calculation does not necessarily validate our theory. To derive the parameters of the energy matrices of any configuration from experimental data, it is essential that the data include the energies of several different terms of the configuration if we are to have any confidence in the derived parameters.

For several of the rare earths there already exists a sufficient number of established levels belonging to f^N type configurations to permit a least-squares derivation of all the parameters without making simplifying assumptions as to the form of the radial integrals. Sugar[32,80] has made a detailed study of the spectrum of Pr III and established many energy levels. Notably, he has reported the energies of 38 of the 41 possible levels of the $4f^3$ configuration. His results allow a deeper insight into the nature of the Slater parameters for the f^N configurations. If $4f$-hydrogenic ratios are used for the Slater integrals, it is found that the levels of the ground multiplet ^4I may be fitted to approximately 4 cm^{-1} using the parameters

$$F_2 = 288.5 \text{ cm}^{-1} \quad \text{and} \quad \zeta_{4f} = 663.6 \text{ cm}^{-1}.$$

Diagonalization of the f^3 energy matrices using these parameters leads to an over-all mean error between the experimental and theoretical levels of approximately 850 cm^{-1}, with some of the deviations being as large as 1960 cm^{-1}. If all the parameters are treated as free variables and their values derived by a least-squares analysis, the mean error is reduced to approximately 484 cm^{-1} using the parameters[81]

$$E^0 = 11024 \text{ cm}^{-1}, \quad E^1 = 4212.4 \text{ cm}^{-1}, \quad E^2 = 20.82 \text{ cm}^{-1},$$
$$E^3 = 400.9 \text{ cm}^{-1}, \quad \zeta_{4f} = 642.6 \text{ cm}^{-1}.$$

Although part of the reduction in the mean error probably comes from the increase in the number of variables, the improvement is nevertheless significant. It is interesting to note that although the over-all agreement is considerably improved, the deviations for the ground multiplet are worsened. This may indicate that the spin-orbit coupling constant varies from one multiplet to another as would be the case if spin-spin or spin-other-orbit interactions were appreciable. Alternatively, it may be that the spin-orbit coupling constant is compensating for an inadequate description of the electrostatic interactions.

The parameter E^0 will not be precisely as defined in Eq. 2-80, but it will differ by some constant since its value will include, among other things, the binding energies of the electrons. The remaining electrostatic parameters have the ratios

$$E^1 : E^2 : E^3 = 14.6818 : 0.07257 : 1.39728$$

compared with the $4f$-hydrogenic ratios of

$$E^1 : E^2 : E^3 = 14.6818 : 0.07685 : 1.48447.$$

The deviations of these ratios although relatively small are nevertheless very significant since quite small changes in the Slater integrals can lead to substantial changes in the energies of the levels.

The discrepancies between the calculated and experimental levels are in some respects still appreciable and are, for the most part, ascribable to the failure to take into account the effects of electrostatic interactions between the $4f^3$ configuration and other configurations of the same parity.

It has frequently been assumed that the f^N configurations exhibit fairly good LS coupling. This assertion has been based on the fact that the lowest multiplets of the lanthanides are usually fairly pure LS multiplets. The upper levels of the lanthanides usually deviate markedly from LS coupling. This is clearly borne out in Trees' analysis of the Pr III ($4f^3$) energy levels.[81] The levels of the ^4I ground multiplet are found to be not less than 98% pure ^4I levels. For the upper levels the purity of the levels varies appreciably. Thus the level at 10,033 cm^{-1}, which is usually designated as a $^2H_{9/2}$ level, is actually made up of 68.3% ^2H, 17.2% ^2G, 10.5% ^4F, 2.2% ^4I, and 1.8% ^4G. It should always be kept in mind that the labels that spectroscopists use in designating energy levels are not necessarily precisely defined. In fact, many of the labels used have little physical meaning.

As the number of f-electrons increases, the spin-orbit coupling constant increases considerably more rapidly than do the electrostatic parameters, with the result that the off-diagonal spin-orbit matrix elements become increasingly more important as the f-shell is filled, and hence the breakdown in LS coupling becomes greater. The role of the density of the levels in determining the degree of breakdown of LS coupling is not usually recognized. As the half-filled shell is approached, the density of the upper levels increases rapidly, with the result that the average spacing between levels of the same total angular momentum J decreases.

Spin-orbit interactions will mix states of the same J but different LS by second-, or higher-order perturbations. The importance of these perturbations increases with the decreasing separation of the levels. Thus, for the upper levels at least, the breakdown of LS coupling increases rapidly with the filling of the f-shell until the half-filled shell is reached and then it starts to decrease at a less rapid rate. This decrease results, in part, from the spreading apart of the energy levels being offset by the increase in magnitude of the spin-orbit coupling constant with atomic number. As a result of the high density of the upper levels and the spin-orbit interaction between levels of the same J, the lanthanides, and more especially the actinides, show a pronounced "*repulsion*" of the energy levels[82] near the middle of the period. This repulsion of the energy levels has the effect of making the spacings of consecutive levels of the same J tend to have equal spacings, or more precisely, the spacings tend to exhibit a Wigner distribution.[83]

Strong spin-orbit mixing of states that differ by more than one unit in L or S occurs frequently if their Coulomb energies are close to being degenerate. Thus in Er IV ($4f^{11}$) the two states $^4F_{9/2}$ and $^4I_{9/2}$ become heavily mixed even though there are no spin-orbit matrix elements coupling them, the $^4F_{9/2}$ level containing a 30% admixture of the $^4I_{9/2}$ state.[56] Levels that are found to be coincident in the Russell-Saunders approximation frequently shift apart in energy by several thousand wave numbers when an intermediate coupling calculation is made. In Russell-Saunders coupling the levels $^2P_{3/2}$ and $^4D_{3/2}$ of Nd IV ($4f^3$) are found to be almost in coincidence.[59] The two states are coupled by a large spin-orbit interaction matrix element, $\sqrt{35}/2\zeta_{4f}$, which is ~ 2540 cm^{-1}. If the two levels are supposed to coincide in Russell-Saunders coupling and the spin-orbit interaction between them taken into account, the levels shift ~ 5080 cm^{-1} apart to give an upper level

$$\frac{1}{\sqrt{2}}\left(|^2D_{3/2}\rangle + |^2P_{3/2}\rangle\right)$$

and a lower level

$$\frac{1}{\sqrt{2}}\left(|^2D_{3/2}\rangle - |^2P_{3/2}\rangle\right).$$

The energy levels of Gd IV ($4f^7$) as deduced from crystal spectra[84] form an interesting example of the importance of intermediate coupling. For the half-filled shell there is no spin-orbit interaction within or between states of the same class and hence the ^6P states cannot split in the Russell-Saunders approximation. Nevertheless it is found that the ^6P state is split into three levels, $^6P_{3/2}$, $^6P_{5/2}$, and $^6P_{7/2}$, with an over-all splitting of approximately 1200 cm^{-1}. This splitting of the ^6P state is a direct result of the spin-orbit coupling of the ^6P state with the ^8S and ^6D states which are of different class.[85] The spin-orbit coupling constants for the $5f^N$ configurations of the actinides are approximately twice those of the corresponding lanthanides, whereas the electrostatic interactions are normally only two-thirds. As a result of the smaller electrostatic interactions the densities of the levels in the actinides are considerably higher than those for the corresponding lanthanides. These higher densities, together with the much greater spin-orbit coupling constants, make for a considerable breakdown in Russell-Saunders coupling. It is to be expected that there will be a well-developed tendency to j-j coupling in the latter half of the actinide period, although probably not sufficient to make j-j coupling a superior basis for making calculations.[86]

Blaise et al.[87] and Bauche et al.[88] have determined the energies of all the levels of the ^7F "multiplet" of Pu I ($5f^67s^2$) as well as that of the first excited level with $J = 0$. The results are compared in Fig. 2-1 with the corresponding levels of Sm I ($4f^66s^2$). In the latter atom the multiplet has approximately 95% ^7F character, whereas in Pu I the multiplet is grossly distorted because of strong spin-orbit mixing with higher states. In particular, the ground state $^7F_0$ is found to have less than 50% ^7F character, and thus the association of the levels with a multiplet has little physical meaning. It is interesting to note that although in Sm I the $^5D_0$ level is

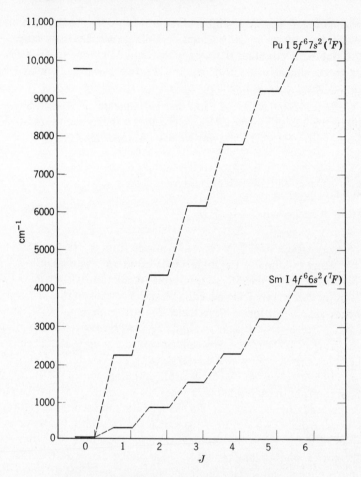

Fig. 2-1　Low-lying energy levels of Sm I and Pu I.

calculated to be at approximately 14,400 cm^{-1}, in Pu I a $J = 0$ level occurs actually *below* the $^7F_6$ level. It is apparent that there can be little resemblance between energy-level structure of these two atoms. Conway[89] has calculated the energy levels for Pu I $(5f^67s^2)$ assuming 5f-hydrogenic ratios for the Slater integrals. By using the parameters

$$F_2 = 230.6 \text{ cm}^{-1} \quad \text{and} \quad \zeta_{5f} = 2174.6 \text{ cm}^{-1},$$

he was able to obtain a remarkably good fit to the observed levels associated with the ^7F "multiplet," although not the same precision as obtained for Sm I $(4f^66s^2)$. However, the calculation fails to place the excited

$J = 0$ level *below* the $^7F_6$ level.   In fact, no set of F_2 and ζ_{5f} parameters will yield the correct result as long as hydrogenic ratios are assumed. Unfortunately, the existent data are insufficient to permit a derivation of all the Slater integrals by a least-squares fitting.

Klinkenberg[90] has determined all the energy levels of the $5f^2$ configuration of Th III in addition to those of several other two-electron configurations.   His results give considerable insight into the magnitude of electrostatic and spin-orbit interactions at the commencement of the actinides.   Racah[91] has made a detailed theoretical analysis of Klinkenberg's results by deriving the electrostatic and spin-orbit parameters by the least-squares method.   Using the parameters

$$F_0 = 26{,}329 \text{ cm}^{-1}, \qquad F_2 = 193 \text{ cm}^{-1}, \qquad F_4 = 36.3 \text{ cm}^{-1},$$
$$F_6 = 3.4 \text{ cm}^{-1}, \quad \text{and} \quad \zeta_{5f} = 1035 \text{ cm}^{-1},$$

he was able to fit the experimental levels with a mean error of approximately 450 cm^{-1} or approximately 1.3% of the width of the configuration. Racah's parameters give the ratios of the Slater integrals as

$$\frac{F_4}{F_2} = 0.1881 \qquad \text{and} \qquad \frac{F_6}{F_2} = 0.01762,$$

which differ appreciably from those of a $5f$-hydrogenic eigenfunction. As with the lanthanides, the ratios of the Slater integrals tend to be larger than those of the hydrogenic eigenfunction.   However, it should be remembered that thorium, the first member of the actinide series, is not typical of the actinides inasmuch as it contains no $5f$-electrons in its ground state, the actinide contraction having scarcely commenced.   The parameters for actinides further on in the series may exhibit a rather different behavior as the actinide contraction progresses.

2-14   Coupling Schemes and Energy-Level Diagrams

Studies of the energy-level structures of the f^N configurations tell us much about the magnitudes of the electrostatic and spin-orbit interactions as well as the nature of the couplings between the f-electrons.   Similarly, studies of the energy levels of the $f^N l$ and $f^N l l'$ type configurations lead to information concerning the interactions and couplings of the nonequivalent electrons with the f^N core.

The simplest configurations of the type $f^N l$ are those in which l is an s-electron.   The electrostatic interaction of the s-electron with the f^N core introduces only one radial integral $G^3(f, s)$, in addition to those of the f^N core.

The low-lying levels of the $4f^46s$-configuration of Nd II form a particularly interesting example of the coupling of a s-electron to a core of equivalent f-electrons. Schuurmans[76] has determined the energies of all the levels that result from the coupling of a $6s$-electron with the ^5I term of the $4f^4$ core. In LS coupling two multiplets, ^6I and ^4I, are to be expected. The levels, arranged in LS coupling, are depicted in Fig. 2-2a.

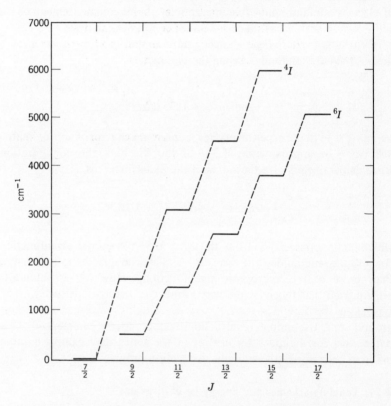

Fig. 2-2a   Energy levels of Nd II $4f^4(^5I)6s$ in LS coupling.

The intervals between the successive levels deviate considerably from those predicted by the Lande interval rule, showing that the two multiplets cannot be considered to follow Russell-Saunders coupling closely. The question arises: Is Russell-Saunders coupling the coupling scheme that describes most closely the physical coupling of the $6s$-electron to the $4f^4$ core? An inspection of Fig. 2-2a shows that the levels can be grouped into rather close pairs as in Fig. 2-2b. The energy-level scheme now has a simple, and physically significant, form.   Each pair of levels corresponds to the coupling of the angular momentum of the 6s-electron to the total angular momentum J_1 of the ^5I state of the $4f^4$ core to form the total angular momentum J of the ion.   The angular momentum of the 6s-electron may couple either parallel to, or antiparallel to, the angular momentum J_1.   Associated with these two couplings are a different

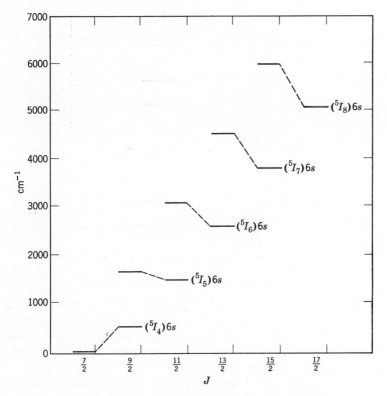

Fig. 2-2b   Energy levels of Nd II $4f^4(^5I)6s$ in J_1j coupling.

electrostatic exchange interaction of the 6s-electron with the $4f^4$ core. The exchange interaction of the 6s-electron with the $4f^4$ core is very weak, and consequently, the occurrence of close pairs of levels is scarcely surprising.   The appropriateness of this coupling scheme is seen in Fig. 2-2c, where the centers of gravities of the pairs of levels are compared with the levels found by Schuurmans for Nd I $4f^4$ (^5I).

The coupling scheme used to describe the $4f^N6s$-configurations is a

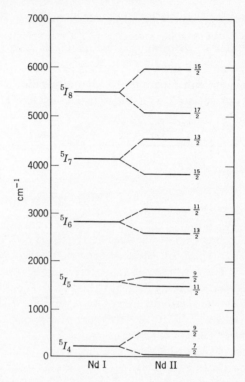

Fig. 2-2c   A comparison of the low-levels of Nd I and Nd II.

special case of the $J_1 j$ coupling scheme, which is, in turn, a generalization of j-j coupling.   In this scheme the electrons of the f^N core are first coupled to form states characterized by the quantum numbers $S_1 L_1 J_1$.   The spin and orbital angular momentum of the nonequivalent electron are then coupled to form states characterized by a total angular momentum j. The angular momenta J_1 and j are now coupled together to form states of the atom or ion characterized by their total angular momentum J. The manner in which the electrons of the core are coupled to form J_1 need not be restricted to LS coupling, although for the purposes of making calculations in the $J_1 j$ coupling scheme it is usually simplest to consider the states of the core in the LS coupling basis.

For the purposes of labeling energy levels it is usual to give the designation of the core level and the quantum numbers $J_1 j J$.   This coupling may be considered as a direct consequence of the strong binding of the core electrons and the weak electrostatic interaction of the nonequivalent electron with the core electrons.   The separation of the levels of given $J_1 j$

will be a measure of the closeness of the physical coupling scheme to that of $J_1 j$ coupling.

In $J_1 j$ coupling the treatment of the spin-orbit interaction is considerably simpler than in LS coupling. Making the abbreviations

$$\psi_1 = l^N \alpha_1 S_1 L_1 \quad \text{and} \quad \psi_1' = l^N \alpha_1' S_1' L_1',$$

we can write the spin-orbit interaction matrix elements for the states of the configuration $l^N l'$ in $J_1 j$ coupling as

$$(\psi_1 J_1, sl'j; JM | H_{s-o} | \psi_1', sl'j'; JM) = \delta(J_1, J_1') \delta(j, j')$$

$$\left[\delta(\psi_1, \psi_1') \zeta_{l'}(sl'j | \mathbf{s} \cdot \mathbf{l} | sl'j) + \zeta_l \left(\psi_1 J_1 | \sum_{i=1}^{n} (\mathbf{s}_i \cdot \mathbf{l}_i) | \psi_1' J_1 \right) \right], \quad (2\text{-}112)$$

where

$$(sl'j | \mathbf{s} \cdot \mathbf{l} | sl'j) = \frac{j(j + 1) - l'(l' + 1) - s(s + 1)}{2}, \quad (2\text{-}113)$$

whereas for the second part of the right-hand side of Eq. 2-112 the spin-orbit matrix elements are just those calculated for the l^N-configuration using Eq. 2-106. The treatment of spin-orbit interaction in $J_1 j$ coupling has the great advantage of being diagonal in J_1 and j. Thus the spin-orbit interaction is taken into account simply by adding the first term in the right-hand side of Eq. 2-112 to the diagonal of the spin-orbit matrices calculated for the f^N core.

The ease of calculating the spin-orbit interaction matrix elements is offset by the difficulty in calculating those for the electrostatic interactions of the added electron with the core in $J_1 j$ coupling. In LS coupling these matrix elements are diagonal in LS and J and are given by Eq. 2-94. In $J_1 j$ coupling the matrix elements are diagonal in J but *not* in J_1 and j.

We may always calculate the matrix elements of any operator H_{op} in the $J_1 j$ coupling scheme by first calculating the matrix elements in the LS coupling scheme and then making a transformation to $J_1 j$ coupling. A state

$$((S_1 L_1) J_1, (sl)j; J|$$

may be expanded in terms of Russell-Saunders states by writing

$$((S_1 L_1) J_1, (sl)j; J| = \sum_{SL} ((S_1 L_1) J_1, (sl)j; J| (S_1 s) S, (L_1 l) L; J)$$
$$\times ((S_1 s) S, (L_1 l) L; J|. \quad (2\text{-}114)$$

The transformation coefficient may be found from Eq. 2-39. Using Eqs. 2-39 and 2-114, we obtain the matrix elements in $J_1 j$ coupling as

$$(\psi_1 J_1, slj; J | H_{op} | \psi_1' J_1', slj'; J') = ([J_1, J_1', j, j'])^{1/2} \sum_{SL} ([S, L, S', L'])^{1/2}$$

$$\times \begin{Bmatrix} S_1 & s & S \\ L_1 & l & L \\ J_1 & j & J \end{Bmatrix} \begin{Bmatrix} S_1' & s & S' \\ L_1' & l & L' \\ J_1' & j' & J' \end{Bmatrix} (\psi_1, sl; SL | H_{op} | \psi_1', sl; S'L'). \quad (2\text{-}115)$$

Except for certain special cases the presence of 9-j symbols in this equation and the necessity for calculating first all the matrix elements in the LS coupling scheme make calculations of the electrostatic interactions in the $J_1 j$ coupling scheme long and tedious, although certainly not beyond the resources of modern computers.

In practice, it is usually simplest to calculate both the electrostatic and the spin-orbit interactions in an LS basis and then to diagonalize the matrices to make the transformation from the LS basis to the physical scheme.   In this case the eigenvectors will be in the LS basis, and the composition of the levels in terms of these basis states given simply by the scalar product of the eigenvectors.   If we wish to determine the composition of the levels in some other basis, we may obtain transformation matrices that will carry the LS basis states into those of the desired basis by diagonalizing the energy matrices for a set of fictitious parameters appropriate to the desired basis.[66]   For example, in $J_1 j$ coupling the transformation matrices may be obtained by diagonalizing the energy matrices for parameters where the spin-orbit parameter of the added electron is made very large and the electrostatic parameters put near to zero.

Fortunately for the $l^N s$ configurations the matrix elements of electrostatic interaction between the s-electron and the l^N-core have a particularly simple form.[53]   If we are only interested in the relative energies of the terms, we may disregard those terms that depend only on N. For $J_1 = J_1'$ we obtain

$$
\begin{aligned}
(\psi_1 &J_1 s; J | H_{el} | \psi_1' J_1 s; J) \\
&= \pm \, \delta(\psi_1, \psi_1') G^l(l, s) \frac{L_1(L_1 + 1) - S_1(S_1 + 1) - J_1(J_1 + 1)}{(2l + 1)(2J + 1)}, \quad (2\text{-}116)
\end{aligned}
$$

where H_{el} is the operator representing the electrostatic interaction. The plus sign is taken for $J = J_1 + \frac{1}{2}$ and the minus sign for $J = J_1 - \frac{1}{2}$. If $J_1 \neq J_1'$, we have $J_1 = J \pm \frac{1}{2}$ and $J_1 = J \mp \frac{1}{2}$. The off-diagonal elements are then given by

$$
\begin{aligned}
(\psi_1 J \pm \tfrac{1}{2}, s; J | H_{el} | \psi_1' J &\mp \tfrac{1}{2}, s; J) = \frac{\delta(\psi_1, \psi_1') G^l(l, s)}{(2J + 1)(2l + 1)} \\
&\times [(S_1 + L_1 + J + \tfrac{3}{2})(S_1 + L_1 + \tfrac{1}{2} - J)(L_1 + J + \tfrac{1}{2} - S_1) \\
&\times (S_1 + J + \tfrac{1}{2} - L_1)]^{1/2}. \quad (2\text{-}117)
\end{aligned}
$$

It is evident from the simplicity of these equations and the ease in which the spin-orbit matrix elements may be obtained that it is simpler to calculate the energy matrices for the $f^N s$ configuration in the $J_1 j$ coupling scheme than in the LS coupling scheme.

In general, a well-defined coupling scheme will be closely followed only if the matrix elements of those interactions that are not diagonal in the quantum numbers characterizing the coupling scheme are small. This requirement will be realized if the radial integrals associated with these interactions are very small. Parts of a configuration may appear to follow a well-defined coupling scheme even though the states of the configuration considered as a whole depart considerably from the scheme. This situation arises whenever the energy separations of the levels connected by the off-diagonal matrix elements are large compared to the connecting matrix elements themselves. Thus, although the low-lying levels of Pu II $5f^6$ $(^7F)6s$ are closely J_1j coupled,[92] the density of the upper core levels is high, with the result that the spacings between the core levels will be small; this makes for a considerable breakdown in J_1j coupling for the upper levels.

The levels that result from the addition of an s-electron to the low-lying states of the f^N configurations of both the lanthanides and the actinides exhibit close J_1j coupling. Thus in Nd II $4f^4(^5I)6s$ the levels are better than 90% pure J_1j coupled states,[93] and in Yb III $(4f^{13}6s)$ the levels are approximately 97% pure J_1j coupled states.[70] In Sm II $4f^6(^7F)6s$ there is some breakdown of J_1j coupling because of the off-diagonal matrix elements of the electrostatic interaction of the $6s$-electron with the $4f^6(^7F)$ core mixing core levels of different J_1, with the result that some levels are only 75% pure J_1j coupled states.[93]

In making detailed calculations of f^Ns systems it is necessary to have an initial estimate of the radial integral $G^3(f, s)$. In the lanthanides the lowest term (^8S) of the $4f^7$ core is well separated from the next lowest term (^6P) of the core, with the result that the ^8S term is a better than 97% pure Russell-Saunders term. To a very good approximation the separation $4f^7(^8S)6s[^7S - {}^9S]$ will be equal to the difference in electrostatic interaction of the $6s$-electron with the $4f^7(^8S)$ core for the two terms. Using Eq. 2-116, this is found to be equal to $8G^3(4f, 6s)/7$. Russell et al.[94] have found the $(^7S - {}^9S)$ separation in Eu II to be 1669.21 cm^{-1}, whereas Callahan[95] has found it to be 2354.47 cm^{-1} in Gd III, from which we deduce the following.

For Eu II $G^3(4f, 6s) = 1460.6$ cm^{-1}.

For Gd III $G^3(4f, 6s) = 2060.2$ cm^{-1}.

Additional values of $G^3(4f, 6s)$ can be deduced from the known energy-level structures of the simple $4f6s$ and $4f^{13}6s$ configurations *provided* configuration interaction can be neglected. The energy levels of these configurations can be calculated in terms of the two radial integrals $G^3(4f, 6s)$ and ζ_{4f}. Meggers[96] has found all the levels of the $4f^{13}6s$

configuration of Tm II, and Bryant[70] has found those of Yb III $4f^{13}6s$. Their results yield the following.

For Tm II $G^3(4f, 6s) = 1432.9$ cm^{-1}.
For Yb III $G^3(4f, 6s) = 2356.2$ cm^{-1}.

Judd and Marquet[97] have studied the low levels of Er II $4f^{12}6s$ and deduced for Er II $G^3(4f, 6s) = 1580$ cm^{-1}. A more recent calculation by Goldschmidt[98] indicates that their values should be reduced to approximately 1475 cm^{-1}.

The radial integral $G^3(4f, 6s)$ exhibits practically no variation with atomic number for a given stage of ionization. This is a direct result of the orbit of the $6s$-electron lying mainly in the outer shells of the ion and hence not changing appreciably if simultaneously a $4f$-electron is added to the core and the nuclear charge is increased by one unit. The smallness of the variation of $G^3(4f, 6s)$ with atomic number permits its extrapolation for the same stage of ionization of all the lanthanides once two or three values have been determined. Thus in the second stage of ionization $G^3(4f, 6s)$ has the almost constant value of 1450 cm^{-1}, and in the third stage of ionization it assumes the almost constant value of 2050 cm^{-1}.

Fred and Tomkins[99] have determined the $^7S - {}^9S$ separation for the $5f^77s$ configuration of Am II, the actinide analogue of Eu II, to be 2598.32 cm^{-1}. It might be thought that a value of $G^3(5f, 7s)$ could be readily deduced from this datum. Such a deduction would almost certainly be in error since the $5f^7(^8S)$ core state can no longer be considered as a pure Russell-Saunders state. It does in fact contain appreciable admixtures of the ^6P and ^6D terms. Reliable values for the actinides can only be made by making intermediate coupling calculations for the $5f^N$-core.

Racah[91] has analyzed the levels of the $5f7s$ configuration of Th III, and Kessler[68] has made a similar study of the levels of the $5f6d7s$ configuration of Th II. They have deduced the following values.

For Th III $G^3(5f, 7s) = 5341$ cm^{-1}.
For Th II $G^3(5f, 7s) = 2023$ cm^{-1}.

Judd[53] has deduced from the data of Schuurmans et al.[100] on U II $5f^4(^5I)7s$ the value

U II $G^3(5f, 7s) = 2600$ cm^{-1},

whereas in Pu II $(5f^67s)$ Bauche et al.[92] find

Pu II $G^3(5f, 7s) = 2478$ cm^{-1}.

As for the lanthanides, the radial integral $G^3(f, s)$ shows little variation with changing atomic number. However, for the actinides $G^3(f, s)$ is considerably larger than in the corresponding lanthanides. The break-down of $J_1 j$ coupling will be proportional to $[G^3(f, s)]^2$ and the inverse of the energy separation of the connected core levels. Since the density of the core levels and the magnitude of $G^3(f, s)$ is greater in the actinides than in the lanthanides, we should anticipate a greater breakdown in $J_1 j$ coupling than in the lanthanides.

The $f^N p$ configurations also exhibit quite good $J_1 j$ coupling. Calla-han's[95] analysis of the spectra of Gd III gives a beautiful illustration of $J_1 j$ coupling in an $f^N p$ configuration. He has determined all the energy levels formed by the coupling of a $6p$-electron to the $4f^7(^8S_{7/2})$ core of Gd III. The matrix elements of electrostatic interaction between the core and the $6p$ electron are given in the $J_1 j$ coupling scheme by

$$\left(f^7(^8S_{7/2})6p_j; J \left| \sum_{i<j}^{7} \frac{e^2}{r_{ij}} \right| f^7(^8S_{7/2})6p_{j'}, J \right)$$

$$= -56([j, j'])^{1/2} \begin{Bmatrix} \frac{7}{2} & J & j' \\ \frac{1}{2} & j & 1 \\ 3 & \frac{7}{2} & \frac{1}{2} \end{Bmatrix} \sum_k \begin{pmatrix} 3 & k & 1 \\ 0 & 0 & 0 \end{pmatrix}^2 G^k(f, p), \quad (2\text{-}118)$$

a result that follows from Eq. 2-94 and 2-115. This formula may be further simplified and the electrostatic interactions expressed in terms of a single parameter G by defining the quantity

$$G(f, p) = 5G_2(f, p) + 4G_4(f, p).$$

The matrix elements of spin-orbit interaction are given by Eq. 2-113 and may be expressed in terms of a single spin-orbit coupling constant ζ_p. Thus the energy level calculation requires only the parameters G and ζ_p to be determined. The parameter G may be fixed by noting that

$$^9P_5 - ^7P_2 = 24G(f, p)$$

independently of the nature of the coupling. Values of ζ_p may then be chosen to minimize the root-mean-square deviation of the calculated and experimentally observed levels. The results of such a calculation by Callahan[95] are shown in Fig. 2-3 and tabulated in Table 2-4. The eigen-vectors of the $J_1 j$ coupled states show clearly that $J_1 j$ coupling is the most appropriate coupling scheme by which to describe the properties of the $4f^7 6p$ configuration.

The physical significance of $J_1 j$ coupling in the $f^N p$ configurations is shown clearly in the structure of the $4f^{13}6p$ configuration of Yb III.[70] The effect of the spin-orbit interaction in the $4f^{13}$ core is to remove the twofold degeneracy of the ^2F term, producing two well-separated core states, $^2F_{7/2}$ and $^2F_{5/2}$. The next largest interaction is the spin-orbit

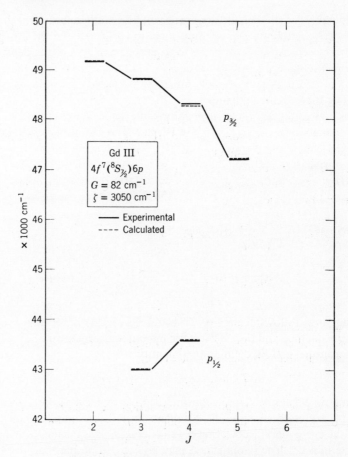

Fig. 2-3 Energy levels of Gd III $4f^7(^8S_{7/2})6p$.

TABLE 2-4   Energy levels of the $4f^7(^8S)6p$ states of Gd III

Level	Calculated	Experimental	Difference	Eigenvector
$[(^8S_{7/2})6p_{3/2}]_2$	49,221	49,195	-26	$1.000p_{3/2}$
$[(^8S_{7/2})6p_{3/2}]_3$	48,857	48,859	2	$0.989p_{3/2} + 0.148p_{1/2}$
$[(^8S_{7/2})6p_{3/2}]_4$	48,284	48,339	55	$0.977p_{3/2} + 0.213p_{1/2}$
$[(^8S_{7/2})6p_{3/2}]_5$	47,253	47,234	-19	$1.000p_{3/2}$
$[(^8S_{7/2})6p_{1/2}]_4$	43,615	43,612	-3	$0.213p_{3/2} - 0.977p_{1/2}$
$[(^8S_{7/2})6p_{1/2}]_3$	43,043	43,020	-23	$0.148p_{3/2} - 0.989p_{1/2}$

interaction of the 6p-electron which has the effect of removing its twofold degeneracy to produce two states $p_{1/2}$ and $p_{3/2}$, approximately $3\zeta_p/2$ apart,

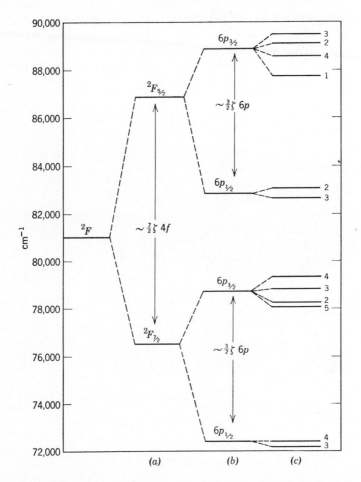

Fig. 2-4 Energy levels of Yb III $4f^{13}(^2F)6p$. (*a*) Spin-orbit interaction of the $4f^{13}$ core; (*b*) spin-orbit interaction of the $6p$ electron; (*c*) electrostatic interaction between $4f^{13}$ and $6p$.

with $p_{1/2}$ lowest. The $p_{3/2}$ and $p_{1/2}$ states may then assume different orientations in the electrostatic field of the core splitting into four and two levels respectively. Because the electrostatic interaction between the $4f^{13}$ core and the $6p$-electron is very weak, these splittings are relatively small. The mechanism of J_1j coupling is illustrated in Fig. 2-4.

J_1j coupling would appear to be a general property of all f^Np configurations, both in the lanthanides and the actinides. Unfortunately, experimentalists have not always labeled the states of f^Np configurations in

this coupling scheme.   In Ce III $4f6p$ the energy levels were labeled in the
LS coupling scheme[101] as shown in Fig. 2-5a.   It is clear from the figure
that the LS multiplets are grossly distorted, with the result that little
physical significance can be attached to the labeling scheme.   In Fig.

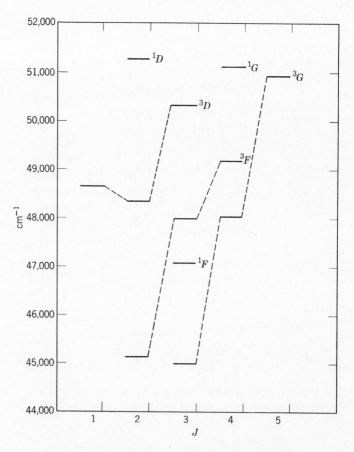

Fig. 2-5a Energy levels of Ce III ($4f6p$) in LS coupling.

2-5b we have labeled the levels in the J_1j coupling scheme, and the physical
significance of the coupling scheme is immediately apparent.

Although the $f^N p$ configurations seem to follow quite good J_1j coupling
throughout the rare earths series, the $f^N d$ configurations are sometimes
found in J_1j coupling and sometimes in LS coupling.   Spector[102] has

shown from the data of Sugar[103] that the $4f5d$ configuration in Ce III is quite closely LS coupled, whereas Bryant[70] has found the analogous $4f^{13}5d$ configuration of Yb III to be $J_1 j$ coupled.   Again in Ce III Spector[102] finds that the $4f7d$ is very nicely $J_1 j$ coupled.   The parameters deduced

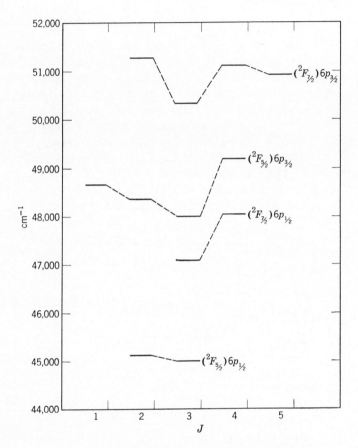

Fig. 2-5b   Energy levels of Ce III ($4f6p$) in $J_1 j$ coupling.

for these three configurations are given in Table 2-5.   It is apparent that, apart from F_0, there is a marked similarity between the electrostatic parameters of Ce III ($4f5d$) and Yb III ($4f^{13}5d$), whereas the spin-orbit coupling constant ζ_{5d} had only shown a slight increase.   The dissimilarities in the couplings of these two configurations arise from two distinct causes.

TABLE 2-5   Interaction parameters for $f^N d$ configurations in Ce III and Yb III (all values in cm^{-1})

	F_0	F_2	F_4	G_1	G_3	G_s	ζ_f	ζ_d
Ce III $4f5d$	9,400	175	21	296	40	5	666	795
Ce III $4f7d$	119,913	17.5	2.2	17.5	3.3	0.5	644	91
Yb III $4f^{13}5d$	44,073	186.8	14.2	193.2	24.62	4.11	2950	1211

First, ζ_{4f} changes markedly in going from Ce III to Yb III. In the language of $J_1 j$ coupling this means that the $^2F_{7/2}$ and $^2F_{5/2}$ states of the core are moved apart by the increasing spin-orbit coupling, with the result that the electrostatic interactions that strive to break down the $J_1 j$ coupling are diminished. Second, in Ce III the dominant electrostatic parameter, $G_1(4f, 5d)$, enters in all the energy matrices, whereas in Yb III the parameter arises only in the $J = 1$ matrix and therefore favors $J_1 j$ coupling in the latter ion. Thus in a sense $J_1 j$ coupling in the $f^{13} d$ configuration constitutes a special case and we cannot infer that the $f^N d$ configurations, in general, will follow $J_1 j$ coupling. This is seen in Callahan's[95] observation that the levels of $4f^7(^8S)5d$ do follow, in fact, almost perfect LS coupling.

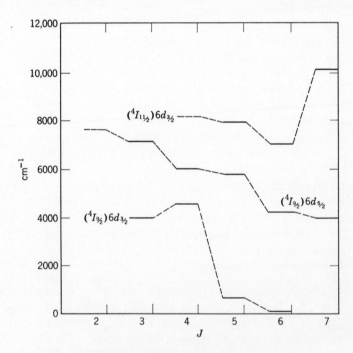

Fig. 2-6   Energy levels of U I $5f^3(^4I)6d$ in $J_1 j$ coupling.

In Ce III $4f7d$ $J_1 j$ coupling is dominant simply as a result of the greatly reduced electrostatic interaction of the $7d$-electron with the tighter bound inner $4f$-electron.

Racah[91] has shown that the energy levels of the $5f6d$ configuration of Th III are intermediate between the well-defined LS and $J_1 j$ coupling schemes. Judd[53] has suggested that the levels of U I $5f^3(^4I)6d7s^2$ determined by Kiess et al.[102a] and Blaise[103a] are *approximately* $J_1 j$ coupled. It is evident from Fig. 2-6 that the levels depart considerably from pure $J_1 j$ coupling as they do also from pure LS coupling. There is appreciable interaction between the $(^4I_{11/2})d_{3/2}$ and $(^4I_{9/2})d_{5/2}$ states as well as between $(^4I_{9/2})d_{5/2}$ and $(^4I_{9/2})d_{3/2}$, which leads to a severe distortion of the level patterns away from those expected from pure $J_1 j$ coupling. It is doubtful if the levels of the $5f^N 6d$ configurations of the actinides can be grouped and labeled in a physically meaningful manner by any of the well-defined coupling schemes.

2-15 $J_1 l$ Coupling in the Rare Earths

The $J_1 l$ coupling scheme, first proposed by Racah,[104] has had considerable application in the interpretation of noble gas spectra.[105,106] A particularly good example of $J_1 l$ coupling has been found by Sugar[103] in the $4f5g$ configuration of Ce III. There seems little doubt that this scheme will be most appropriate for the $f^N g$ configurations throughout both the lanthanide and the actinide series. $J_1 l$ coupling arises in $l^n l'$ configurations when the electrostatic interaction of the outer l'-electron with the l^N core is weak compared to the spin-orbit interaction of the core, but it is strong compared to the spin-orbit interaction of the external electron l'. Here the orbital momentum l' is first coupled to the total angular momentum J_1 of the core to give a resultant angular momentum K; then K is coupled to the spin of the external electron to yield a total angular momentum J.

The angular momentum K will be a good quantum number as long as the spin-dependent interactions between the outer electron and the core are negligible. Thus for good $J_1 l$ coupling it is necessary that *both* the spin-orbit coupling and the electrostatic exchange interactions associated with the outer electron be very weak. In the absence of spin-dependent interactions with the outer electron, each level, classified according to its K-value, will be twofold degenerate. The effect of weak spin-dependent interactions will be to remove this degeneracy, which gives rise to the appearance pairs of levels.

For a hydrogen-like atom or ion the spin-orbit coupling constant ζ_{nl} will be given by

$$\zeta_{nl} = \frac{Z^{*4}}{n^{*3}l(l+1)(2l+1)} \, 11.64 \, \text{cm}^{-1},$$

where Z^* is the effective nuclear charge and n^* is the effective principal quantum number. For a nonpenetrating outer electron the effective nuclear charge will tend to be approximately $(Z - N + 1)$, where Z is the atomic number and N is the number of electrons in the atom or ion; consequently, the spin-orbit interaction will be extremely small. This will indeed be the case for outer electrons having high principal and orbital quantum numbers. For example, the spin-orbit coupling constant for a $5f$ or $5g$ electron in the lanthanides will be less than 0.1 cm^{-1}. From this result we might anticipate that both the $4f^N5f$ and the $4f^N5g$ configurations would display good J_1l coupling. However, the $4f^N5f$ configuration involves a large electrostatic exchange interaction through the $G^0(4f, 5f)$ parameter, with the result that the $4f5f$ configuration of Ce III is actually close to LS coupling*. In the $4f5g$ configuration this term is nonexistent and very good J_1l coupling is found.

The matrix elements of operators in the J_1l coupling scheme may be calculated by determining first the matrix elements in the LS scheme and then making a transformation to J_1l coupling. A state $((S_1L_1)J_1l; Ks; J|$ may be expanded in terms of LS states by writing[45]

$$((S_1L_1)J_1l'; Ks; J| = \sum_{SL} ((S_1L_1)J_1l'; Ks; J|(S_1s)S, (L_1l')L; J)$$

$$\times ((S_1s)S, (L_1l')L; J| = \sum_{SL} (-1)^{S_1 + L_1 + s + l' + S + L + 2K}([J_1, S, L, K])^{1/2}$$

$$\times \begin{Bmatrix} S_1 & L_1 & J_1 \\ l' & K & L \end{Bmatrix} \begin{Bmatrix} S & L & J \\ K & s & S_1 \end{Bmatrix}((S_1s)S, (L_1l')L; J|. \quad (2\text{-}119)$$

The matrix elements for the electrostatic interaction of an electron $n'l'$ with a nl^N core of equivalent electrons may be written as

$$(l^N(S_1L_1)J_1l'; Ks; J|H_{el}|l^N(S_3L_3)J_3l'; K's; J)$$

$$= \sum_k [\delta(S_1, S_3)\delta(K, K')f_k(J_1J_3K)F^k(nln'l') + g_k(J_1J_3KK'J)G^k(nl, n'l'),$$

$$(2\text{-}120)$$

where

$$f_k(J_1J_3K) = (-1)^{J_3 + K + l'}(l||\mathbf{C}^{(k)}||l)(l'||\mathbf{C}^{(k)}||l')$$

$$\times \begin{Bmatrix} J_1 & J_3 & k \\ l' & l' & K \end{Bmatrix}(l^NS_1L_1J_1||\mathbf{U}^{(k)}||l^NS_1L_3J_3), \quad (2\text{-}121)$$

---

* However, in the $4f^{13}\,5f$ configuration $G^0(4f, 5f)$ will only arise for the $J = 0$ states and the remaining levels could be expected to show pair coupling.

and

$$g_k(J_1 J_3 K K' J) = -N([J_1, J_3, S_1, S_3, L_1, L_3, K, K'])^{1/2}$$

$$\times (l||\mathbf{C}^{(k)}||l')^2(-1)^{L_1+L_3} \sum_{\bar{\psi}} (\psi_1\{|\psi)(\bar{\psi}|\}\psi_3)$$

$$\times \sum_{\kappa} [\kappa] \begin{Bmatrix} S_1 & L_1 & J_1 \\ l' & K & \kappa \end{Bmatrix} \begin{Bmatrix} S_3 & L_3 & J_3 \\ l' & K' & \kappa \end{Bmatrix} \begin{Bmatrix} \bar{S} & s & S_1 \\ s & J & K \\ S_3 & K' & \kappa \end{Bmatrix} \begin{Bmatrix} \bar{L} & l & L_1 \\ l & k & l' \\ L_3 & l' & \kappa \end{Bmatrix}$$

$$\tag{2-122}$$

The expression for the matrix elements of the exchange interaction is particularly complicated by the summation over the running index which represents a species of the 18-j symbol.[48] Fortunately, where the $J_1 l$ coupling scheme is most appropriate the exchange interactions are negligible and frequently need not be calculated.

The matrix elements of the spin-orbit interaction within the l^N core are just those computed in the absence of the added electron and are diagonal in J_1. The corresponding matrix elements for the added electron $n'l'$ are given by

$$(l^N(S_1 L_1)J_1 l'; Ks; J|\zeta_{n'l'}(\mathbf{s} \cdot \mathbf{l'})|l^N(S_1 L_1)J_1 l'; K's; J)$$

$$= (-1)^{K+K'+J_1+J+l'+s}\zeta_{n'l'}([K, K'])^{1/2}$$

$$\times \begin{Bmatrix} K & K' & 1 \\ s & s & J \end{Bmatrix} \begin{Bmatrix} K & K' & 1 \\ l' & l' & J_1 \end{Bmatrix}[s(s+1)(2s+1)l'(l'+1)(2l'+1)]^{1/2}$$

$$\tag{2-123}$$

Again where $J_1 l$ coupling is valid these matrix elements will be negligible. In fact, for f^N configurations containing an outer f- or g-electron the spin-orbit interaction may be entirely neglected and only the spin-dependent electrostatic interaction need be considered in calculating departures from $J_1 l$ coupling.

Since the direct electrostatic interaction leaves K as a good quantum number, we may calculate the energies of the twofold degenerate levels characterized by different K values in *pure* $J_1 l$ coupling by simply adding the matrix elements of the direct electrostatic interaction between the added electron $n'l'$ and the nl^N core to the energy matrices of the nl^N core. The direct interactions will normally be very weak because of the external nature of the added electron, and consequently, if the terms of the l^N core are well separated, we may to a good approximation neglect the matrix elements that couple the different terms.

For g-electrons the direct interaction is nonnegligible only for the $F^2(nlng)$ integral and as an added approximation we may neglect all other terms.*   Within this approximation we may write out the 6-j symbol of Eq. 2-121 explicitly to obtain the coefficients of $F^2(nl, n'l')$ as

$$f_2(J_1 K) = (l||\mathbf{C}^{(2)}||l)(l'||\mathbf{C}^{(2)}||l')(l^N S_1 L_1 J_1||\mathbf{U}^{(2)}||l^N S_1 L_3 J_1)$$
$$\times [3h(2h + 1) - 2J_1(J_1 + 1)l'(l' + 1)] ((2J_1 - 1)J_1$$
$$\times (J_1 + 1)(2J_1 + 1)(2J_1 + 3)(2l' - 1)l'(l' + 1)(2l' + 1)(2l' + 3))^{-1/2},$$

$$\tag{2-124}$$

where

$$h = \frac{K(K + 1) - J_1(J_1 + 1) - l'(l' + 1)}{2}. \tag{2-125}$$

Thus for a particular term $\alpha_1 J_1$ of the l^N core the energies $E(\alpha_1 J_1 K)$ of the levels formed by adding an electron l' in pure $J_1 l$ coupling will be given by the expression

$$E(\alpha_1 J_1 K) = ah(2h + 1) + b, \tag{2-126}$$

where b is a constant and a is the coefficient of the quantity $h(2h + 1)$ appearing in Eq. 2-124.   Hence where there is good $J_1 l$ coupling and where the preceding approximations are satisfied, the energy levels derived from a given term of the l^N core should lie on a parabola when plotted as a function of h.   The minima of this parabola will occur at $h = -\frac{1}{4}$ regardless of the term being studied.

The energy levels of the $4f5g$ configuration of Ce III are plotted as a function of h in Fig. 2-7.   It is apparent here that the levels lie very close to two parabolas.   In this figure the upper parabola was drawn for $a(\frac{7}{2}) = 0.25$ cm^{-1} and $b = \frac{125}{57}$ cm^{-1}.   Using Eqs. 2-122 or 2-124, we find†

$$a(\tfrac{7}{2}) = \frac{5}{7}F_2(4f, 5g),$$

from which we readily deduce

$$F_2(4f, 5g) = 0.35 \text{ cm}^{-1},$$

which is indeed very small.   The lower parabola was then drawn by requiring that

$$\frac{a(\frac{5}{2})}{a(\frac{7}{2})} = \frac{9}{5},$$

a result that is consistent with Eq. 2-124.   The small splittings of the pairs is a direct indication that the electrostatic exchange interactions are very small.

---

* Note, however, that in $ngn'g$ configurations this need not be the case since the terms in $G^0(ng, n'g)$ would be important.

† In relating the integral $F^2(4f, 5g)$ to $F_2(4f, 5g)$, we use the tables of Shortley and Fried.[107]

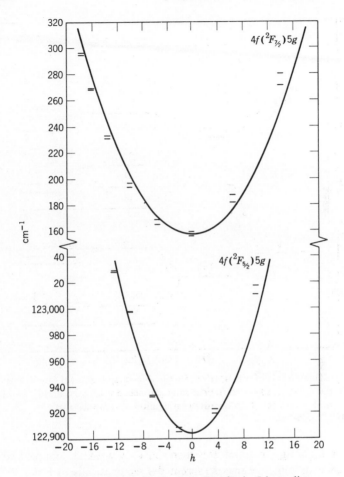

Fig. 2-7　Energy levels of Ce III $4f5g$ in J_1l coupling.

2-16　Coupling Schemes for $f^N ll'$ Configurations

The configurations $f^n ll'$ give many more possibilities for coupling schemes. These systems have not been studied as extensively as the $f^n l$ configurations. However, in a few cases sufficient is known to allow some understanding of the coupling schemes involved.[108,109]　In Yb II $4f^{13}6s6p$[110] we have a clear case of $J_1 J_2$ coupling. In this scheme the core levels are coupled to form J_1; the electrons l' and l'' are then coupled together to form states characterized by a total angular momentum J_2, and finally J_1 and J_2 are coupled together to form states characterized by the total angular momentum J. This coupling scheme is found when the external

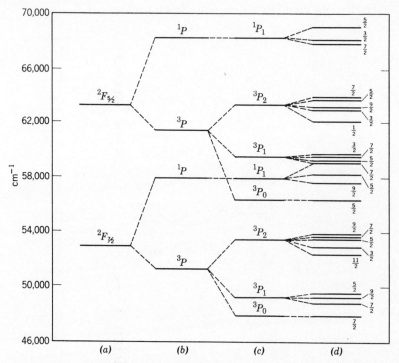

Fig. 2-8 Energy levels of Yb II $4f^{13}(^2F)6s6p$ in J_1J_2 coupling. (*a*) Spin-orbit inter-action in the $4f^{13}$ core; (*b*) electrostatic interaction between the $6s$ and $6p$ electrons; (*c*) spin-orbit interaction of the $6s6p$ configuration; (*d*) electrostatic interaction between $4f^{13}$ and $6s6p$.

electrons are strongly coupled together and only weakly coupled to the core. The coupling scheme is represented schematically in Fig. 2-8.

The $4f^{13}5d6s$ configuration of Yb II[110] exhibits J_1L_2 coupling. This coupling scheme arises from the strong electrostatic interaction of the $5d$ electron with the core. The $5d$ and $6s$ electrons are coupled by their electrostatic interaction to form states characterized by an orbital angular momentum L_2. The L_2 of the pair is then coupled to the state J_1 of the core and orientated in the electrostatic field of the core to form a resulting angular momentum K. The spin of the pair is then coupled to K to form states of total angular momentum J. The coupling scheme is represented schematically in Fig. 2-9. In J_1L_2 coupling we designate the states by the labels of the core, K in brackets with the multiplicity of the pair of external electrons as a superscript, and finally give the total angular momentum J of the state. J_1L_2 coupling is characterized by the appearance of groups of three levels and isolated levels.

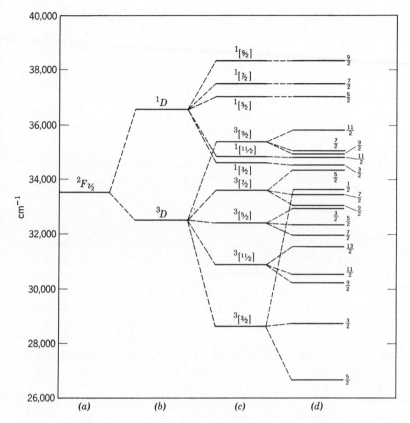

Fig. 2-9 Energy levels of Yb II $4f^{13}(^2F_{7/2})5d6s$ in J_1L_2 coupling. (*a*) $4f^{13}$ core; (*b*) electrostatic interaction between $5d$ and $6s$; (*c*) electrostatic interaction between $4f^{13}$ core and $5d6s$; (*d*) spin-orbit interaction in $5d6s$.

In the early stages of term analyses of rare earth spectra much can be learned by setting up simple energy-level diagrams. By observing the way the levels are grouped, it is frequently possible to decide on the coupling scheme which most appropriately describes the energy levels. By knowing the coupling schemes, it is then possible to make simple predictions as to the magnetic behavior of the levels and the intensities of the transitions without becoming involved in extensive calculations.

2-17 Configuration Interaction
The diagonalization of the combined electrostatic and spin-orbit interaction matrices for a particular configuration yields energy levels that

frequently deviate by hundreds of wave numbers from the observed energy levels even when the radial integrals are treated as parameters to be freely varied. These deviations arise, to a large extent, from our neglect of interaction *between* different configurations of the same parity* that differ in the coordinates of not more than two electrons. Configuration interaction plays a very important, and frequently unrecognized, role in the electronic properties of rare earths, which sometimes has a profound effect on their hyperfine structure,[111] spectral intensities, and their behavior in crystal fields.[112]

We may somewhat arbitrarily divide the configuration interactions into two classes: (1) strong configuration interactions where the perturbing configurations are energetically close to the perturbed configuration and there is appreciable coupling of the configurations by way of the Coulomb field; and (2) weak configuration interactions where the perturbing configurations are well separated from the perturbed configuration and the coupling of the configurations in the Coulomb field is weak.

Where the configuration interaction is strong it becomes necessary to diagonalize energy matrices which include all the electrostatic interactions *within* and *between* the connected configurations. The eigenvectors resulting from the diagonalization then allow us to express the states in terms of linear combinations of the states of the connected configurations. Clearly, for complex configurations this method entails the construction of very large matrices and a substantial increase in the number of radial integrals.

Racah has considered the simple case of configuration interaction between the $5f6d$ and $5f7s$ configurations of Th III and obtained a substantial improvement in the energy-level calculation. Here the mixing of the configurations is quite severe, with the result that some of the states are represented by almost equal combinations of $5f6d$ and $5f7s$ states, which makes it meaningless to say a state belongs to a particular configuration.

Where there is a near degeneracy of several configurations of the same parity, as does, in fact, occur for some of the rare earths, it may be desirable and physically more significant, to consider the configurations as a single entity and adopt a collective model approach analogous to that developed by Elliott[113–114] for the nuclear shell. Spectroscopists have been somewhat slow in adopting some of the powerful techniques developed for handling the nuclear shell. The author is convinced that nuclear shell

---

* We define the *parity* of a configuration to be *even* or *odd* as the sum of the one-electron orbital angular momenta of the electrons is even or odd. Thus f^2p is of odd parity, and f^2d is of even parity.

theorists and atomic spectroscopists could learn much by studying each other's approaches to problems of common interest.

Even when the strong interactions have been included there remain the perturbations produced by all the weakly interacting configurations. Although individually their effects may be quite small, their accumulative effects may be considerable because of the high density of states as the continuum is approached. It would be an impossible, and physically meaningless, task to construct matrices including all the interactions. Rather we should direct our attention towards modifying the energy matrices of the principal electron configuration so that we include the greater part of the effects of *all* the weakly perturbing configurations. This approach has the advantage of requiring no increase in the dimensions of the energy matrices and relatively few additional parameters. Rajnak and Wybourne[48] have given a detailed treatment of the problem for l^N type configurations using second-order perturbation theory.

There are only five basic types of interacting configurations that can modify the energy-level structure of an l^N type configuration:

1. $l^{N-2}l'^2$ and $l^{N-2}l'l''$.
2. $l'^{4l'}l^{N+2}$ and $l'^{4l'+1}l''^{4l''+1}l^{N+2}$.
3. $l'^{4l'+1}l^N l''$.
4. $l^{N-1}l'$.
5. $l'^{4l'+1}l^{N+1}$.

The interactions 2, 3, and 5 are core excitations where an electron is promoted from a closed shell to either an unfilled shell or to the partially filled l^N shell. The two-electron core excitations which involve the excitation of not more than one core electron into the l^N shell produce effects that are indifferent to the energy-level structure of the l^N configuration and, at the most, give rise to a shift of the center of gravity of the entire configuration. Consequently, we may exclude them from our discussion.

In general, for a given perturbing configuration there will be several states m_τ that will interact with the states $|\Psi)$ and $|\Psi')$ of the l^N configuration. Rajnak and Wybourne have shown that the effect of these perturbations may be largely accommodated by adding to each electrostatic matrix element of the type $(l^N\Psi|G|l^N\Psi')$ a correction factor

$$C(\Psi, \Psi') = - \sum_\tau \frac{(l^N\Psi|G|m_\tau)(m_\tau|G|l^N\Psi')}{E}, \qquad (2\text{-}127)$$

where G is an operator representing the Coulomb energy of repulsion,*

---

* For excitations of the type $nl \rightarrow n'l$ the operator G should also include the one-electron radial terms of the Hamiltonian. Since the inclusion of these effects leaves the qualitative conclusions of this section, we shall for simplicity omit them.

$\sum_{i>j} e^2/r_{ij}$, between electrons and E is the (positive) energy of excitation of the electrons to the perturbing configuration.

Rajnak and Wybourne were able to perform the summations in Eq. 2-127 for all five types of configuration interaction by making extensive use of the algebra of tensor operators and n-j symbols. They found that the interactions of type 1 to 5 produced correction factors for the f^N configuration that could be represented by a correction factor of the form

$$C(\Psi, \Psi') = \sum_k P^k (f^N \Psi| \sum_{i>j}^N (\mathbf{U}_i^{(k)} \cdot \mathbf{U}_j^{(k)}) | f^N \Psi'). \qquad (2\text{-}128)$$

The quantities P^k contain the radial factors and excitation energies of the summation in Eq. 2-127 and may be treated as parameters. In this way they will then represent the weighted contributions of many interacting configurations including those lying in the continuum.

For k-even the angular dependent part of Eq. 2-128 has the same form as the coefficients of the Slater radial integrals F^k associated with the matrix element $(f^N \Psi |G| f^N \Psi')$. This part of the correction factor will be included wherever the F^k integrals are treated as parameters since its effect will be simply to "screen" the integrals. Those effects will be concealed in the Slater parameters even though configuration interaction may have been ignored. The degree of "screening" produced will vary with k. For example, $s \leftrightarrow d$ excitations will give a contribution to the "screening" of the F^2 radial integral but not to the F^4 and F^6 integrals.

The terms with k-odd represent effects that are not included even when the Slater integrals are treated as parameters. These overt effects can be included only by introducing additional parameters. Rajnak and Wybourne have used the properties to the Casimir operators[39] to replace the terms with k-odd by the equivalent expression

$$\delta(\Psi, \Psi')[\alpha L(L + 1) + \beta G(G_2) + \gamma G(R_7)]. \qquad (2\text{-}129)$$

In this case $G(G_2)$ and $G(R_7)$ are the eigenvalues of Casimir's operators for the groups G_2 and R_7 used to classify the states of the f^N configuration. These eigenvalues may be calculated in terms of the integers $(u_1 u_2)$ and $(w_1 w_2 w_3)$ used to label the irreducible representations of the groups G_2 and R_7 and are tabulated in Tables 2-6 and 2-7. The α, β, and γ are associated parameters corresponding to particular linear combinations of the P^k (k-odd) parameters. Equation 2-129 represents a particular set of two body scalar interactions that are equivalent to the k-odd terms of Eq. 2-128. This set is by no means unique. For example, Trees[81] has used the eigenvalues of the seniority operator Q in place of $G(R_7)$.

TABLE 2-6   Eigenvalues of Casimir's operator for the group G_2

$U = (u_1, u_2)$	$12G(G_2)$
(00)	0
(10)	6
(11)	12
(20)	14
(21)	21
(22)	30
(30)	24
(31)	32
(40)	36

TABLE 2-7   Eigenvalues of Casimir's operator for the group R_7

$W = (w_1, w_2, w_3)$	$5G(R_7)$
(000)	0
(100)	3
(110)	5
(111)	6
(200)	7
(210)	9
(211)	10
(220)	12
(221)	13
(222)	15

It should be emphasized that the various possible substitutions for Eq. 2-129 will result in different sets of parameters, although the accuracy of the calculation will be unchanged. This point is frequently overlooked in comparison of the Hartree-Fock F^k integrals with those derived from experiment.

The effects of interactions with configurations of the type 4 and 5 result in a correction factor equivalent to that of Eq. 2-128 but with the addition of a term

$$\sum_{k, k', k'' \text{ even}} \Theta(k, k', l')([k''])\begin{Bmatrix} k & k' & k'' \\ f & f & l' \end{Bmatrix}(f^N\Psi| \sum_{i \neq j \neq h} (\{\mathbf{U}_i^{(k)}\mathbf{U}_j^{(k'')}\}^{(k')}\mathbf{U}_h^{(k')})^{(0)}$$
$$\times |f^N\Psi'), \quad (2\text{-}130)$$

where $\Theta(k, k', l')$ contain the radial factors and excitation energies. The angular factor involves the coordinates of three electrons and thus represents an effective three-body interaction. Although the effects of he two-body scalar interactions of Eq. 2-128 are fully included by at number of parameters equal to the number of LS terms in f^2, the three-body interactions could be completely described only if the number of parameters was equivalent to the number of LS terms in f^3. Thus, except where many terms of a configuration of equivalent electrons with more than three electrons (or holes) are known, the introduction of effective three-body terms is scarcely feasible. The three-body terms arise only with single-electron excitations either from the l^N-shell into unfilled orbitals or from a closed shell into the l^N-shell. A large part of the effect of these excitations on the l^N-shell is included in the two-body scalar interaction terms of Eq. 2-128, and therefore the three-body terms of Eq. 2-130 will normally be of lesser importance than those contained in Eq. 2-128.*

The calculations of the energy levels of f^N configurations should be substantially improved by adding the terms given in Eq. 2-129 to the diagonal of the energy matrices. Trees[81] has calculated the energy levels of the $4f^3$ configuration of Pr III and found the mean error to be reduced from 528 cm^{-1} to 369 cm^{-1} when the additional terms $\alpha L(L + 1)$ and $\beta G(G_2)$ are introduced. Since the only term with seniority $v = 1$ was missing, it was not possible to fix the value of all three of the additional two-body scalar interactions. As more rare earth spectra are studied it should be possible to examine the validity of introducing effective interactions to mime the effects of configuration interaction in greater detail and to interpolate the parameters throughout the rare earth series.

The methods just outlined will also hold for configurations containing electrons outside an l^N core with some restrictions; the effects, to second-order, of perturbing configurations in which the quantum numbers of the added electrons do not change will be taken into account if the corrections given here are applied to the states of the l^N core. Thus, for the $f^N p$ configuration, the effects of the perturbations produced by the $f^{N-2}d^2p$ configuration would be included, but not for those produced by the $f^N f'$ configuration.† Trees[81] has found that the addition of the terms $\alpha L(L + 1)$ and $\beta G(G_2)$ to the terms of f^2 in the $f^2 d$ configuration of Pr III reduces the mean error from 255 cm^{-1} to 182 cm^{-1}.

Rajnak and Wybourne[115] have also examined the effect of configuration interaction on the spin-orbit matrix elements of an l^N configuration. Their results indicate that configuration interaction leads to a "screening" of the spin-orbit coupling radial integral and the appearance of pseudo-

---

* Rajnak (*J. Opt. Soc. Am.*, in press) has examined the role of three-body interactions in the $4f^3$ configuration of Pr III.

† The generalization of the linear theory to configurations containing nonequivalent electrons has been discussed by Wybourne (*Phys. Rev.*, in press).

spin-other orbit interactions.[116]   In the limit of LS coupling these latter interactions will not produce deviations from the Lande interval rule, but it will result in the association of different spin-orbit coupling constants for different multiplets of the configuration.

2-18   Atomic Wave Functions and the Empirical Parameters

Having computed the energy levels of a particular electron configuration and obtained a set of empirical parameters, it is of considerable interest to compare the parameters with the radial integrals obtained from *ab initio* calculations of atomic wave functions. The methods of calculating atomic wave functions have been well described elsewhere,[35,36,117] so we shall consider them only briefly.

The atomic wave function calculations usually performed belong to one or the other of two basic methods: (1) Hartree self-consistent field (SCF) calculations and (2) Hartree-Fock calculations.

In the Hartree SCF calculation the wave function is taken to be simply the product of the one-electron eigenfunctions.   Each of the one-electron eigenfunctions should satisfy Schrodinger's equation for its own central field as in Eq. 2-6.   Trial one-electron eigenfunctions, hopefully close to the final ones, are used to calculate the approximate potential energies of the N-electrons of the atom or ion under consideration.   Schrodinger's equation is then solved for each electron to yield new eigenfunctions from which new potentials may be calculated and thereby a new solution of the Schrodinger's equations obtained.   The process is repeated until the resulting wave function becomes consistent with the fields from which it was calculated.   The Hartree SCF method does not use the properly antisymmetrized wave functions of Eq. 2-13.   Antisymmetrization is only considered inasmuch as the quantum numbers of the one-electron states are chosen to be in agreement with the Pauli exclusion principle. Thus in the SCF method there is no correlation between the motions of the individual electrons, and the SCF method does not include the effects of exchange.

The Hartree-Fock method endeavors to remove this defect of the SCF method by constructing correctly antisymmetrized wave functions and thus includes the effects of exchange.   Frequently, the calculation of the Hartree-Fock wave functions is made using parametrized analytical functions to represent the one-electron orbitals.   Using these analytical functions, we may calculate the total energy of the atom or ion for a particular multiplet or for the average energy of the configuration and then use a variational procedure to adjust the parameters of the analytical functions until the energy is minimized.   If sufficient parameters are used to specify the analytical functions, wave functions essentially identical to those obtained by numerical procedures will result.

Relativistic effects become appreciable in the rare earths and ideally should be included in the calculation of the atomic wave functions. For a truly relativistic wave function the one-electron eigenfunctions should be solutions of the relativistic Dirac equation. This requirement leads to a considerable complication in the calculation of the atomic wave functions since both exchange and relativistic effects must be included in the Dirac formulation if correctly antisymmetrized wave functions are to be obtained. There are, however, some advantages in using a completely relativistic formulation of the N-electron problem. The phenomena, which in nonrelativistic electron theory are ascribed to the electron spin and to the spin-orbit interaction, are built into the theory from the beginning and not as an addition to the nonrelativistic Schrodinger equation. With the development of large, high-speed computers it should be possible to compute relativistic wave functions, with the inclusion of exchange, for all the rare earths. However, if full use is to be made of these wave functions, it will be essential to use a completely relativistic formulation of the N-electron problem. Grant[118] has discussed some of the problems associated with the relativistic treatment of the many electron problems using the j-j coupling representation, and Rose[119] has given a detailed treatment of relativistic electron theory.

Freeman and Watson[120] have obtained nonrelativistic Hartree-Fock analytical wave functions for Ce^{3+}, Pr^{3+}, Nd^{3+}, Sm^{3+}, Eu^{2+}, Gd^{3+}, Dy^{3+}, Er^{3+}, and Yb^{3+}, and Ridley has made Hartree SCF calculations (without exchange) of the wave functions of Pr^{3+} and Tm^{3+}. In addition, Herman and Skillman[122] have made Slater-modified Hartree-Fock calculations[123] for the neutral atoms of all elements up to $Z = 103$. The results of these calculations reveal much about the nature of the $4f$-wave functions, the effects of exchange, and the relationship of the empirical parameters to the calculated radial integrals.

In Fig. 2-10 we plot the radial charge density $P^2(r)[P(r) = rR(r)]$ as a function of r for the $4f$, $5s$, $5p$, and $6s$ electrons of Gd^+ from Freeman and Watson's results. This plot provides a vivid demonstration that the $4f$-shell is indeed deeply imbedded inside the $5s$- and $5p$-shells and are relatively unaffected by the $6s$-electrons. The $4f$-radial wave functions calculated using the Hartree-Fock method differ rather strongly from those calculated for a $4f$-hydrogenic wave function. Both the Hartree-Fock and the SCF wave functions possess a much greater concentration of charge in the exponential "tail" than does the hydrogenic wave function. The effect of the exchange has been to cause the $4f$-orbitals to contract relative to those of the SCF wave function. The Hartree-Fock

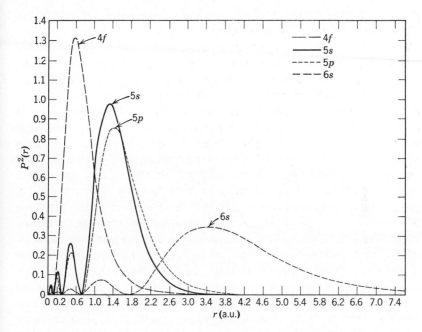

Fig. 2-10   Radial charge distribution $P^2(r)$ as a function of r for the $4f$, $5s$, $5p$, and $6s$ orbitals of Gd^+.

wave functions of Freeman and Watson should in principle give a better representation of the free ion wave functions than the SCF wave functions which neglect exchange effects.

Cohen[124] has made a relativistic Hartree SCF calculation for the normal uranium, and Boyd et al.[125] have calculated nonrelativistic Hartree SCF wave functions. A comparison of their calculations shows that the electrons of lower angular momentum are more tightly bound in the relativistic calculation and hence they shield the nuclear charge more effectively. The $5f$-eigenvalue is changing rapidly as a function of the atomic number throughout the actinide series and is very sensitive to small changes in the atomic potential. Boyd et al. noted that the eigenvalues of the $5f$- and $6d$-electrons in U were, respectively, 5.69 and 1.06 eV greater than those in the relativistic calculation of Cohen's.

Freeman and Watson[120] have calculated the radial integrals $F^k(4f, 4f)$ and ζ_{4f} from their Hartree-Fock wave functions and found them to be considerably *greater* than the corresponding empirical parameters. The calculated radial integrals predict multiplets that are considerably more expanded that those observed experimentally. Slater[35] has commented that for the d^N transition ions it appears as if configuration interaction with higher configurations is very important in pushing down the higher multiplets in the low configurations more than in the lower multiplets, and thereby squeezing the levels of the observed configurations in comparison with the separations determined by the simple theory.

It is at first sight surprising that the Slater-Condon methods of calculating energy levels on the assumption of no configuration interaction yields such good results when, in fact, it is evident that there must be considerable configuration interaction. The "true" wave function must contain admixtures of the states of many configurations. These admixtures, although individually quite small, may well account for an appreciable accumulative contribution to the final wave function. Thus the "f^N" configuration might well contain 50% f^N character, with the remaining 50% being made up of many small contributions from the virtually infinite number of interacting configurations. It is evident from the work of Rajnak and Wybourne[49,115] that in this case the elementary theory for a *pure f^N* configuration would still give a reasonably good account of the observed energy levels provided the $F^k(4f, 4f)$ and ζ_{4f} radial integrals are treated as parameters. The net result will be that the radial integrals will be scaled *down* to be *less* than those calculated using a Hartree-Fock wave function without configuration interaction. Thus it would be surprising indeed if the Hartree-Fock wave functions yielded radial integrals which agreed with the empirical parameters. No substantial improvement in the agreement would be expected if relativistic effects were to be included in the wave function calculation.

2-19 Remaining Interactions

The inclusion of the normal Coulomb and spin-orbit interactions accounts by far for the greatest part of the energy of the states of the configurations encountered in the rare earths. The relativistic derivation of the many-electron Hamiltonian[126] shows that there are additional magnetic interactions that need to be considered in a precise treatment of the calculation of the energy levels of an atom. In general, these additional terms in the Hamiltonian do not make very substantial energy contributions. We shall limit ourselves to the effects of orbit-orbit, spin-spin, and spin-other-orbit interaction in the f^N-shell.

The Hamiltonian for the orbit-orbit interaction[127] has the form (in atomic units)

$$H_{o-o} = \frac{\alpha^2}{2} \sum_{i>j} \left[\frac{1}{r_{ij}} (\nabla_i \cdot \nabla_j) + \frac{1}{2r_{ij}^3} \{ (\mathbf{r}_{ij} \cdot \nabla_i)(\mathbf{r}_{ij} \cdot \nabla_j) \right.$$
$$\left. + (\mathbf{r}_{ji} \cdot \nabla_j)(\mathbf{r}_{ji} \cdot \nabla_i) \} + \frac{1}{2r_{ij}^3} (\mathbf{r}_{ij} \cdot \nabla_i - \nabla_j) \right], \quad (2\text{-}131)$$

where here α is the fine-structure constant. Yanagawa[128] has discussed the calculation of the matrix elements of orbit-orbit interactions. His results may be simplified to yield for f^N configurations,[129]

$$(f^N\tau SLJ|H_{o-o}|f^N\tau'S'L'J') = -\delta(\tau, \tau')\delta(J, J')\delta(S, S')\delta(L, L')$$
$$\times [\alpha L(L + 1) + \beta G(G_2) + \gamma G(R_7) + N\omega], \quad (2\text{-}132)$$

where

$$\alpha = -2\left(M^0 - \frac{5M^4}{121}\right), \qquad \beta = 32\left(M^2 - \frac{35M^4}{121}\right),$$

$$\gamma = -40M^2, \quad \text{and} \quad \omega = 8\left(3M^0 + M^2 + \frac{5M^4}{11}\right),$$

and M^x is a radial integral defined by Marvin[130] as

$$M^x = \frac{\alpha^2}{4} \iint\limits_{r_i > r_j} R_{nf}^2(r_i)R_{nf}^2(r_j) \frac{r_i^x}{r_j^{x+3}} \, dr_i \, dr_j. \quad (2\text{-}133)$$

We note that the orbit-orbit interaction has the same angular form as the three terms of Eq. 2-121, but the radial parts of the orbit-orbit interaction are of opposite sign. Hence in the parametrization of the effects of configuration interaction due to two-electron excitations, the effects of the orbit-orbit interactions will be accommodated in the derived parameters*.

The Hamiltonian for the spin-spin interaction has the form

$$H_{s-s} = \alpha^2 \sum_{i>j} \left[\frac{(\mathbf{s}_i \cdot \mathbf{s}_j)}{r_{ij}^3} - \frac{3(\mathbf{r}_{ij} \cdot \mathbf{s}_i)(\mathbf{r}_{ij} \cdot \mathbf{s}_j)}{r_{ij}^5}\right]. \quad (2\text{-}134)$$

The calculation of the matrix elements of spin-spin interaction have been discussed by Horie[116] and Innes[131] among others.[132-134] Horie has shown the matrix elements for a configuration l^N to be of the form

$$(l^N\tau SLJM|H_{s-s}|l^N\tau'S'L'J'M') = (-1)^{S'+L+J}\begin{Bmatrix} S & S' & 2 \\ L' & L & J \end{Bmatrix}$$

$$\times \sum_k Z_k M^{k-1} \sum_{\tau''S''L''} (l^N\tau SL||\mathbf{V}^{(1,k-1)}||l^N\tau''S''L'')(l^N\tau''S''L''||\mathbf{V}^{(1,k+1)}$$

$$\times ||l^N\tau'S'L')(-1)^{S+L+S'+L'}\begin{Bmatrix} S & S' & 2 \\ 1 & 1 & S'' \end{Bmatrix}\begin{Bmatrix} L & L' & 2 \\ k-1 & k+1 & L'' \end{Bmatrix}, \quad (2\text{-}135)$$

where

$$Z_k = -4[5k(k + 1)(2k - 1)(2k + 1)(2k + 3)]^{1/2}(l||\mathbf{C}^{(k-1)}||l)(l||\mathbf{C}^{(k+1)}||l),$$
$$(2\text{-}136)$$

---

* For a detailed account of the calculation of the matrix elements of the orbit-orbit interaction see the paper of Dagys, Rudzikas, Katilius, and Jucys, *Lietuvos Fizikos Rinkinys* III, Nos. 3-4, page 365 (1963).

and the double tensors are as defined in Eq. 2-101. The radial integrals M^{k-1} are identical to those of the orbit-orbit interaction. The matrix elements of the spin-spin interaction are diagonal in the seniority number v and unchanged under conjugation ($l^N \rightarrow l^{4l+2-N}$). In addition, they are vanishing for terms belonging to different classes for the half-filled shell.

An alternative method of calculating these matrix elements has been discussed by Trees.[134] This method avoids the summations over the double tensors, but requires that the matrix elements of the l^{N-1} configuration be first evaluated. An example for the f^2 configuration has been given by Judd,[39] who has also shown[135] that within a given LS multiplet the spin-spin interaction has matrix elements equal to

$$-\rho\left[(L \cdot S)^2 + \frac{L \cdot S}{2} - \frac{L(L + 1) S(S + 1)}{3}\right],\tag{2-137}$$

and has given tables permitting the calculations for the states of maximum multiplicity of all the f^N configurations to be carried out in terms of the radial integrals M^{k-1}.

The Hamiltonian for the spin-other-orbit interaction has the form

$$H_{\text{s-o-o}} = \frac{\alpha^2}{2} \sum_{i>j} \left[\mathbf{V}_i\left(\frac{1}{r_{ij}}\right) \times \mathbf{p}_i\right](\mathbf{s}_i \times 2\mathbf{s}_j).\tag{2-138}$$

Horie[116] has discussed methods of calculating the matrix elements of the spin-other-orbit interaction. The J-dependence of the matrix elements is given by

$$(l^N \tau SLJ|H_{\text{s-o-o}}|l^N \tau' S'L'J') = \delta(J, J')(-1)^{S' + L + J}\begin{Bmatrix} S & S' & 1 \\ L' & L & J \end{Bmatrix}$$
$$\times (l^N \tau SL||H_{\text{s-o-o}}||l^N \tau' S'L').\tag{2-139}$$

We note that the J-dependence of the matrix elements is identical to that of the spin-orbit interaction. Following Horie we may write the reduced matrix elements as the sum of two terms H^{I} and H^{II}. For H^{I} we have

$$(l^N \tau SL||H^{\text{I}}||l^N \tau' S'L') = \left[-2NM^0 + 6\left\{\frac{3}{l(l + 1)(2l + 1)}\right\}^{1/2}\right.$$
$$\left.\times \sum_{kK} (-1)^{K+k}(l||\mathbf{C}^{(K)}||l)(l||\mathbf{U}^{(Kk)}||l)\begin{Bmatrix} K & l & l \\ l & k & 1 \end{Bmatrix}M^{k-1}\right]$$
$$\times (l^N \tau SL||\mathbf{V}^{(11)}||l^N \tau' S'L')[l(l + 1)(2l + 1)]^{1/2},\tag{2-140}$$

where k is an odd integer (1, 3, and 5 for f-electrons) and $K = k \pm 1$.

$U^{(Kk)}$ is a quantity defined by Horie as

$$(l\|\mathbf{U}^{(k-1,k)}\|l) = (-1)^{(k-1)/2}(2l + 1)[k + 1)(2k - 1)(2k + 1)/3]^{1/2}$$
$$\times \left[\frac{(k - 1)!(k + 1)!(2l - k)!}{(2l + k + 1)!}\right]^{1/2}\left(\frac{2l + k + 1}{2}\right)! \bigg/ \left[\left(\frac{k - 1}{2}\right)!\right.$$
$$\times \left.\left(\frac{k + 1}{2}\right)!\left(\frac{2l - k + 1}{2}\right)!\right], \quad \text{(2-141a)}$$

and

$$(l\|\mathbf{U}^{(k+1,k)}\|l) = -\left[\frac{k(2k + 3)}{(k + 1)(2k - 1)}\right]^{1/2}(l\|\mathbf{U}^{(k-1,k)}\|l). \quad \text{(2-141b)}$$

The matrix elements of H^{I} are proportional to those of the spin-orbit interaction; therefore the effect of this portion of the spin-orbit interaction is to modify the spin-orbit coupling constant.

The second term H^{II} is somewhat more complicated and has the form

$$(l^N\tau SL\|H^{\mathrm{II}}\|l^N\tau'S'L') = -2(3)^{1/2}\sum_{kK}(-1)^{k+K+L+L'}(l\|\mathbf{C}^{(K)}\|l)$$

$$\times (l\|\mathbf{U}^{(K,k)}\|l)M^{k-1}\bigg[\sum_{\tau''L''}(l^N\tau SL\|\mathbf{U}^{(K)}\|l^N\tau''SL'')(l^N\tau''SL''\|\mathbf{V}^{(1k)}\|$$

$$\times l^N\tau'S'L')\begin{Bmatrix} L & K & L'' \\ k & L' & 1 \end{Bmatrix} + 2\sum_{\tau''L''}(l^N\tau SL\|\mathbf{U}^{(k)}\|l^N\tau''SL'')(l^N\tau''SL''\|\mathbf{V}^{(1K)}\|$$

$$\times \|l^N\tau'S'L')\begin{Bmatrix} L & k & L'' \\ K & L' & 1 \end{Bmatrix}\bigg]; \quad \text{(2-142)}$$

where we omit the term with $k = 1$, $K = 0$ from the summation for the first term in braces since it is already included in Eq. 2-140.

For systems with two or more equivalent electrons the contribution to the spin-other-orbit interaction given by Eq. 2-140 may be absorbed by the spin-orbit coupling parameter, whereas the contribution from Eq. 2-142 will represent an overt effect that can only be included by introducing the M^k integrals as additional parameters. Fortunately, usually the first contribution will be dominant because of the presence of the term $-2NM^0$. It is important in making comparisons of spin-orbit coupling constants computed from atomic wave functions with those derived by least-squares analyses of experimental data to realize that the latter may contain the effects of interactions other than those of the spin-orbit interaction.[136,137]

The matrix elements of the orbit-orbit, spin-spin, and spin-other-orbit interactions for the l^N configuration may be expressed in terms of just three radial integrals, M^0, M^2, and M^4. Using a 4f-hydrogenic eigen-function in Eq. 2-133 to evaluate these integrals, we find[39] (in atomic units)

$$M^0 = \frac{3473}{32,768} \alpha^2 \langle r^{-3} \rangle, \qquad M^2 = \frac{2115}{32,768} \alpha^2 \langle r^{-3} \rangle, \qquad \text{and}$$

$$M^4 = \frac{1485}{32,768} \alpha^2 \langle r^{-3} \rangle,$$

where α is the fine-structure constant. Bleaney[138] has deduced for the $4f^2$ configuration of Pr IV the value

$$\langle r^{-3} \rangle = 5.06 \text{ a.u.}$$

Inserting these values in Eq. 2-132, we obtain for the orbit-orbit interaction in Pr IV $4f^2$

$$\alpha = -12.4 \text{ cm}^{-1}, \quad \beta = 175.7 \text{ cm}^{-1}, \quad \text{and} \quad \gamma = -107.3 \text{ cm}^{-1}.$$

The shifts in the LS terms of $4f^2$ (assuming Russell-Saunders coupling) are given in Table 2-8. Although the approximations of this calculation are rather gross, it would seem that these shifts are by no means negligible.

TABLE 2-8 Energy-level shifts in Pr IV $4f^2$ due to orbit-orbit interaction

^3H	-303.3
^3F	-168.3
^1G	-193.4
^1D	-19.7
^3P	43.6
^1I	-466.3
^1S	$0 \quad \text{cm}^{-1}$

Again, assuming Russell-Saunders coupling and a $4f$-hydrogenic eigenfunction, we may calculate the shifts produced by spin-spin interaction among the triplets of Pr IV $4f^2$. The results are shown in Table 2-9. These shifts are much smaller than those produced by the orbit-orbit interaction and may in most practical cases be ignored.

TABLE 2-9 Energy-level shifts in Pr IV $4f^2$ due to spin-spin interaction

$^3H_4$	-5.5
$^3H_5$	8.3
$^3H_6$	-3.2
$^3F_2$	5.2
$^3F_3$	-6.7
$^3F_4$	2.2
$^3P_0$	0
$^3P_1$	20.0
$^3P_2$	$-4.0 \quad \text{cm}^{-1}$

CHAPTER 3

Intensities in Rare Earth Spectra

3-1 Transition Probabilities

In this chapter we shall consider some of the problems that arise in the interpretation of the intensities of optical transitions in rare earth spectra. The results we shall give are quite general and applicable to the spectra of other atoms and ions. In developing the initial parts of the theory we shall follow the treatment of Condon and Shortley[33] rather closely and then show how the theory of tensor operators leads to quite general formulas for calculating transition probabilities.

In the absence of perturbing fields each energy level characterized by a total angular momentum J will be $(2J + 1)$-fold degenerate, each of the different states being characterized by a different value of J_z. A *spectral line* is defined as the radiation associated with all possible transitions between the states belonging to two levels. The radiation resulting from a transition between a particular pair of states will be called a *component* of the line.

We may write the emitted intensity of the component from a state $\alpha J J_z$ to a state $\alpha' J' J_z'$ in ergs per second as

$$\mathbf{I}(\alpha J J_z; \alpha' J' J_z') = \mathbf{N}(\alpha J J_z) h c \sigma \mathscr{A}(\alpha J J_z; \alpha' J' J_z'), \qquad (3\text{-}1)$$

where $N(\alpha J J_z)$ is the number of atoms in state $\alpha J J_z$, σ is the wave number (in cm^{-1}) of the transition, and $\mathscr{A}(\alpha J J_z; \alpha' J' J_z')$ is the *spontaneous-emission transition probability* for the transition. This equation assumes there is no induced emission and the absence of other modes of energy degradation. For an *electric-dipole* transition we may write

$$\mathscr{A}(\alpha J J_z; \alpha' J' J_z') = \frac{64\pi^4 \sigma^3}{3h} |\langle \alpha J J_z | \mathbf{P} | \alpha' J' J_z' \rangle|^2, \qquad (3\text{-}2)$$

where $\langle \alpha J J_z | \mathbf{P} | \alpha' J' J_z' \rangle$ is the matrix element of the electric-dipole operator

$$\mathbf{P} = -e \sum_i \mathbf{r}_i. \tag{3-3}$$

The *total intensity* of a line is the sum of the intensities of its components; therefore for the transition from a level αJ to a level $\alpha' J'$

$$\mathbf{I}(\alpha J; \alpha' J') = N(\alpha J J_z) \frac{64\pi^4 \sigma^4 c}{3} \sum_{J_z, J_z'} |\langle \alpha J J_z | \mathbf{P} | \alpha' J' J_z' \rangle|^2.$$

The *strength* of the line may be defined as the sum of the squared electric-dipole matrix elements, namely,

$$\mathscr{S}(\alpha J; \alpha' J') = \sum_{J_z, J_z'} |\langle \alpha J J_z | \mathbf{P} | \alpha' J' J_z' \rangle|^2. \tag{3-4}$$

The line strength, as just defined, is quite independent of the conditions under which the atom or ion is radiating. Noting that $N(\alpha J J_z) = N(\alpha J)/(2J + 1)$, we obtain the intensity as

$$\mathbf{I}(\alpha J; \alpha' J') = \frac{N(\alpha J)}{2J + 1} \frac{64\pi^4 \sigma^4 c}{3} \mathscr{S}(\alpha J; \alpha' J'). \tag{3-5}$$

For practical calculations we shall define the transition probability as

$$\mathscr{A}(\alpha J; \alpha' J') = \frac{1}{2J + 1} \frac{64\pi^4 \sigma^3}{3h} \mathscr{S}(\alpha J; \alpha' J'). \tag{3-6}$$

Thus we see that the intensities of spectral lines are determined by the line strengths, the fourth power of the wave number of the transition, and the population of the upper energy level. The determination of the population of the energy levels depends on the rates at which the atoms or ions enter and leave by all processes, and hence, requires a detailed knowledge of the excitation process of the spectral source. Where thermal equilibrium exists it is possible to deduce the population of the levels using the Boltzmann distribution

$$N(\alpha J) = (2J + 1) e^{-E(\alpha J)/kT}. \tag{3-7}$$

However, such an ideal excitation is seldom achieved, thus making the determination of reliable *absolute* intensities one of the outstanding problems in experimental spectroscopy.[139,140] It is normally possible to obtain only reliable *relative* intensities and it is to their interpretation we shall restrict our discussions. This means that we must restrict our attention to those transitions that originate from a common upper level αJ because different upper levels will possess different populations.

3-2   Calculation of Line Strengths

Numerous tabulations of line strengths have appeared in the literature.[141] These tabulations suffer from two major defects: (1) they are not extensive enough to include many of the transitions that are encountered in the spectroscopy of the rare earths and (2) no indication is given of what phase must be taken if the square root of the line strength is required. The latter defect is particularly serious since it is not possible to make intermediate coupling calculations[142] with most of the existing tables.

The electric-dipole operator **P** may be written in the tensorial form as[45]

$$\mathbf{P} = -e \sum_{q,i} r_i (\mathbf{C}_q^{(1)})_i, \tag{3-8}$$

where $\mathbf{C}_q^{(1)}$ is as defined in Eq. 2-26.   The line strengths may then be written as

$$\mathscr{S}(\alpha J; \alpha' J') = e^2 \sum_{J_z, J_{z'}, q} |(\alpha J J_z| \sum_i r_i (\mathbf{C}_q^{(1)})_i | \alpha' J' J_{z'})|^2$$

$$= e^2 |(\alpha J \| \sum_i r_i \, \mathbf{C}_i^{(1)} \| \alpha' J')|^2. \tag{3-9}$$

We wish, however, to calculate the *square root* of the line strength, namely

$$\mathscr{S}^{1/2}(\alpha J; \alpha' J') = -e(\alpha J \| \sum_i r_i \mathbf{C}_i^{(1)} \| \alpha' J'), \tag{3-10}$$

where we retain the phases of the matrix elements of the tensor operator $\mathbf{C}^{(1)}$.

Let us now consider the calculation of line strengths in LS coupling. The J-dependency of the line strengths in LS coupling may be determined by use of Eq. 2-49 to be given by

$$\mathscr{S}^{1/2}(\alpha SLJ; \alpha' SL'J') = (-1)^{J+L'+S+1}([J, J'])^{1/2} \begin{Bmatrix} J & 1 & J' \\ L' & S & L \end{Bmatrix}$$

$$\times -e(\alpha SL \| \sum_i r_i \mathbf{C}_i^{(1)} \| \alpha' SL'). \tag{3-11}$$

The angular momenta appearing in the 6-j symbol must satisfy the triangular conditions of Eq. 2-31 to be nonvanishing.   Application of these conditions leads to the selection rules

$$\Delta S = 0, \qquad \Delta L = 0, \pm 1, \qquad \text{and} \quad \Delta J = 0, \pm 1, \quad \text{but not } 0 \leftrightarrow 0.$$

The J selection rule is independent of the coupling scheme.   The selection rules on S and L are weaker in the sense that they are dependent on the details of the coupling scheme.   A departure from LS coupling will lead to a breakdown of these latter selection rules.   It is important to realize that the fact that the angular momenta of two states satisfy a set of selection rules does not in itself ensure a nonvanishing transition probability.

To complete the evaluation of the line strengths in LS coupling we must evaluate the matrix elements

$$-e(\alpha SL\|\sum_i r_i \mathbf{C}_i^{(1)}\|\alpha' SL'), \tag{3-12}$$

which will be different for different transition arrays.*

We shall now consider the calculation of these matrix elements for several transition arrays that are commonly encountered in rare earth spectra.

1. $l^N l' \leftrightarrow l^N l''$.

The tensor operator $\mathbf{C}^{(1)}$ is a one-particle type F operator, and hence the matrix elements may be evaluated using Eq. 2-49 to give

$$-e(l^N\alpha_1 S_1 L_1, n'l'; SL \|\sum_i r_i \mathbf{C}_i^{(1)}\| l^N\alpha_1 S_1 L_1, n''l''; SL')$$

$$= (-1)^{L_1 + L + l'' + 1 + g}([L, L'])^{1/2}\begin{Bmatrix} L & 1 & L' \\ l'' & L_1 & l' \end{Bmatrix} l_>^{1/2} s(n'l', n''l''), \tag{3-13}$$

where
$$s(n'l', n''l'') = -e\int_0^\infty r\, R(n'l')R(n''l'')\, dr, \tag{3-14}$$

and we have used the fact that

$$(l'\|\mathbf{C}^{(1)}\|l'') = l_>^{1/2}(-1)^g,$$

where $g = (l'' - l' + 1)/2$ and $l_>$ is the greater of l' and l''. We note that in pure LS coupling the line strengths are diagonal in the quantum numbers that characterize the states of the l^N core. It follows from Eq. 3-14, and the fact that $\mathbf{C}^{(1)}$ is a type F operator, that the line strengths in any coupling scheme will be nonzero only for transitions occurring between states of opposite parity and where the configuration change is by just the nl of a single electron, the change in l being restricted to $\Delta l = \pm 1$. The selection rule on l may be broken if there is configuration interaction but not the parity selection rule.

The transitions $f^N p \leftrightarrow f^N d$ are a typical example of this particular transition array.

2. $l^N l' l'' \leftrightarrow l^N l' l'''$.

---

* A transition array is defined as the totality of lines resulting from the transitions between two configurations.

The matrix elements for this transition array may be found by using Eq. 2-49 twice to yield

$$-e(l^N\alpha_1 S_1 L_1, (n'l', n''l'')S_2 L_2; SL \parallel \sum_i r_i \mathbf{C}_i^{(1)} \parallel l^N\alpha_1 S_1 L_1,$$

$$(n'l', n'''l''')S_2 L_2'; SL') = (-1)^{L+L_1+L_2+L_2'+l'+l'''+g}([L, L', L_2, L_2'])^{1/2}$$

$$\begin{Bmatrix} L & 1 & L' \\ L_2' & L_1 & L_2 \end{Bmatrix} \begin{Bmatrix} L_1 & 1 & L_2' \\ l''' & l' & l'' \end{Bmatrix} l_>^{1/2} s(n''l''; n'''l'''). \quad (3\text{-}15)$$

We note that in writing the matrix element we have assumed a particular species of LS coupling. In this coupling scheme we obtain the additional selection rules

$$\Delta S_2 = 0 \quad \text{and} \quad \Delta L_2 = 0, \pm 1.$$

The transitions $f^N sp \leftrightarrow f^N sd$ are typical of this array. The matrix elements for the transition array $l^N l'' l' \leftrightarrow l^N l''' l'$ are the same as for Eq. 3-15 apart from the replacement of the phase factor by $(-1)^{L+L_1+l'+l''+g}$.

3. $l^N \leftrightarrow l^{N-1} l'$.

The matrix elements for this array readily follow on application of Eq. 2-75 and then Eq. 2-49 to yield

$$-e(l^N\alpha SL \parallel \sum_i r_i \mathbf{C}^{(1)} \parallel l^{N-1}\alpha_1 S_1 L_1, n'l'; SL') = (-1)^{L_1+L+l'+1+g}$$

$$\times ([L, L'])^{1/2} \begin{Bmatrix} L & 1 & L' \\ l' & L_1 & l \end{Bmatrix} N^{1/2}(l^N\alpha SL\{|l^{N-1}\alpha_1 S_1 L_1)l_>^{1/2}\, s(nl; n'l'). \quad (3\text{-}16)$$

For the more than half-filled shell we make use of Eq. 2-22 to calculate the coefficients of fractional parentage. This type of transition array is important in the $f^N \leftrightarrow f^{N-1}d$ and $f^N \leftrightarrow f^{N-1}g$ transitions of the rare earths.

4. $l^N l' \leftrightarrow l^{N-1} l'^2$.

The evaluation of the matrix elements for this array is slightly more complicated than for preceding examples. We first use Eq. 2-75 to obtain

$$-e(nl^N\alpha_1 S_1 L_1, n'l'; SL \parallel \sum_i r_i \mathbf{C}_i^{(1)} \parallel nl^{N-1}\alpha_1' S_1' L_1', (n'l')^2 S_2 L_2; SL')$$

$$= -N^{1/2}(l^N\alpha_1 S_1 L\{|l^{N-1}\alpha_1' S_1' L_1')e(nl^{N-1}\alpha_1' S_1' L_1', nl; S_1 L_1, n'l'; SL$$

$$\times \parallel r_N \mathbf{C}_N^{(1)} \parallel nl^{N-1}a_1' S_1' L_1', (n'l')^2 S_2 L_2; SL'). \quad (3\text{-}17)$$

We now recouple the angular momenta on the left-hand side:

$$(S_1'L_1', sl)S_1L_1, sl'; SL|S_1'L_1', (sl, sl')S_2\lambda; SL) = (-1)^{S+L+S_1'+L_1'+l+l'+2s}$$

$$\times \; [(S_1, L_1, S_2, \lambda)]^{1/2} \begin{Bmatrix} S_1' & s & S_1 \\ s & S & S_2 \end{Bmatrix} \begin{Bmatrix} L_1' & l & L_1 \\ l' & L & \lambda \end{Bmatrix}.$$

Inserting this result in Eq. 3-17 and then applying Eq. 2-49 to the matrix element, we obtain

$$(-1)^{S+S_1'+L_2+l+l'}(l^N\alpha_1 S_1 L_1\{|l^{N-1}\alpha_1'S_1'L_1') \sum_\lambda (N[S_1, L_1, L, L', S_2, \lambda])^{1/2}$$

$$\times \begin{Bmatrix} S_1' & s & S_1 \\ s & S & S_2 \end{Bmatrix} \begin{Bmatrix} L_1' & l & L_1 \\ l' & L & \lambda \end{Bmatrix} \begin{Bmatrix} L & 1 & L' \\ L_2 & L_1' & \lambda \end{Bmatrix} - e((nl, n'l')S_2\lambda$$

$$\times \; \|r\mathbf{C}^{(1)}\|(n'l')^2 S_2 L_2).$$

The matrix element may then be evaluated using Eq. 2-75 followed by Eq. 2-48 and then Eq. 2-40 used to perform the sum over the three 6-j symbols involving λ to yield Eq. 3-17 as

$$= (-1)^{S+S_1'+g+1}(2N[S, L, S_2, L_2, S_1, L'])^{1/2}(l^N\alpha_1 S_1 L_1\{|l^{N-1}\alpha_1'S_1'L_1')$$

$$\times \begin{Bmatrix} S' & S & S_1 \\ s & S & S_2 \end{Bmatrix} \begin{Bmatrix} l' & L_2 & l' \\ L & L' & 1 \\ L_1 & L_1' & l \end{Bmatrix} l_>^{1/2} s(nl; n'l'). \quad (3\text{-}18)$$

The most commonly encountered transition array of this type in rare earth spectra is that of $f^N d \leftrightarrow f^{N-1} d^2$.

The calculation of the line strengths for other transition arrays may be made using the methods outlined in the preceding examples and introduce no new problems; they are therefore left as an exercise for the reader.

The formulas we have just derived for calculating line strengths are valid for transitions only between two LS-coupled configurations. These formulas will not give the correct line strengths if one or both of the configurations deviate from this well-defined coupling scheme. In some cases it is preferable to work in a coupling scheme other than LS coupling. In general, however, it is best to work in the coupling scheme that corresponds most closely to the actual physical coupling, for it is then frequently possible to make simple predictions of the intensity characteristics of the spectra without extensive computation. The choice of the coupling scheme is, however, as we shall see, somewhat dictated by the coupling scheme in which the energy matrices of the configurations were calculated.

3-3   Line Strengths in $J_1 j$ Coupling

The line strengths in $J_1 j$ coupling may be readily calculated using the methods developed in Sec. 3-2. The J-dependency of the line strengths is found by use of Eq. 2-49 to be

$$\mathscr{S}^{1/2}(\alpha_1 J_1 jJ; \alpha_1 J_1 j'J') = (-1)^{J+J_1+j'+1}([J, J'])^{1/2}$$

$$\times \begin{Bmatrix} J & 1 & J' \\ j' & J_1 & j \end{Bmatrix} -e(n'sl'j\|r\mathbf{C}^{(1)}\|n''sl''j'), \qquad (3\text{-}19)$$

from which follow the selection rules

$$\Delta J_1 = 0, \qquad \Delta j = 0, \pm 1, \qquad \text{and} \quad \Delta J = 0, \pm 1, \quad \text{but not } 0 \leftrightarrow 0.$$

The matrix element in Eq. 3-19 may be readily evaluated as

$$= (-1)^{j+l''+s+1+g}([j, j'])^{1/2} \begin{Bmatrix} j & 1 & j' \\ l'' & s & l' \end{Bmatrix} l_>^{1/2} s(n'l'; n''l'') \qquad (3\text{-}20)$$

The selection rule on J_1 holds quite independently of the form of the coupling of the f^N core. Clearly, the $J_1 j$ selection rules will only be valid if both configurations follow $J_1 j$ coupling. These selection rules are especially important in understanding the intensity characteristics of the spectra that arise from allowed transitions between the $f^N s$ and $f^N p$ configurations. Their spectra are characterized by the appearance of two groups of intense lines. These intense lines correspond to those $p \to s$ transitions that occur without a change in the quantum numbers of the states of the f^N core. The lower energy group of $p \to s$ transitions originate from the $p_{1/2}$ states, whereas the higher energy group of $p \to s$ transitions originate from the $p_{3/2}$ states. The energy separation of the two groups is approximately independent of the core levels since in pure $J_1 j$ coupling the $(p_{3/2} \to p_{1/2})$ separation is just $\frac{3}{2}\zeta_p$. The application of the $J_1 j$ selection rules can constitute a very powerful tool in analyzing these spectra.

3-4   Line Strengths in Intermediate Coupling

In many practical cases encountered in rare earth spectra the configurations involved in a particular transition array depart appreciably from the well-defined coupling schemes, making calculations of the line strengths in intermediate coupling essential. The calculation of line strengths in intermediate coupling commences by calculating the square root of the line strength, $\mathscr{S}^{1/2}(\alpha J; J')$, in some well-defined coupling scheme, which need not be limited to LS coupling, and then making a transformation to the actual coupling to obtain the intermediate coupling line strengths $\mathscr{S}^{1/2}(aJ; bJ')$.

Thus we may write[33]

$$\mathscr{S}^{1/2}(aJ; bJ') = \sum_{\alpha,\beta} (aJ|\alpha J)\mathscr{S}^{1/2}(\alpha J; \beta J')(\beta J'|bJ'), \qquad (3\text{-}21)$$

where $(aJ|\alpha J)$ represents the transformation matrix that transforms the states $|\alpha J)$ into the state $(aJ|$ of the actual coupling and analogously for $(\beta J'|bJ')$. We note that the states $|\alpha J)$ and $(\beta J'|$ need not be in the same coupling scheme.

The transformation matrices will normally depend on the degree of departure from some well-defined coupling scheme unless a simple transformation is being made from one well-defined coupling scheme to some other well-defined coupling scheme. The simplest way to obtain the transformation matrices is to construct the energy matrices of the two configurations in the same well-defined coupling scheme, and with the same choice of phases as the line strengths were calculated, and then diagonalize the energy matrices for the set of parameters that yields energy levels that correspond as closely as possible to the observed energy levels. The matrices that diagonalize the energy matrices (that is, the eigenvectors of the diagonalized energy matrices) will be the same as the transformation matrices we require. The line strengths in intermediate coupling then follow by a simple matrix multiplication. Since the radial part of the line strength is unaffected by the transformation, we frequently make use of *relative* line strengths where the radial part is removed; this leaves us free to fix the radial part at some later time should we desire to calculate *absolute* line strengths.

As an example of the calculation of relative line strengths in intermediate coupling consider the $J = 2 \to J = 3$ transitions of the transition array $4f^{13}6p \to 4f^{13}6s$ of Yb III studied by Bryant.[70] The energy matrices have been constructed in the LS coupling scheme and diagonalized to yield a set of energy levels that correspond quite closely to the observed levels which Bryant actually labeled in the $J_1 j$ coupling scheme and which we shall retain for labeling the levels. The eigenvectors resulting from the diagonalization give the linear combinations of the LS states that correspond to the levels in intermediate coupling. The square roots of the line strengths, in LS coupling, follow from Eq. 3-13. The two transformation matrices found from the diagonalization of the energy matrices are shown in Table 3-1 together with the square roots of the line strengths in the order given by Eq. 3-21. The result of the matrix multiplication, which gives the square roots of the relative line strengths in intermediate coupling, is shown immediately below. For comparison, the square roots of the relative line strengths for pure $J_1 j$ coupling are given directly below the square roots of the intermediate coupling line strengths. This comparison shows clearly that pure $J_1 j$ coupling calculations give results almost identical to those found from the considerably more tedious intermediate coupling calculation. It is apparent that the LS coupling calculation gives a completely unrealistic picture of the intensity characteristics of this spectra, thus justifying Bryant's labeling of the energy levels in the $J_1 j$ coupling notation. We note that the line strengths of the transitions (that is, the squares of the tabulated values) that violate the $J_1 j$ selection rules are extremely small when compared with those of the allowed transitions, which is as observed in Bryant's study.

TABLE 3-1 Calculation of line strengths in intermediate coupling for the $J = 2$ to $J = 3$ transitions of Yb III $4f^{13}6p \rightarrow 4f^{13}6s$

	$^3F_3$	$^1F_3$			$^3F_2$	$^3D_2$	$^1D_2$
$(\frac{7}{2},\frac{1}{2})_3$	0.6792	0.7339	$^3F_3$		0.4303	1.2171	0
$(\frac{5}{2},\frac{1}{2})_3$	0.7339	-0.6792	$\times$ $^1F_3$		0	0	1.2910

	$(\frac{7}{2},\frac{3}{2})_2$	$(\frac{5}{2},\frac{3}{2})_2$	$(\frac{5}{2},\frac{1}{2})_2$
$^3F_2$	0.2128	0.8051	0.5536
$\times$ $^3D_2$	0.6851	-0.5269	0.5030
$^1D_2$	-0.6967	-0.2723	0.6637

	$(\frac{7}{2},\frac{1}{2})_2$	$(\frac{5}{2},\frac{3}{2})_2$	$(\frac{5}{2},\frac{1}{2})_2$	
$(\frac{7}{2},\frac{1}{2})_3$	1.2887	0.0570	0.0512	$S^{1/2}$ Intermediate
$=$ $(\frac{5}{2},\frac{1}{2})_3$	-0.0683	0.4552	1.2061	coupling

	$(\frac{7}{2},\frac{1}{2})_2$	$(\frac{5}{2},\frac{3}{2})_2$	$(\frac{5}{2},\frac{1}{2})_2$	
$(\frac{7}{2},\frac{1}{2})_3$	1.2910	0	0	
$(\frac{5}{2},\frac{1}{2})_3$	0	0.6085	1.1389	$S^{1/2}(J_1 jJ; J_1 j'J')$

3-5 Transitions between Differently Coupled Configurations

The selection rules that have been given so far apply only when both configurations involved in the transition array follow the same well-defined coupling scheme. Sometimes, however, the configurations will follow different coupling schemes. For example, in the $4f5f$-$4f5g$ transitions of Ce III the $4f5f$ configuration exhibits good LS coupling, whereas the $4f5g$

configuration follows J_1l coupling very closely. Clearly, here the application of *all* of the selection rules for LS or for J_1l coupling would be physically meaningless. We may apply only those selection rules that are common to both coupling schemes; that is, (for $l^N l' \leftrightarrow l^N l''$) the quantum numbers α, S, L, associated with the l^N core will not change, $\Delta J = 0$, ± 1, but not $0 \leftrightarrow 0$, and $\Delta l = \pm 1$.

For making practical calculations it is usually simplest to first calculate the square roots of the line strengths, assuming both configurations are LS coupled, and then to transform by an intermediate coupling-type calculation to the actual coupling scheme since rarely do we find that both configurations follow well-defined coupling schemes.

3-6 Estimation of the Radial Integrals

Where interest is limited to the interpretation of relative intensities there is little point in trying to calculate the absolute line strengths, because relative line strengths will clearly suffice *provided the effects of configuration interaction* can be neglected.

In calculating *absolute* line strengths or intensities, the calculation of the radial integral in Eq. 3-14 is of fundamental importance and is, in addition to the problem of determining the population distributions among the levels, a serious limiting factor in making precise calculations. These two problems represent the major obstacles facing the development of a precise interpretation of the intensities of spectral lines and constitute one of the great problems of present-day theoretical spectroscopy. Even when precise calculations are made it is usually found that the experimental determinations lack the precision necessary to give an adequate test of the theoretical methods. We can, however, expect that these problems will be attacked with renewed vigor because of their tremendous importance in the fields of astrophysics. It is well known that rare earth spectra are present in stellar and solar spectra; [143] thus as more lines are clearly identified there will be the possibility of using these spectroscopic observations for studying the physical conditions existing in stellar objects, provided we can understand the problems associated with the interpretation of their intensity characteristics.

The same difficulties are involved in estimating both the radial integrals associated with intensity calculations and in estimating the radial integrals associated with energy-level calculations—the lack of adequate wave functions. There is, however, an important difference; in energy-level calculations we are principally interested in the wave function of a single configuration, whereas in intensity calculations we are interested in the overlap of the wave functions of two configurations. This means that we must have excited-state wave functions when normally only the wave functions of the ground configurations are given in the literature.   To date there are no such Hartree-Fock calculations for rare earths.   Even if such calculations were available, it is unlikely that they would yield very accurate radial integrals.   We can expect the overlap of the wave functions to be very sensitive to the effects of correlation, and it will probably be some time before correlated Hartree-Fock wave functions of suitable accuracy will become possible for atoms as heavy as the rare earths.   In the meantime it may well be desirable to derive the appropriate integrals from the experimental data, which, however, will only be feasible when really precise experimental determinations become possible.

Bates and Damgaard[144] have shown that in some cases it is permissible to neglect the departure of the potential of an atom or ion from its asymptotic Coulomb form for the purposes of calculating transition integrals. This Coulomb approximation enables a general analytical expression for the transition integrals to be derived.   These authors have given tables from which the transition integrals for s-p, p-d, and d-f transitions may be calculated, provided the term values of the upper and lower levels are known.   Comparison with experimental data shows that for systems involving a single electron outside closed shells Bates and Damgaard's method gives remarkably accurate results.   Their method is, however, likely to be of questionable validity for most of the examples in rare earth spectra, where systems involving unclosed shells are most frequently encountered, thus making it difficult to identify the energy parameters associated with their method.

3-7   The Oscillator Strengths of Eu II

The calculation of the oscillator and line strengths of the $[4f^7(^8S_{7/2})6p - 4f^7(^8S_{7/2})6s]$ transition array of Eu II gives an interesting example of some of the great problems that are likely to be encountered in the interpretation of the intensity characteristics of rare earth spectra.

The strongest lines of the spectrum of Eu II arise from transitions based on the ground level of Eu III, $4f^7(^8S)$.   The levels of Eu II that result from the addition of a 6s-, 6p-, or 5d-electron to the lowest level of the $4f^7$ configuration are well known from the work of Russell et al.[94] Meggers et al.[139] have made a study of these transitions reporting their intensities on a uniform energy scale.   Using these intensity measurements, Corliss and Bozman[140] have deduced the oscillator strengths and transition probabilities of the $[4f^7(^8S_{7/2})6p \rightarrow 4f^7(^8S_{7/2})6s]$ transition array.   These particular transitions are of particular interest, for they represent transitions between two quite closely J_1j-coupled configurations.

The calculation of the energy levels of Eu II $4f^7(^8S_{7/2})6p$ is identical to that of the isoelectronic Gd III ion discussed on page 57.   By treating the parameters $G(4f, 6p)$ and ζ_{6p} as free variables, it is found that the energy levels calculated using the values

$$G(4f, 6p) = 45.15 \text{ cm}^{-1} \quad \text{and} \quad \zeta_{6p} = 1725 \text{ cm}^{-1}$$

agree quite closely with the experimental levels of Russell et al. On diagonalizing the energy matrices for these values, we obtain the eigenvectors for the different levels. The results of the calculation are given in Table 3-2. It is apparent from an inspection of the eigenvectors that the levels do, in fact, follow $J_1 j$ coupling very closely.

TABLE 3-2   Calculated and observed energy levels of Eu II $4f^7(^8S_{7/2})6p$

$J_1 jJ$	E_{calc}	E_{obs}	Eigenvector
$[a6p_{1/2}]_3$	23,835	23,774	$-0.136\,p_{3/2} + 0.991\,p_{1/2}$
$[a6p_{1/2}]_4$	24,148	24,208	$-0.207\,p_{3/2} + 0.978\,p_{1/2}$
$[a6p_{3/2}]_5$	26,217	26,173	$p_{3/2}$
$[a6p_{3/2}]_4$	26,782	26,839	$0.978\,p_{3/2} + 0.207\,p_{1/2}$
$[a6p_{3/2}]_3$	27,091	27,104	$0.991\,p_{3/2} + 0.136\,p_{1/2}$
$[a6p_{3/2}]_2$	27,300	27,256	$p_{3/2}$

$a \equiv 4f^7(^8S_{7/2})$

The levels of the $4f^7(^8S)6s$ configuration may clearly be treated as pure $J_1 j$ or pure LS levels since there are just two levels and these two are of different J. For the purposes of this calculation we shall consider them to be in the $J_1 j$ coupling scheme.

The square roots of the line strengths may then be calculated in the $J_1 j$ coupling scheme, and then by using the eigenvectors of Table 3-2 and Eq. 3-21 transformed to intermediate coupling. On squaring these transformed values we obtain the line strengths of the transitions in intermediate coupling. The results are given in Table 3-3.

TABLE 3-3   Line strengths of Eu II $4f^7(^8S_{7/2})6p$ in intermediate coupling

$4f^7 6s$	$4f^7 6p$					
	$[a6p_{3/2}]_5$	$[a6p_{3/2}]_4$	$[a6p_{1/2}]_4$	$[a6p_{3/2}]_3$	$[a6p_{1/2}]_3$	$[a6p_{3/2}]_2$
$[a6s]_4$	3.6667	2.3244	0.6719	0.8776	1.4556	0
$[a6s]_3$	0	0.6719	2.3264	1.4556	0.8776	1.6667

$a \equiv 4f^7(^8S_{7/2})$

Experimental results of intensity studies are usually reported in terms of the transition probabilities of Eq. 3-6 or as oscillator strengths. The *emission* oscillator strength is related to the line strength by[33]

$$f(\alpha J; \alpha' J') = \frac{8\pi^2 mc}{3e^2 h\lambda} \frac{\mathscr{S}(\alpha J; \alpha' J')}{2J + 1}$$

$$= \frac{303.75}{\lambda} \frac{\mathscr{S}(\alpha J; \alpha' J')}{2J + 1}, \qquad (3\text{-}22)$$

where λ is the wavelength in angstroms.

The measured wavelengths and oscillator strengths of the transitions are given in Table 3-4. Using these values, we may readily calculate the

TABLE 3-4 Observed wavelengths and oscillator strengths for the $4f^7(^8S_{7/2})6p \rightarrow 4f^7(^8S_{7/2})6s$ transition array of Eu II

Transition	Wavelength	Intensity	$(2J + 1)f$
$[a6p_{3/2}]_5 \rightarrow [a6s]_4$	3819.67	3400_{cw}	1.0
$[a6p_{3/2}]_4 \rightarrow [a6s]_4$	3724.94	1700_{cw}	0.59
$\rightarrow [a6s]_3$	3971.96	2000_{cw}	0.84
$[a6p_{1/2}]_4 \rightarrow [a6s]_4$	4129.70	2200_{cw}	0.49
$\rightarrow [a6s]_3$	4435.56	900_{cw}	0.25
$[a6p_{3/2}]_3 \rightarrow [a6s]_4$	3688.42	550	0.20
$\rightarrow [a6s]_3$	3930.48	2800_{cw}	1.2
$[a6p_{1/2}]_3 \rightarrow [a6s]_4$	4205.05	4000_{cw}	0.84
$\rightarrow [a6s]_3$	4522.57	200	0.052
$[a6p_{3/2}]_2 \rightarrow [a6s]_3$	3907.10	2400_{cw}	1.1

oscillator strengths in terms of $s^2(6p; 6s)$ from the line strengths of Table 3-3. The results are given in Table 3-5. The absolute oscillator strengths would require the evaluation of the transition integral $s^2(6p, 6s)$. It might at first be thought that the value of the transition integral $s^2(6p; 6s)$ could be obtained from a least squares fit of the observed absolute oscillator strengths and the calculated relative oscillator strengths of Table 3-5. A comparison of Tables 3-4 and 3-5 reveals, however, several disturbing features.

It is clear that no choice of the transition integral $s(6p; 6s)$ could possibly lead to the correct ratios of the oscillator strengths for the two $J = 4$ files or to the correct ratio of the oscillator strengths from the $J = 5$ and $J = 2$ upper states. Thus there must be a serious discrepancy between the calculated and experimentally determined oscillator strengths. An examination of the sources of this discrepancy reveals some of the great difficulties that will have to be faced if the intensities of the spectra of the rare earths are to be understood properly.

TABLE 3-5   Relative emission oscillator strengths of the $4f^7(^8S_{7/2})6p \rightarrow$ $4f^7(^8S_{7/2})6s$ transition array of Eu II

$$(2J + 1)f(a6p_jJ; a6sJ') \times 10$$

4f⁷6s \ 4f⁷6p	$[a6p_{3/2}]_5$	$[a6p_{3/2}]_4$	$[a6p_{1/2}]_4$	$[a6p_{3/2}]_3$	$[a6p_{1/2}]_3$	$[a6p_{3/2}]_2$
$[a6s]_4$	2.916	1.895	0.494	0.723	1.051	0
$[a6s]_3$	0	0.514	1.592	1.125	0.589	1.296

Oscillator strengths given in terms of $s^2(6p; 6s)$.

The discrepancy between the observed and calculated oscillator strengths is almost certainly larger than the residual errors of the theoretical treatment.   The predicted ratios of the oscillator strengths for the different J-files should be quite close to the actual ratios since the effects of the breakdown of $J_1 j$ coupling have been included.   Some change in the ratios would occur if there is configuration interaction; however, it is most unlikely that the entire discrepancy is due to the neglect of configuration interaction.   Rather the bulk of the discrepancy is more likely to be associated with the complexities of the experimental determination of oscillator strengths.

Most of the very strong lines of the Eu II spectrum are quite complex and wide structures.   This complexity of the lines arises from the presence of large isotope shifts[30] for the different isotopes that occur in natural europium compounds and metal.   To further complicate the structure of the spectral lines there is considerable hyperfine structure associated with each of the isotopes.   In most of the reported intensity measurements for Eu II there has been sufficient resolution to at least partially resolve the structure of the lines.   If the structure is resolved, it becomes essential to integrate the intensities of the different components of each line.   In many of the methods used for measuring intensities this is not done, so that substantial errors occur in the intensity measurements.   This is particularly true of measurements using the stepped sector method.[139]

Before any attempt can be made to interpret the experimental intensities it is necessary to perform very careful intensity measurements with an accuracy of at least a few percent.   Accurate absolute intensity and oscillator strength measurements could lead to very good tests of wave function calculations since the radial integrals involved depend critically on the overlap of the wave functions.

CHAPTER 4

The Zeeman Effect in the Rare Earths

4-1 The Zeeman Effect

The energy levels of an atom or ion are $(2J + 1)$-fold degenerate in the absence of external electric or magnetic fields.* This degeneracy persists regardless of the form of the coupling of the electrons, but it may be removed by applying a magnetic field, with the result that each level characterized by a particular value of J splits into $2J + 1$ components. The different components are characterized by the quantized projections J_z of J on the axis of the applied field which is normally taken to be in the z-direction.

The study of the splittings of energy levels in an applied magnetic field can lead to a knowledge of the magnetic properties of the energy levels which may later be of value in interpreting the solid-state magnetic properties of rare earth metals and compounds. The Zeeman effect also provides spectroscopists with a powerful tool for the analysis of rare earth spectra.

In the first-order theory of the Zeeman effect the Hamiltonian H_M for the interaction between the N-electrons and an external magnetic field $\mathcal{H}$ is written as [33]

$$H_M = \beta \mathcal{H} \cdot \sum_{i=1}^{N} (\mathbf{l}_i + 2\mathbf{s}_i), \qquad (4\text{-}1a)$$

where β is the Bohr magneton. Schwinger[145] has shown from the use of quantum electrodynamics that the gyromagnetic ratio g_s of the electron

---

* However, note the introductory remarks of Sec. 5-1.

spin is actually slightly larger than 2.   Sommerfield[146] has found that to the fourth-order g_s is given by

$$g_s = 2 \left(1 + \frac{\alpha}{2} - 0.328 \frac{\alpha^2}{2} + \cdots \right) = 2(1.001160),$$

where α is the fine-structure constant.   Thus Eq. 4-1 may be more accurately written as

$$H_M = \mathscr{H} \cdot \sum_{i=1}^{N} (\mathbf{l}_i + g_s \mathbf{s}_i). \tag{4-1b}$$

The calculation of the Zeeman effect (neglecting certain relativistic and diamagnetic corrections) centers about the evaluation of the matrix elements of

$$\left(\alpha J J_z \mid \sum_{i=1}^{N} (\mathbf{l}_i + g_s \mathbf{s}_i) \mid \alpha J' J_z \right). \tag{4-2}$$

H_M commutes with J_z, although not with $\mathbf{J}^2$, regardless of the form of the coupling; therefore the matrix elements are rigorously diagonal in J_z but not in J.

4-2   LS Coupling

In LS coupling H_M also commutes with $\mathbf{L}^2$ and $\mathbf{S}^2$ and hence the matrix elements are also diagonal in S and L.   The J_z-dependence of the matrix elements may be obtained by using the Wigner-Eckart theorem, Eq. 2-30, to yield

$$(\alpha SLJJ_z | \mathbf{L} + g_s \mathbf{S} | \alpha SLJ'J_z) = (-1)^{J-J_z} \begin{pmatrix} J & 1 & J' \\ -J_z & 0 & J_z \end{pmatrix}$$
$$(\alpha SLJ \| \mathbf{L} + g_s \mathbf{S} \| \alpha SLJ'). \tag{4-3}$$

Application of Eqs. 2-48 and 2-49 to the spin and orbital parts of the matrix element followed by the explicit evaluation of the 3-j and 6-j symbols[46] yields, for the diagonal elements,

$$(\alpha SLJJ_z | \mathbf{L} + g_s \mathbf{S} | \alpha SLJJ_z) = J_z g, \tag{4-4}$$

where

$$g = 1 + (g_s - 1) \frac{J(J+1) - L(L+1) + S(S+1)}{2J(J+1)}, \tag{4-5}$$

and for the off-diagonal elements

$$(\alpha SLJJ_z | \mathbf{L} + g_s \mathbf{S} | \alpha SLJ - 1J_z) = (g_s - 1)(J^2 - J_z^2)^{1/2}$$
$$\times \left[\frac{(S+L+J+1)(S+L+1-J)(L+J-S)(S+J-L)}{4J^2(2J+1)(2J-1)} \right]^{1/2}. \tag{4-6}$$

g is the well-known Lande g-factor which has been tabulated extensively.[8]

If the energy levels that differ in J by one unit are well separated, the effect of the applied magnetic field will be to split each level into $(2J+1)$-

equidistant components, forming a pattern which is symmetrical about the energy of the field-free level. When the energy levels are not well separated and the magnetic fields are large, it becomes essential to include the off-diagonal elements given by Eq. 4-6, which then results in the formation of asymmetrical Zeeman patterns. In second-order perturbation theory the shift in the components by the off-diagonal elements (Paschen-Back effect) are proportional to the square of the matrix elements and hence quadratic in the magnetic field strength $\mathscr{H}$. When there is appreciable coupling in the magnetic field of the levels differing in J by one unit, J ceases to be a "good" quantum number and violations of the J selection rules may result. Then the experimental g-values can have little physical meaning, for it no longer describes, by itself, the Zeeman splittings. A detailed analysis of the asymmetries of Zeeman patterns has been given by Catalan.[147]

4-3 J_1j Coupling

The $f^N s$ and $f^N p$ configurations usually exhibit close J_1j coupling, and as a result the Zeeman splittings of the levels are most readily interpreted in terms of the J_1j coupling scheme. In this scheme the *diagonal* matrix elements are found to be

$$\left(\alpha_1 S_1 L_1 J_1, slj; JJ_z \middle| \sum_i (\mathbf{l}_i + g_s \mathbf{s}_i) \middle| \alpha_1 S_1 L_1 J_1, slj; JJ_z \right) = J_z g(J_1 jJ), \quad (4\text{-}7)$$

where

$$g(J_1 jJ) = [J(J+1) + J_1(J_1+1) - j(j+1)]g(S_1 L_1 J_1)/2J(J+1)$$
$$+ [J(J+1) + j(j+1) - J_1(J_1+1)]g(slj)/2J(J+1). \quad (4\text{-}8)$$

In *pure* J_1j coupling the levels based on different states of the l^N core will normally be sufficiently separated to allow us to neglect matrix elements that are nondiagonal in J_1. Similarly, the matrix elements that are nondiagonal in j can usually be neglected *if* this coupling holds. The matrix elements that are diagonal in all the quantum numbers other than J will be given by

$$\left(\alpha_1 S_1 L_1 J_1, slj; JJ_z \middle| \sum_i (\mathbf{l}_i + g_s \mathbf{s}_i) \middle| \alpha_1 S_1 L_1 J_1, slj; J-1J_z \right) = (J^2 - J_z^2)^{1/2}$$
$$\times \left[\frac{(J + J_1 + j + 1)(J_1 + j + 1 - J)(J + J_1 - j)(J + j - J_1)}{4J^2(2J+1)(2J-1)} \right]^{1/2}$$
$$\times [g(S_1 L_1 J_1) - g(slj)], \quad (4\text{-}9)$$

where $g(S_1 L_1 J_1)$ and $g(slj)$ are LS coupling Lande g-factors.

In the limit where pure J_1j coupling is attained, levels having common J_1j quantum numbers and built from the same state of the l^N core will be degenerate and the off-diagonal terms of Eq. 4-9 will lead to large Paschen-Back effects. Small departures from pure J_1j coupling will result in the removal of this degeneracy and the spreading apart of the states with different J. This then diminishes the Paschen-Back effects so that for weak fields the off-diagonal elements of Eq. 4-9 may be neglected. However, J_1 and j will now cease to be good quantum numbers and it becomes essential to include off-diagonal elements of the type

$$(\alpha_1 S_1 L_1 J_1, slj, JJ_z | 1 + g_s s | \alpha_1 S_1 L_1 J_1, slj - 1; JJ_z) = \frac{(g_s - 1)J_z}{4jJ(J + 1)}$$

$$\times \left[\frac{(J + J_1 + j + 1)(J + j - J_1)(J_1 + j - J)(J + J_1 - j + 1)}{\times (s + l + j + 1)(l + j - s)(s + l - j + 1)(s + j - l)}{(2j + 1)(2j - 1)} \right]^{1/2}$$

$$(4-10)$$

and

$$(\alpha_1 S_1 L_1 J_1, slj, JJ_z | L_1 + g_s S_1 | \alpha_1 S_1 L_1 J_1 - 1, slj; JJ_z) = \frac{-(g_s - 1)J_z}{4J J_1 (J + 1)}$$

$$\times \left[\frac{(J+J_1+j+1)(J+J_1-j)(J_1+j-J)(J+j-J_1+1)}{\times (S_1+L_1+J_1+1)(L_1+J_1-S_1)(S_1+J_1-L_1)(S_1+L_1-J_1+1)}{(2J_1 - 1)(2J_1 + 1)} \right]^{1/2}.$$

$$(4-11)$$

It is clear that the inclusion of these matrix elements would complicate greatly the calculation of the Zeeman patterns. In practice, it is usually simplest to make the calculations in an LS-basis and then to make a transformation to the actual coupling. We note that whenever a well-defined coupling scheme is actually attained by a physical system it is essential to consider the matrix elements that are nondiagonal in the total angular momentum J of the atom or ion. When the physical system cannot be represented by a well-defined coupling scheme, it then becomes essential to consider the effects of the matrix elements that are non-diagonal in the other quantum numbers that characterize the coupling scheme.

4-4 $J_1 l$ **Coupling**

The magnetic splittings of the $f^N g$ configurations should be very well described in terms of $J_1 l$ coupling. The diagonal matrix elements will be given by

$$\left(\alpha_1 S_1 L_1 J_1 l; Ks; JJ_z \Big| \sum_i (l_i + g_s s_i) \Big| \alpha_1 S_1 L_1 J_1 l; Ks; JJ_z \right)$$

$$= J_z \Big\{ 2[g(S_1 L_1 J_1) - 1] \frac{J_1(J_1 + 1) + K(K + 1) - l(l + 1)}{(2J + 1)(2K + 1)} + (g_s - 1)$$

$$\times \frac{J(J + 1) - K(K + 1) + s(s + 1)}{2J(J + 1)} + 1 \Big\}. \quad (4-12)$$

In the $f^N g$ configurations the pair splittings are very small and the matrix elements between the levels of the pairs will lead to large Paschen-Back effects. These matrix elements may be written as

$$\left(\alpha_1 S_1 L_1 J_1 l; Ks; JJ_z \Big| \sum_i (l_i + g_s s_i) \Big| \alpha_1 S_1 L_1 J_1 l; Ks; J - 1J_z \right)$$
$$= \frac{(J^2 - J_z^2)^{1/2}}{4J} \left[\frac{4[g(S_1 L_1 J_1) - 1][J_1(J_1 + 1) - l(l + 1)]}{4J^2 - 1} + g(S_1 L_1 J_1) - 2g_s \right].$$
$$(4\text{-}13)$$

It must, of course, be remembered that where there are appreciable departures from $J_1 l$ coupling it is also necessary to consider the matrix elements that are nondiagonal in J_1 and K.

In many cases of practical interest the energy levels of the configuration being studied will not be adequately described by any of the well-defined coupling schemes and a transformation to intermediate coupling becomes necessary.

4-5 Intermediate Coupling

Calculations in intermediate coupling may be made by first calculating the reduced matrix elements of Eq. 4-3 in LS coupling and then making a transformation to intermediate coupling, namely,

$$(aJ\|\mathbf{L} + g_s\mathbf{S}\|bJ') = \sum_{\alpha SL} (aJ|\alpha SLJ)(\alpha SLJ\|\mathbf{L} + g_s\mathbf{S}\|\alpha SLJ')\,(\alpha SLJ'|bJ'),$$
$$(4\text{-}14)$$

where $(aJ|\alpha SLJ)$ and $(\alpha SLJ'|bJ')$ are transformation matrices that transform the LS coupling states $|\alpha SLJ)$ and $(\alpha SLJ'|$ to the intermediate coupling states $(aJ|$ and $|bJ')$. The transformation matrices may be obtained by diagonalizing the energy matrix calculated in the LS coupling scheme as discussed in Sec. 3-4. If the energy matrices have been calculated in the $J_1 j$ coupling scheme, the transformation matrices resulting from the diagonalization of the energy matrices should be used to transform the reduced matrix elements $\left(J_1 jJ \| \sum_i (l_i + g_s s_i) \| J_1' j'J' \right)$ to intermediate coupling.

Where the states differing in J are well separated and only the diagonal elements need be calculated, the intermediate coupling g-value becomes

$$g(\gamma J) = \sum_{\alpha SL} g(SLJ)(\alpha SLJ|\gamma J)^2. \qquad (4\text{-}15)$$

If we sum over the variable γ for all the levels of a particular J-value, we obtain

$$\sum_\gamma g(\gamma J) = \sum_{\alpha SL} g(SLJ). \qquad (4\text{-}16)$$

since $\sum_{\gamma} (\alpha SLJ | \gamma J)^2$ is equal to unity, the transformation being unitary. Equation 4-16 expresses the result known as the *g-sum rule*. This sum holds regardless of the form coupling of the electrons. However, the g-sum rule must be used with considerable caution. It is *exact only if the summation is made over the complete set of states of a given J*. To sum over the complete set of states yields a result of no value and any restriction of the summation to less than a complete set of states represents a definite approximation.[148]   In its most common usage the g-sum is restricted to the states of a given J of a particular configuration. Where there is appreciable configuration interaction this restriction is no longer valid. The g-sum rule is of particular value in checking calculations of theoretical g-values in well-defined coupling schemes. Thus the sum of the LS coupling g-values for the states of a particular configuration characterized by a particular value of J must equal the sum of the $J_1 j$ coupling g-values over the same set of states.

Considerable caution must be exercised before making statements about the coupling of a configuration solely on the basis of the measured g-values because these quantities are frequently insensitive to the details of the couplings and thus can prove very deceptive.

Hubbs et al.[149] have measured g for the $^7F_1$ level of Pu I ($5f^6 7s^2$) using the atomic beam method[10] and found

$$g = 1.4975,$$

which may be compared with the Russell-Saunders g-value of 1.5012. The close agreement of these two values might be interpreted as indicating that the $5f^6 7s^2$ configuration of Pu I exhibits Russell-Saunders coupling to a very good approximation. Diagonalization of the energy matrix, however, reveals that the $^7F_1$ state is admixed with 27% $^5D_1$ and with smaller admixtures of $^3P_1$. It is scarcely surprising that a g-value close to that for a pure $^7F_1$ state is measured when it is realized that $^5D_1$ and $^3P_1$ both have $g = 1.05116$.

In Pr II $4f^3(^4I)6s$ the energy-level structure clearly follows $J_1 j$ coupling. This, however, is not directly evident from a comparison of the g-values calculated for the pure LS and $J_1 j$ states with the measured values.[150] The calculated and experimental g-values are listed in Table 4-1, and it is evident that the g-values calculated for the two coupling schemes are too similar to allow a positive identification of the coupling scheme for these data alone.

Measurements of g-values by the usual methods of optical spectroscopy are seldom accurate to more than 1 in 200. Atomic beam measurements yield the g-values of the low-lying levels (usually, less than 5000 cm^{-1}) of the rare earths with an accuracy up to 1 in 10^6. The extraordinary

TABLE 4-1　Magnetic g-factors for Pr II $4f^3(^4I)6s$

SLJ	J_1j	Energy (cm^{-1})	g_{LS}	g_{exp}	g_{J_1j}
$^5I_4$	$(\frac{9}{2}, s)_4$	0.00	0.600	0.605	0.600
$^5I_5$	$(\frac{9}{2}, s)_5$	441.94	0.900	0.875	0.854
$^5I_6$	$(\frac{11}{2}, s)_6$	1649.01	1.072	1.064	1.061
$^3I_5$	$(\frac{11}{2}, s)_5$	1743.65	0.833	0.860	0.879
$^5I_7$	$(\frac{13}{2}, s)_7$	2998.31	1.179	1.177	1.172
$^3I_6$	$(\frac{13}{2}, s)_6$	3403.12	1.024	1.037	1.044
$^5I_8$	$(\frac{15}{2}, s)_8$	4437.09	1.251	1.250	1.251
$^3I_7$	$(\frac{15}{2}, s)_7$	5079.31	1.143	1.143	1.150

accuracy of the atomic beam measurements affords a very sensitive test of the validity of the theoretical interpretation of the Zeeman effect? The g-values calculated with the full inclusion of intermediate coupling do not usually agree with the atomic beam values to better than 1 in 10^3. Judd and Lindgren,[151] following from the earlier work of Abragam and Van Vleck,[152] have shown that the bulk of these discrepancies is a consequence of the neglect of certain relativistic and diamagnetic effects.*

4-6　Relativistic and Diamagnetic Corrections

In atoms as heavy as the rare earths relativistic and diamagnetic effects become quite important. The relativistic effect is associated with the change in the interaction between the atomic moment and the external field, due to the velocity of the electron, and with the change in the spin-orbit coupling, due to the external field. These corrections follow as a direct consequence of the Dirac equation for a single electron and are proportional to the kinetic energy T of the electron in the first approximation. For the N-electron problem the relativistic correction to the magnetic Hamiltonian H_M of Eq. 4-1a corresponds to the Breit-Margenau correction[155] and may be written as

$$\delta H_{M1} = -\alpha^2\beta \sum_i [\mathscr{H} \cdot (\mathbf{l}_i + 2\mathbf{s}_i)T_i - \mathbf{s}_i \cdot (\nabla_i V_i \times \mathbf{A}_i)], \quad (4\text{-}17)$$

where $\mathbf{A}_i$ is the magnetic vector potential and V_i the electrostatic potential of the ith electron in the central field. The first part of this correction is the relativistic mass correction, and the second part is a correction to the spin-orbit coupling.

---

* Several extensions of Abragam and Van Vleck's paper[152] have been made by K. Kambe and J. H. Van Vleck, *Phys. Rev.*, **111**, 194 (1958). Their results have been very elegantly expressed in the framework of the theory of tensor operators by Innes and Ufford.[54]

The diamagnetic correction is caused by changes in the spin-other-orbit and orbit-orbit interactions produced by the external field and depends essentially on the electron density in the core of closed shells. The diamagnetic correction to Eq. 4-1a can be derived from the Breit equation for electron-electron interactions and may be written as[151,153]

$$\delta H_{M2} = \alpha^2 \beta \sum_{i < j} \left[2\mathbf{s}_i \cdot \left(\nabla_j \left(\frac{1}{r_{ij}} \right) \times \mathbf{A}_j \right) - \frac{\mathbf{A}_j \cdot \mathbf{p}_i}{r_{ij}} - \frac{(\mathbf{r}_{ij} \cdot \mathbf{A}_j)(\mathbf{r}_{ij} \cdot \mathbf{p}_i)}{r_{ij}^3} \right].$$

(4-18)

The first term represents a correction to the spin-other-orbit interaction, and the last two terms represent corrections to the orbit-orbit interactions.

By transforming the two-electron operators into one-electron operators by integrating over one of the electrons and assuming the charge density from all the electrons is spherically symmetric, Judd and Lindgren were able to write the expectation value of the total correction as

$$\delta H_M = -\alpha^2 \beta \mathscr{H} \cdot \Theta,$$ (4-19)

where

$$\Theta = \langle T + Y \rangle \sum_i (l_i + 2\mathbf{s}_i) - \langle T + U \rangle \sum_i \left(\mathbf{s}_i - \frac{(\mathbf{s}_i \cdot \mathbf{r}_i)\mathbf{r}_i}{r_i^2} \right),$$ (4-20)

and

$$U(r) = \frac{1}{r^3} \int_0^r r'^2 \rho'(r') \, dr' \quad \text{and} \quad Y(r) = \frac{1}{3} \left[U(r) + \int_r^\infty \frac{\rho'(r') \, dr'}{r'} \right],$$

and $\rho'(r')$ is the radial density of all the electrons except i.

Within the approximation of Russell-Saunders coupling the correction to g may be written as

$$\delta g = -\alpha^2 \Theta$$
$$= -\alpha^2 (g \langle T + Y \rangle - h \langle T + U \rangle),$$ (4-21)

where g is the classical g-value and h is a factor, depending on the angular part of the eigenfunction, which is very similar to that of the magnetic hyperfine-structure operator discussed in Chapter 5. For equivalent electrons and a Hund's rule ground state, the factor h becomes[151]

$$h = \frac{2(2l - 2N + 1)}{3N(2L - 1)(2l - 1)(2l + 3)}$$
$$\times \left[\frac{L(L + 1)[J(J + 1) - L(L + 1) + S(S + 1)]}{2J(J + 1)} \right.$$
$$- \frac{3}{4} \frac{[J(J+1) - L(L+1) - S(S+1)][J(J+1) + L(L+1) - S(S+1)]}{J(J+1)}$$
$$\left. + \frac{1}{3} \frac{[J(J + 1) - L(L + 1) + S(S + 1)]}{J(J + 1)} \right].$$ (4-22)

Judd and Lindgren have tabulated h for the ground multiplets of all the f^N configurations of the rare earth atoms.

The relativistic and diamagnetic corrections, unlike the classical g-value, are not diagonal in the αSL quantum numbers. In the actinides the breakdown of Russell-Saunders coupling is considerable even for the low-lying levels, and the diagonal term in h no longer gives an adequate treatment of the correction. Conway and Wybourne[79] have shown that the matrix elements of h that are diagonal in J but not in αSL may be written as

$$h = \frac{2}{3}\left[(g - 1) - \mathscr{S}\right], \tag{4-23a}$$

where

$$\mathscr{S} = \left[\frac{2(2l + 1)(2J + 1)}{J(J + 1)}\right]^{1/2}\begin{Bmatrix} S & S' & 1 \\ L & L' & 2 \\ J & J & 1 \end{Bmatrix}(l^N\alpha SL\|\mathbf{V}^{(12)}\|l^N\alpha'S'L'), \tag{4-23b}$$

with the matrix elements of $\mathbf{V}^{(12)}$ given by Eq. 2-101. Furthermore, they were able to show that, in general, the correction resulting from the $\mathscr{S}$ term in Eq. 4-23, although extremely sensitive to small deviations from Russell-Saunders coupling, is negligible when compared with the rest of the correction. As a result the relativistic diamagnetic correction, with the inclusion of intermediate coupling, may be represented to a very good approximation by the expression

$$\delta g = \frac{-\alpha^2}{3}\left[g(3\langle T + Y\rangle - 2\langle T + U\rangle) + 2\langle T + U\rangle\right], \tag{4-24}$$

where g is the classical g-value corrected for intermediate coupling.

The actual calculation of the relativistic-diamagnetic correction requires an estimate of the expectation values of the integrals $\langle T\rangle$, $\langle U\rangle$, and $\langle Y\rangle$. Judd and Lindgren were able to calculate their approximate values for the lanthanides using a modified analytical hydrogenic eigenfunction and deriving the electron density from the Thomas-Fermi model.[33] The associated parameters were determined by choosing values that yielded eigenfunctions that reproduce closely the eigenfunctions of Pr^{3+} and Tm^{3+} calculated by Ridley.[121] They estimate the error in the resultant integrals as probably not exceeding 10%. Although their values could no doubt be improved slightly by using better eigenfunctions, as they become available, the agreement is already so good that the resulting improvements are unlikely to be significant for they will be comparable with the approximations of the theory of the corrections.

The corresponding calculation of the integrals for the actinides remains to be performed and should be of considerable interest. In the actinides intermediate coupling corrections to the g-values will be essential even if an accuracy of only the order of optical spectroscopic measurements is to be considered.

Conway and Wybourne[79] have made a detailed study of the relativistic-diamagnetic and intermediate-coupling corrections to the g-values of the low-lying levels of the lanthanides. Using the observed energy levels of the ^7F multiplet of Sm I $(4f^6)$, they diagonalized the energy matrices to obtain theoretical levels that agreed to within approximately 1 cm^{-1}. The g-values in intermediate coupling were then calculated from the eigenvectors of the different levels. The relativistic and diamagnetic corrections computed by Judd and Lindgren were added to the inter-mediate coupling g-values to yield the final theoretical g-values, which were found to agree with the results of the atomic beam measurements of Pichanick and Woodgate[154] to practically the order of magnitude of the experimental error. The diamagnetic and relativistic corrections all enter in the third decimal place.

4-7   Relative Intensities and Polarization of Zeeman Spectra

The study of the relative intensities and polarization properties of Zeeman spectra constitutes a powerful tool in the analysis of the complex spectra of the rare earths. This study makes it possible to determine the J- and g-values of the upper and lower states of a spectral line.

At optical frequencies the wave number separation of the levels that give rise to the spectral lines is very large compared with the wave number separations of the Zeeman components of the lines. If one is interested solely in the *relative* intensities of the Zeeman components of a spectral line, the frequency-dependent terms in the usual intensity formulas may be suppressed and the relative intensities taken as proportional to the line strengths of the components. Thus for transitions between the levels αJ and $\alpha' J'$, the relative intensities could be written as

$$I(\alpha J J_z \alpha' J' J_z') = \mathscr{S}(\alpha J J_z; \alpha' J' J_z')$$

$$= e^2 \left| \left(\alpha J J_z \middle| \sum_i r_i (C_q^{(1)})_i \middle| \alpha' J' J_z' \right) \right|^2, \tag{4-25}$$

where $q = 0, \pm 1$. Applying the Wigner-Eckart theorem to Eq. 4-25, we obtain the right-hand side as

$$= \begin{pmatrix} J & 1 & J' \\ -J_z & q & J_z' \end{pmatrix}^2 \mathscr{S}(\alpha J; \alpha' J'), \tag{4-26}$$

where $\mathscr{S}(\alpha J; \alpha' J')$ is simply the line strength of the field-free spectral line. Retaining only the quantities that depend directly on the J_z quantum numbers, the relative intensity for the Zeeman components of a given spectral line may be defined as

$$I_r(JJ_z; J'J_z') = \begin{pmatrix} J & 1 & J' \\ -J_z & q & J_z' \end{pmatrix}^2. \tag{4-27}$$

The 3-j symbol will be nonvanishing only if $\Delta J_z = q$, and hence the selection rule

$$\Delta J_z = 0, \pm 1 \quad \text{(but not } \Delta J_z = 0 \quad \text{if} \quad J = 0 \leftrightarrow 0). \tag{4-28}$$

The Zeeman components that arise from transitions with $\Delta J_z = 0$ have their radiating light linearly polarized parallel to the direction of the magnetic field and are known as the π-components, and the components with $\Delta J_z = \pm 1$ which have their radiating light circularly polarized in planes perpendicular to the direction of the magnetic field are known as the σ-components.

Since the light emitted by an atom in the absence of a magnetic field is unpolarized, so should the total light emitted in a magnetic field in every direction. Thus the sum of the intensities of all the π-components is equal to the sum of the intensities of all the σ-components. In observing the Zeeman effect in a direction perpendicular to the magnetic field, only half the intensity of the σ-components is observed. The other half of the intensity is observed in the direction parallel to the magnetic field.

For the transverse Zeeman effect (that is, for the radiation emitted in any direction perpendicular to the magnetic field), the relative intensities of the π- and σ-components will be given by

$$J_z \rightarrow J_z \quad I_\pi = \begin{pmatrix} J & 1 & J' \\ -J_z & 0 & J_z \end{pmatrix}^2$$

$$J_z \rightarrow J_z \pm 1 \quad I_\sigma = \frac{1}{2}\begin{pmatrix} J & 1 & J' \\ -J_z & \mp 1 & J_z \pm 1 \end{pmatrix}^2.$$

The 3-j symbols may be expressed explicitly in terms of J, J' and J_z to yield the formulas

$$J \rightarrow J \qquad J_z \rightarrow J_z \pm 1 \quad I_\sigma = (J \pm J_z + 1)(J \mp J_z)A,$$
$$J_z \rightarrow J_z \qquad I_\pi = 4J_z^2 A, \tag{4-29a}$$

$$J \rightarrow J + 1 \qquad J_z \rightarrow J_z \pm 1 \quad I_\sigma = (J \pm J_z + 1)(J \pm J_z + 2)B,$$
$$J_z \rightarrow J_z \qquad I_\pi = 4(J + J_z + 1)(J - J_z + 1)B, \tag{4-29b}$$

where

$$A = \tfrac{1}{4}J(J + 1)(2J + 1) \quad \text{and} \quad B = \tfrac{1}{4}(J + 1)(2J + 1)(2J + 3).$$

In tabulations of the relative intensities of the components of a spectral line, it is usual to put A and B equal to unity. The relative intensities given by the formulas of Eq. 4-29 depend only on the JJ_z values of the levels involved in the transition and are thus independent of the couplings of the electronic states of the field-free atom or ion.

4-8   Characteristics of Zeeman Patterns

The components arising from a spectral line when the source is placed in a magnetic field are said to form a *Zeeman pattern*. The Zeeman pattern is characterized by the magnitude of the separations of the components and their intensities. In the absence of Paschen-Back effects the positions Γ of the components of the Zeeman pattern will be given by

$$\Gamma_\pi = \Gamma_0 + (J_z g - J_z' g')\beta\mathcal{H}$$
$$\Gamma_\sigma = \Gamma_0 + [(g - g')J_z - g'\Delta J_z](4.670 \times 10^{-5})\mathcal{H} \text{ cm}^{-1}, \quad (4\text{-}30)$$

where the primed values of $J_z g$ refer to a level $\alpha'J'$ and the unprimed values to those of a level αJ, $\Delta J_z = J_z - J_z'$, and $\mathcal{H}$ is the magnetic field strength measured in gauss. Γ_0 is the position of the field-free spectral line and it is readily seen that the pattern will be symmetrical about it. Applying the selection rule for J_z we obtain the displacements $\Delta\Gamma$ about the field-free spectral line as

$$\Delta\Gamma_\pi = \Gamma_\pi - \Gamma_0 = J_z(g - g') \quad (J_z \to J_z), \quad (4\text{-}31a)$$

for the π-components and as

$$\Delta\Gamma_\sigma = \Gamma_\sigma - \Gamma_0 = [(g - g')J_z - \Delta J_z g'] \quad (J_z \to J_z \pm 1)\,(4\text{-}31b)$$

for the σ-components with $\Delta\Gamma$ in units of $\beta\mathcal{H}$.

In experimental spectroscopy the π- and the σ-components may be separated from one another by photographing the spectra in both polarizations, so that the π-components appear in one exposure and the σ-components in the other on a single plate that also contains an exposure of the field-free spectra.

It is apparent from Eq. 4-31a that the spacings of the π-components will depend directly on the difference in the g-values of the two levels participating in the transition. Because of the relatively large angular momenta associated with many of the electronic states of the rare earths, it frequently happens that the two g-values are almost equal. In this case the π-components coalesce and appear as either a single line or as a relatively broadened line, whereas the σ-components coalesce into two lines placed symmetrically about the central π-component, each having an intensity equal to half that of the π-component. The pattern is then said to form a *pseudo triplet*. Only at very high magnetic fields is it possible to resolve many of the Zeeman patterns found in rare earth spectra. This great difficulty of obtaining resolved Zeeman patterns for all spectral lines of the rare earth spectra constitutes a major limitation to applying the results of Zeeman studies to the term analysis of the spectra.

When the Zeeman patterns can be resolved, it is possible to determine the J- and g-values of both the upper and lower levels involved in the transition. This information can be of great value in determining the term structure of the configurations. The J-values can be determined from resolved Zeeman patterns merely by visual inspection, without any detailed calculations or measurements but by simply noting the characteristics of the pattern. The chief characteristics of the Zeeman patterns may be summarized as follows.

Transitions with $\Delta J = \pm 1$. The number of π-components is $2J_< + 1$, where $J_<$ is the lesser of J and J'. Thus by simply counting the number of π-components, the J-values of *both* levels may be found. The pattern may be readily recognized by noting that the intensity of the π-components for these transitions *increases* toward the center of the pattern. There is always a central π-component at the position of the field-free spectral line. If the number of π-components is even, J is integer, but if it is odd, J is half-integer. This latter fact can be of value in sorting out the different spectral lines according to the stage of ionization of the atoms.

Transitions with $\Delta J = 0$. These patterns may be recognized by the absence of a central π-component (unless $g = g'$ as in a pseudo-triplet). The intensity of the π-components *decreases* toward the center of the pattern. There are $2J_< + 1$-components if J is half integer and $2J_<$ if J is integer (in this case the $\Delta J_z = 0$, $J_z \leftrightarrow J_z$ transition is forbidden). Again the J-values are established by simply counting the π-components.

These characteristics of Zeeman patterns allow the assignment of J-values to be made with very little difficulty if well-resolved Zeeman patterns are observed. The situation is considerably more complicated when there is an appreciable hyperfine structure, such structures are frequently encountered in the spectra of rare earths. In the particular case of the rare earths with zero nuclear spin (that is, the even-even rare earths) isotopes may be used to advantage. Unfortunately, there are only a few suitable isotopes and, of course, none for the odd atomic number rare earths.

The study of the π-component separations can establish only the difference in the g-values of the levels. It is to the σ-components we must turn if we wish to extract g-values from observations of Zeeman patterns. These can be found only by careful measurement of the positions of the components of the pattern. After measuring the positions, it is necessary to assign J_z-values to the components. This may be done by first assigning the J-values and then calculating the relative intensities of the components using Eq. 4-29. Having assigned the J_z-values, it is then possible to calculate the g-values of both levels by setting up pairs of equations in g and g' from Eq. 4-31b and solving for g and g'.

The g-values obtained from Zeeman patterns may be used to assist in making term analyses of rare earth spectra. However, the levels of rare earth atoms or ions seldom follow any of the well-defined coupling schemes close enough to permit unambiguous assignments to be made solely on the basis of Zeeman data. The g-values may, however, be of value where a calculated energy-level scheme exists together with the appropriate calculated g-values.

CHAPTER 5

Hyperfine Structure and Isotope Shifts

5-1 Nuclear Moments

The energy levels of an atom or ion whose electrons are moving in a purely central field are $(2J + 1)$-fold degenerate. This degeneracy may be removed not only by an external noncentral field but also by the interaction of the spin and orbital moments of the electrons with the nuclear magnetic (or electric quadrupole) moment. The interaction between the nuclear and electronic moments gives rise to the hyperfine structure of spectral lines.

An atomic nucleus possesses a nuclear moment only if it has a nonzero nuclear spin. Hyperfine-structure studies are usually, although not always, performed on nuclei in their ground state. The nuclear ground-state spins are found to satisfy the following rules.

1. All nuclei with both Z- and $(A-Z)$-even have zero spin. Z is the atomic number and A the nuclear mass number.
2. Nuclei with both Z- and $(A-Z)$-odd have integer spin.
3. Nuclei with A-odd have half-integer spin.

The nuclear magnetic-dipole moment vector μ_I for a nucleus may be written as

$$\mu_I = g_I \beta_N \mathbf{I},\tag{5-1}$$

where g_I is called the nuclear g-factor by analogy with the electronic Lande g-factor and β_N is the nuclear magneton, which is defined as

$$\beta_N = \frac{e\hbar}{2M_p c} = \frac{m_e \beta}{M_p},\tag{5-2}$$

where M_p is the proton mass, m_e is the electron mass, and β is the Bohr magneton. The magnetic-moment vector of the nucleus can be taken as proportional to its spin-angular momentum I and written as

$$\mathbf{\mu}_I = \frac{\mu_I \mathbf{I}}{I},\tag{5-3}$$

where μ_I is the *nuclear magnetic moment* expressed in units of nuclear magnetons. It is evident from Eq. 5-2 that the nuclear magneton will be approximately 1/1836 that of the electronic Bohr magneton, and hence the hyperfine splittings produced by the electron-nucleus interaction will be smaller than that of the fine-structure splittings by a factor of this order. In the rare earths the hyperfine splittings may be as large as 1 cm^{-1}.

Nuclei with spin greater than or equal to unity may also possess, in addition to the nuclear magnetic-dipole moment, an electric-quadrupole moment. The electric-quadrupole moment gives a measure of the departure from spherical symmetry of the nuclear charge distribution and can lead to information concerning nuclear deformations.[155] In general, we can treat the effects of higher multipole magnetic and electrostatic moments as negligible in comparison with those of the magnetic-dipole and electric-quadrupole moments.*

In this chapter we shall limit our discussion to the spectroscopic effects produced by the interaction of the nuclear moments with the electronic moments. The reader is referred to the literature for details of the interpretations of the nuclear moments and their relationships to the various nuclear models.[155,157-160]

5-2   Magnetic Hyperfine Structure in f^N Configurations

Each f-electron will produce a magnetic field $\mathscr{H}_i$ at the nucleus, and if we regard the nucleus as a point magnet, the energy of magnetic interaction H_{hfs} between this field and the nuclear magnetic moment vector $\mathbf{\mu}_I$ becomes

$$H_{hfs} = -\sum_{i=1}^{N} \mathscr{H}_i \cdot \mathbf{\mu}_I.\tag{5-4}$$

The magnetic field produced at the nucleus by an orbital electron ($l \neq 0$) is[158]

$$\frac{-e(\mathbf{v} \times \mathbf{r})}{r^3} + \frac{\mu r^2 - 3\mathbf{r}(\mathbf{\mu} \cdot \mathbf{r})}{r^5} = -2\beta \frac{[\mathbf{l} - \mathbf{s} + 3\mathbf{r}(\mathbf{s} \cdot \mathbf{r})/r^2]}{r^3},\tag{5-5}$$

where $\mathbf{\mu} = -2\beta\mathbf{s}$.

---

* For a discussion of the calculation of general multipole interactions, see Schwartz.[156]

Thus for N-electrons Eq. 5-4 becomes

$$H_{\text{hfs}} = 2\beta\beta_N g_I \sum_{i=1}^{N} \frac{\mathbf{N}_i \cdot \mathbf{I}}{r_i^3},\tag{5-6}$$

where $\mathbf{N}_i = \mathbf{l}_i - \mathbf{s}_i + \dfrac{3\mathbf{r}_i(\mathbf{s}_i \cdot \mathbf{r}_i)}{r_i^2}.$ (5-7)

$\mathbf{N}_i$ may be put into tensorial form to yield[39]

$$\mathbf{N}_i = \mathbf{l}_i - (10)^{1/2}(\mathbf{s}\mathbf{C}^{(2)})_i^{(1)}.\tag{5-8}$$

Equation 5-6 then becomes

$$H_{\text{hfs}} = a_l \sum_{i=1}^{N} [\mathbf{l}_i - (10)^{1/2}(\mathbf{s}\mathbf{C}^{(2)})_i^{(1)}] \cdot \mathbf{I},\tag{5-9}$$

with

$$a_l = 2\beta\beta_N g_I \langle r^{-3}\rangle = \frac{2\beta\beta_N \mu_I \langle r^{-3}\rangle}{I},\tag{5-10}$$

where $\langle r^{-3}\rangle$ is the expectation value of the inverse-cube radius of the electron orbital.

The matrix elements of H_{hfs} may be evaluated in one or the other of two coupling schemes. In the absence of external fields we may regard J and I coupling together to form states characterized by a total angular momentum F. In this scheme the states will be characterized by the quantum numbers $JIFM$. In the presence of external fields where the interaction with the field is large compared with the interaction between I and J, it is advantageous, and physically more realistic, to work in the scheme $JJ_z II_z M$. In both schemes the matrix elements will be diagonal in M. The matrix elements are not, however, diagonal in J. Usually the hyperfine coupling between states differing in J is so small, because of the smallness of the matrix elements and the appreciable separation of the states, that it may be safely neglected.*

The evaluation of the matrix elements in Eq. 5-9 proceeds by first applying Eq. 2-47 to obtain in the $JIFM$ scheme

$$(\alpha JIFM|H_{\text{hfs}}|\alpha' JIFM) = (-1)^{J+I+F} a_l \begin{Bmatrix} J & J & 1 \\ I & I & F \end{Bmatrix} (I\|\mathbf{I}^{(1)}\|I)$$

$$\times \left(\alpha J \Big\| \sum_{i=1}^{N} \mathbf{N}_i \Big\| \alpha' J\right). \tag{5-11}$$

---

* For an interesting exception of astrophysical importance see Garstang.[161]

Using Eq. 2-34 to evaluate the matrix element in $I^{(1)}$ and writing out the 6-j symbol explicitly in terms of J, I and F, we obtain[162]

$$(\alpha JIFM | H_{\text{hfs}} | \alpha' JIFM) = \frac{a_l}{2} [F(F + 1) - J(J + 1) - I(I + 1)]$$

$$\times \left(\alpha J \| \sum_{i=1}^{N} \mathbf{N}_i \| \alpha' J \right) / [J(J + 1)(2J + 1)]^{1/2} \quad (5\text{-}12)$$

$$= \tfrac{1}{2} AK, \quad (5\text{-}13)$$

where

$$K = F(F + 1) - J(J + 1) - I(I + 1) \quad (5\text{-}14)$$

and

$$A = \frac{a_l \left(\alpha J \| \sum_{i=1}^{N} \mathbf{N}_i \| \alpha' J \right)}{[J(J + 1)(2J + 1)]^{1/2}}. \quad (5\text{-}15)$$

The *measured* value of A is known as the *magnetic hyperfine-structure constant* and may be positive or negative. a_l will be a constant for all the states of a given electron configuration. The second factor in A will be different for each of the states of the configuration and constant only within the hyperfine splittings of a given level. K gives the dependence of the hyperfine splittings on I and F and hence characterizes the hyperfine intervals. If A is positive, the smallest F-value lies lowest in energy but if A is negative, it lies highest in energy. For $J \geq I$ each level will be split into $2I + 1$ hyperfine components, and for $I \leq J$ each level splits into $2J + 1$ hyperfine components.

The magnetic hyperfine constant A may be determined from high-resolution spectroscopic measurements of hyperfine patterns or from atomic beam data. Knowing A from experiment it is possible to deduce a value for the nuclear magnetic moment if we can calculate $\langle r^{-3} \rangle$ and the angular part of Eq. 5-15.

Evaluation of the angular part of $\sum_{i=1}^{N} \mathbf{N}_i$ for the f^N configuration proceeds by first noting that

$$\frac{(\alpha SLJ \| \mathbf{L} \| \alpha SLJ)}{[J(J + 1)(2J + 1)]^{1/2}} = 2 - g, \quad (5\text{-}16)$$

where g is the Lande g-factor. The matrix element in $(s\mathbf{C}^{(2)})_i{}^{(1)}$ may be evaluated using Eq. 2-45 to yield[162]

$$\left(f^N \alpha SLJ \| (10)^{1/2} \sum_{i=1}^{N} (s\mathbf{C}^{(2)})_i{}^{(1)} \| f^N \alpha' S'L'J \right) = (30)^{1/2} (2J + 1)$$

$$\times \begin{Bmatrix} S & S' & 1 \\ L & L' & 2 \\ J & J & 1 \end{Bmatrix} (f \| \mathbf{C}^{(2)} \| f)(f^N \alpha SL \| \mathbf{V}^{(12)} \| f^N \alpha' S'L'). \quad (5\text{-}17)$$

The matrix element in $\mathbf{C}^{(2)}$ follows from Eq. 2-37 to give

$$(f\|\mathbf{C}^{(2)}\|f) = -\left[\frac{f(f+1)(2f+1)}{(2f+3)(2f-1)}\right]^{1/2} = -\frac{2(105)^{1/2}}{15}. \qquad (5\text{-}18)$$

Using Eqs. 5-16, 5-17, and 5-18 in Eq. 5-15, we obtain the final result

$$A = a_l\left\{2 - g + 2\left[\frac{14(2J+1)}{J(J+1)}\right]^{1/2}(f^N\alpha SL\|\mathbf{V}^{(12)}\|f^N\alpha'S'L')\begin{Bmatrix} S & S' & 1 \\ L & L' & 2 \\ J & J & 1 \end{Bmatrix}\right\} \qquad (5\text{-}19)$$

$$= a_l(\mathscr{L} + \mathscr{S}), \qquad (5\text{-}20)$$

where $\mathscr{L} = 2 - g$ and represents the interactions of the electron orbital moments with the nuclear magnetic moment, and $\mathscr{S}$, the remaining part of the bracketed expression, represents the interactions of the electron-spin moments with the nuclear magnetic moment.

Equation 5-19 may be specialized for the Hund's rule ground state to yield[149]

$$A = a_l\left[2 - g + \frac{2(2L - N^2)}{N^2(2L-1)(2f-1)(2f+3)}\left\{\frac{L(L+1)}{2J(J+1)}[J(J+1)\right.\right.$$
$$+ S(S+1) - L(L+1)]$$
$$\left.\left. - \frac{3}{4}\frac{[J(J+1)-L(L+1)-S(S+1)][J(J+1)+L(L+1)-S(S+1)]}{J(J+1)}\right\}\right], \qquad (5\text{-}21)$$

where N is the number of electrons or holes. We note that for the ground state of the half-filled shell, A vanishes and no hyperfine splittings would be anticipated.

In the JJ_zII_z scheme the diagonal matrix elements are given by[162]

$$(\alpha SLJJ_zII_z|H_{\text{hfs}}|\alpha'SL'JJ_zII_z) = J_zI_zA, \qquad (5\text{-}22a)$$

and the off-diagonal elements are given by

$$(\alpha SLJJ_zII_z|H_{\text{hfs}}|\alpha'S'L'JJ_z \pm 1II_z \mp 1) = \tfrac{1}{2}A[(J \mp J_z)$$
$$\times (J \pm J_z + 1)(I \pm I_z)(I \mp I_z + 1)]^{1/2}, \qquad (5\text{-}22b)$$

where A is as given in Eq. 5-15. Only those hyperfine-interaction matrix elements that are diagonal in $M = J_z + I_z$ have nonzero values.

The matrix elements of H_{hfs} will usually require correction for the effects of intermediate coupling. The value of $\mathscr{L}$ in intermediate coupling may be found readily by replacing the Lande g-factor in Eq. 5-19 by its intermediate coupling value. The matrix elements of $\mathscr{S}$, unlike those of

$\mathscr{L}$, are not diagonal in the quantum numbers αSL. The intermediate coupling value of $\mathscr{S}$ may be readily found once the eigenvectors of the energy matrix are known.[79]

As a practical example consider the case of ^{165}Ho. Goodman et al.[163] have measured the magnetic hyperfine-structure constant A of the ground state ($4f^{11}6s^2\,^4I_{15/2}$) of the ^{165}Ho atom by the atomic beam method and obtained the value (in megacycles per second)

$$A = (800.583 \pm 0.003)\ \text{Mc/sec.}$$

Using Eq. 5-19, we obtain for the pure Russell-Saunders ground state the values

$$\mathscr{L} = \tfrac{4}{5} \quad \text{and} \quad \mathscr{S} = -\tfrac{4}{225},$$

and it therefore follows from Eq. 5-30, and the measured value of A, that

$$a_l = \frac{225}{176}\,A = 1023.473\ \text{Mc/sec.}$$

This value should, however, be corrected for departures from pure Russell-Saunders coupling. Wybourne[162] has given the eigenvector of the ground state of Ho I as

$$0.9855|^4I) - 0.1691|^2K) + 0.0158|^2L).$$

The intermediate coupling corrected value of $\mathscr{L}$ becomes

$$0.9855^2(^4I|\mathscr{L}|^4I) + 0.1691^2(^2K|\mathscr{L}|^2K) + 0.0158^2$$
$$(^2L|\mathscr{L}|^2L) = \tfrac{4}{5}(1.0048).$$

The corresponding value of $\mathscr{S}$ is given by

$$0.9855^2(^4I|\mathscr{S}|^4I) + 0.1691^2(^2K|\mathscr{S}|^2K) + 0.0158^2(^2L|\mathscr{S}|^2L)$$
$$-2[(0.9855)(0.1691)(^4I|\mathscr{S}|^2K) - (0.9855)(0.0158)(^4I|\mathscr{S}|^2L)$$
$$+ (0.1691)(0.0158)(^2K|\mathscr{S}|^2L)] = -\tfrac{4}{225}(2.8549)$$

We note that although the breakdown of Russell-Saunders coupling is quite small, its effect on $\mathscr{S}$ is considerable. The extreme sensitivity of $\mathscr{S}$ to small departures from Russell-Saunders coupling arises directly from the fact that $V^{(12)}$, unlike the Lande g-factor, is nondiagonal in the quantum numbers αSL.

Using the intermediate coupling corrected values of $\mathscr{L}$ and $\mathscr{S}$, the corrected value of

$$a_l = \frac{225}{176}\,(1.0387)A = 1063.081\ \text{Mc/sec}$$

is obtained.

The change in a_l for Ho I resulting from the effects of intermediate coupling is relatively small. For the actinides and the excited states of the lanthanides the intermediate-coupling corrections can be of considerable importance.

To complete the derivation of the nuclear magnetic moment for ^{165}Ho from the observed hyperfine structure, it is necessary to obtain a value of $\langle r^{-3} \rangle$. Judd and Lindgren [151] have obtained the value of

$$\langle r^{-3} \rangle = 8.82 \text{ a.u.}$$

from theoretical considerations. Using this value in Eq. 5-10 and the intermediate-coupling corrected value of a_l, we find

$$g_I = 1.2545 = \frac{\mu_I}{I}.$$

Goodman et al. were able to determine the spin I as $\frac{7}{2}$, from which the nuclear magnetic moment

$$\mu_I = 4.39\beta_N$$

follows immediately.

The accuracy of the nuclear moment just derived clearly depends on the accuracy of our estimate of $\langle r^{-3} \rangle$. It is in calculating this quantity that the greatest uncertainty arises in deriving nuclear moments from hyperfine observations. Attempts to calculate accurate values of $\langle r^{-3} \rangle$ have been made by several workers and have yielded rather widely varying results. Bleaney [164] has related the spin-orbit coupling constants of the triply ionized lanthanides to $\langle r^{-3} \rangle$ by assuming a simple hydrogenic function and deduced the expression

$$\langle r^{-3} \rangle = 0.89(Z - 47)^{3/2} A^{-3},$$

where Z is the atomic number. Foglio and Pryce [165] have made a somewhat similar derivation for the actinides using a Thomas-Fermi type potential. Judd and Lindgren, [163] and later Lindgren, [166] have endeavored to calculate values of $\langle r^{-3} \rangle$ for both the neutral and triply ionized lanthanides using a modified hydrogenic function having the form

$$R(r) = Nr^4 e^{-ar} \cosh [k(ar - 4)],$$

where N is a normalizing constant, and a and k are adjustable parameters whose values were chosen to match Ridley's Hartree $4f$-functions [121] and the experimentally deduced spin-orbit coupling constants. Freeman and Watson [120] have computed values of $\langle r^{-3} \rangle$ from the Hartree-Fock wave functions for most of the triply ionized lanthanides. The values of $\langle r^{-3} \rangle$ calculated by Bleaney,[164] Lindgren,[166] and Freeman and Watson[120] for the lanthanides are collected in Table 5-1. It is interesting to note

TABLE 5-1   Values (in atomic units) of $\langle r^{-3} \rangle$ for neutral and triply ionized lanthanides

Z	Ion	Bleaney	Lindgren	Freeman and Watson	Atom	Lindgren
58	Ce^{3+}	4.8	3.66	4.72	Ce	3.03
59	Pr^{3+}	5.5	4.26	5.37	Pr	3.67
60	Nd^{3+}	6.2	4.86	6.03	Nd	4.29
61	Pm^{3+}	6.9	5.46	–	Pm	4.92
62	Sm^{3+}	7.5	6.07	7.36	Sm	5.55
63	Eu^{3+}	8.4	6.70	–	Eu	6.19
64	Gd^{3+}	9.2	7.35	8.84	Gd	6.86
65	Tb^{3+}	10.0	8.03	–	Tb	7.54
66	Dy^{3+}	10.9	8.74	10.34	Dy	8.27
67	Ho^{3+}	11.8	9.50	–	Ho	9.03
68	Er^{3+}	12.7	10.32	12.01	Er	9.84
69	Tm^{3+}	13.6	11.20	–	Tm	10.73
70	Yb^{3+}	14.5	12.18	13.83		

that the Hartree-Fock values of Freeman and Watson are quite similar to the hydrogenic values of Bleaney, whereas those for the modified hydrogenic function (which should follow the Hartree functions quite closely) differ appreciably. The discrepancies between the different tabulations show that the nuclear magnetic moments derived from the hyperfine splitting factors of f^N configurations may be in substantial error.

5-3   Electric-Quadrupole Splittings in f^N Configurations

Nuclei with spin $I \geq 1$ may possess, in addition to the nuclear magnetic moment, an electric-quadrupole moment. Interaction of the electron moments with the nuclear-quadrupole moment may make an appreciable contribution to the observed hyperfine structure and give rise to derivations in magnetic hyperfine-structure interval rule of Eq. 5-14.

If we consider the nucleus to be of finite extension, then the electrostatic interaction between the charged nucleons and electrons may be written as[167]

$$H_{\text{elec}} = -e^2 \int\limits_{\tau_e} \int\limits_{\tau_n} \frac{\rho_e(r_e)\rho_n(r_n) \, d\tau_e \, d\tau_n}{|\mathbf{r}_e - \mathbf{r}_n|}, \qquad (5\text{-}23)$$

where $e\rho_e(r_e)$ and $e\rho_n(r_n)$ are the electron and nuclear charge densities and r_e and r_n are measured relative to the center of the nucleus. The denominator in Eq. 5-23 may be expanded in terms of spherical harmonics exactly as in the treatment of electrostatic interaction (page 17) to yield

$$\frac{1}{|\mathbf{r}_e - \mathbf{r}_n|} = \sum_k \frac{r_n^k}{r_e^{k+1}} (\mathbf{C}_e^{(k)} \cdot \mathbf{C}_n^{(k)}). \qquad (5\text{-}24)$$

Parity considerations[158] allow us to drop all the k-odd terms in the expansion since if all nuclear electric effects arise from electrical charges, then the nuclear Hamiltonian must be invariant with respect to inversion of the coordinate system. The $k = 0$ term corresponds to a monopole, or single charge, and hence is of no interest in discussions of electron-nuclear interactions and may be ignored. The $k = 2$ term in the expansion corresponds to the electric-quadrupole interaction. Higher electric-multipole moments have been found to be smaller than the limits of current observations, and hence we shall only retain the $k = 2$ term in Eq. 5-24. Thus for the electric-quadrupole interaction we may write Eq. 5-23 as

$$H_Q = -e^2 \int_{\tau_e} \int_{\tau_n} \rho(r_e)\rho(r_n) \frac{r_n^{\,2}}{r_e^{\,3}} (\mathbf{C}_e^{\,(2)} \cdot \mathbf{C}_n^{(2)}) \, d\tau_e \, d\tau_n. \qquad (5\text{-}25)$$

The matrix elements of H_Q may be evaluated by first applying Eq. 2-47 to yield the elements diagonal in J as

$$(\alpha JIF|\mathbf{H}_Q \cdot \mathbf{I}|\alpha'JIF) = (-1)^{J+I+F} - e^2 \begin{Bmatrix} J & J & 2 \\ I & I & F \end{Bmatrix} (\alpha J \| r_e^{-3}\mathbf{C}_e^{(2)} \| \alpha'J)$$
$$\times \, (I \| r_n^{\,2}\mathbf{C}_n^{(2)} \| I). \qquad (5\text{-}26)$$

Following Casimir[169] we define the nuclear quadrupole moment Q as a matrix element over the space of the nuclear coordinates evaluated when I has its largest component in the z-direction, that is,

$$Q = (II|r_n^{\,2}\mathbf{C}_n^{(2)}|II)$$
$$= \begin{pmatrix} I & 2 & I \\ -I & 0 & I \end{pmatrix} (I \| r_n^{\,2}\mathbf{C}_n^{(2)} \| I).$$

On evaluating the 3-j symbol explicitly, we obtain[44]

$$Q = \left[\frac{2I(2I - 1)}{(I + 1)(2I + 1)(2I + 3)}\right]^{1/2} (I \| r_n^{\,2}\mathbf{C}_n^{(2)} \| I). \qquad (5\text{-}27)$$

Inserting this result into Eq. 5-26 and evaluating the 6-j symbol explicitly, we obtain, after some rearrangement,[162]

$$(\alpha JIF|\mathbf{H}_Q \cdot \mathbf{I}|\alpha' JIF) = -e^2 Q \langle r^{-3} \rangle \left[\frac{4J(2J-1)}{(J+1)(2J+1)(2J+3)} \right]^{1/2}$$

$$(\alpha J \| \mathbf{C}_e^{(2)} \| \alpha' J) \left[\frac{\frac{3}{4}K(K+1) - I(I+1)J(J+1)}{2I(2I-1)J(2J-1)} \right], \qquad (5\text{-}28a)$$

$$= b_l X_J \left[\frac{\frac{3}{4}K(K+1) - I(I+1)J(J+1)}{2I(2I-1)J(2J-1)} \right], \qquad (5\text{-}28b)$$

where

$$b_l = e^2 Q \langle r^{-3} \rangle. \qquad (5\text{-}29)$$

The electric-quadrupole hyperfine constant B, as usually defined, is given by

$$B = b_l X_J, \qquad (5\text{-}30)$$

and K is as defined by Eq. 5-14. X_J will be different for different electronic states, and b_l is a constant for the states of a given configuration. The dependence of the hyperfine splittings on F is contained in the term enclosed in brackets in Eq. 5-28b and characterizes the quadrupole hyperfine intervals. In practice, the observed hyperfine structure results from the effects of the interactions of both the nuclear magnetic moment and the electric-quadrupole moment (if $I \geq 1$) with the electron moments; the hyperfine splittings in the $JIFM$ scheme in the absence of external fields are then given by

$$H_{\text{hfs}} = \frac{AK}{2} + B \left[\frac{\frac{3}{4}K(K+1) - I(I+1)J(J+1)}{2I(2I-1)J(2J-1)} \right]. \qquad (5\text{-}31)$$

By fitting this expression to the observed hyperfine structure, it is possible to deduce A and B for a given energy level of an atom or ion.

In the JJ_zII_z scheme the matrix elements of the nuclear electric-quadrupole interaction become[162]

$$(\alpha JJ_zII_z|H_Q|\alpha' JJ_z \pm qII_z \mp q) = (-1)^{J-J_z} \begin{pmatrix} J & 2 & J \\ -J_z \mp q & J_z \pm q \end{pmatrix}$$

$$\times (-1)^{I-I_z} \begin{pmatrix} I & 2 & I \\ -I_z \pm q & I_z \mp q \end{pmatrix}$$

$$\times \frac{B}{4} \left[\frac{(2I+1)(I+1)(2I+3)(2J+1)(J+1)(2J+3)}{I(2I-1)J(2J-1)} \right]^{1/2}, \qquad (5\text{-}32)$$

where q is limited to the values of 0, 1 and 2. The only nonzero matrix elements are those that are diagonal in $M = J_z + I_z$. The matrix elements that are diagonal in J_z and I_z may be found by the explicit evaluation of the two 3-j symbols to be

$$(\alpha J J_z I I_z | H_Q | \alpha' J J_z I I_z) = \frac{B}{4} \left[\frac{3I_z^2 - I(I+1)}{IJ(2I-1)(2J-1)} \right] [3J_z^2 - J(J+1)]. \quad (5\text{-}33)$$

Thus, in the approximation that the off-diagonal matrix elements may be ignored (that is, that J_z and I_z are good quantum numbers), we may write for H_{hfs} in the $J J_z I I_z$ scheme

$$H_{hfs} = J_z I_z A + B \frac{[3I_z^2 - I(I+1)][3J_z^2 - J(J+1)]}{4IJ(2J-1)(2I-1)}. \quad (5\text{-}34)$$

The evaluation of the matrix elements of the electric-quadrupole interaction requires the determination of the matrix elements of the tensor operator $\mathbf{C}^{(2)}$ for the particular configuration being studied. For the f^N configuration we have

$$(f^N \alpha SLJ \| \sum_{i=1}^{N} \mathbf{C}_i^{(2)} \| f^N \alpha' SL'J)$$

$$= (f \| \mathbf{C}^{(2)} \| f)(f^N \alpha SLJ \| \mathbf{U}^{(2)} \| f^N \alpha' SL'J)$$

$$= (-1)^{S+L'+J}(2J+1) \begin{Bmatrix} J & J & 2 \\ L' & L & S \end{Bmatrix} (f^N \alpha SL \| \mathbf{U}^{(2)} \| f^N \alpha' SL')(f \| \mathbf{C}^{(2)} \| f).$$

$$(5\text{-}35)$$

The matrix element in $\mathbf{C}^{(2)}$ may be evaluated from Eq. 2-37 and that in $\mathbf{U}^{(2)}$ from Eq. 2-92 or obtained from the tables of Nielson and Koster.[43] We note that the matrix elements of the electric-quadrupole interaction, unlike those of the magnetic-dipole interaction, are diagonal in the spin-quantum numbers. When there are departures from pure Russell-Saunders coupling, we must determine the intermediate-coupling corrected value of the matrix element in Eq. 5-35 to yield an intermediate-coupling, corrected electric-quadrupole hyperfine constant B. If B is determined experimentally, we may deduce the value of b_l. Knowing b_l and calculating $\langle r^{-3} \rangle$ as in Sec. 5-3, it would be possible to arrive at a value for the nuclear electric-quadrupole moment. This value will, of course, have associated with it all the inaccuracies of the $\langle r^{-3} \rangle$ value. Unfortunately, it does not appear possible as yet to determine directly the nuclear electric-quadrupole moments without requiring an explicit knowledge of the electron-nuclear interaction.

5-4 Hyperfine Splittings in $f^N l$ Configurations

The hyperfine splittings in $f^N l$ configurations arise from the combined effects of the interaction of the f^N core electrons with the nucleus and that of the added electron l with the nucleus.   We shall consider first magnetic hyperfine structure.

Using Eq. 5-12 and Eq. 5-13 we may write the matrix elements of H_{hfs} for $f^N l$ ($l \neq 0$) as

$$(\alpha JIFM | H_{\text{hfs}} | \alpha' JIFM) = \frac{\frac{Ka'}{2} \left(\alpha J \left\| \sum_{i=1}^{N+1} r_i^{-3} \mathbf{N}_i \right\| \alpha' J \right)}{[J(J+1)(2J+1)]^{1/2}}, \tag{5-36}$$

where $\mathbf{N}_i$ is as defined in Eq. 5-7 and

$$a' = \frac{2\beta\beta_N\mu_I}{I}.$$

The problem of calculating the magnetic hyperfine splittings for any configuration reduces to calculating the appropriate matrix elements of $\mathbf{N}_i$.

Consider $J_1 j$ coupling, which should be moderately well followed in the $f^N p$ configurations of the rare earths.   The matrix elements of $\mathbf{N}_i$ may be found by using Eq. 2-48 to operate on the f^N electrons and Eq. 2-49 to operate on the added electron l to yield

$$a' (f^N \alpha_1 J_1 jJ \| \sum_{i=1}^{N+1} r_i^{-3} \mathbf{N}_i | f^N \alpha_1' J_1' j'J) = (2J+1)(-1)^{J_1+J+1}$$

$$\times \left[(-1)^j \begin{Bmatrix} J & J & 1 \\ J_1' & J_1 & j \end{Bmatrix} (f^N \alpha_1 J_1 \| \sum_{i=1}^{N} \mathbf{N}_i \| f^N \alpha_1' J_1') \delta(j, j') a_f \right.$$

$$\left. + (-1)^{j'} \begin{Bmatrix} J & J & 1 \\ j' & j & J_1 \end{Bmatrix} (j \| \mathbf{N} \| j') \delta(J_1, J_1') a_l \right], \tag{5-37}$$

where we have written $a_f = a' \langle r_f^{-3} \rangle$ and $a_l = a' \langle r_l^{-3} \rangle$ in keeping with Eq. 5-10.   The matrix element diagonal in J_1 and j may be found by explicit evaluation of the 6-j symbol and the use of Eq. 5-15 to be given by

$$(f^N \alpha_1 J_1 jJIFM | H_{\text{hfs}} | f^N \alpha_1' J_1 jJIFM) = \frac{K}{2} \frac{1}{2J(J+1)}$$

$$\times [[J(J+1)+J_1(J_1+1)-j(j+1)]A_f + [J(J+1)+j(j+1)-J_1(J_1+1)]a_l] \tag{5-38}$$

where A_f and a_l are the magnetic hyperfine-structure constants associated with the f^N core and the added electron l respectively.

The result of Eq. 5-38 is well known as a result of the early vector model method [169] and has frequently been applied in the analysis of hyperfine patterns.   In using this formula it must be realized that the submatrices in $\sum_{i=1}^{N} \mathbf{N}_i$ and $\mathbf{N}$ in Eq. 5-37 are *not* diagonal in the quantum numbers J_1

and j respectively. Thus a small departure from pure $J_1 j$ coupling may lead to serious errors if Eq. 5-38 alone is used since the nondiagonal matrix elements of Eq. 5-37 may be comparable to those of Eq. 5-38. Furthermore, it must be emphasized that for large values of J and J_1 the multiplicative factor associated with A_f is substantially larger than that associated with a_l. Even if A_f is much smaller than a_l, it is seldom a valid approximation to omit the contribution of the f^N core even when we are concerned with configurations involving unpaired s-electrons. The simplicity of Eq. 5-38 can be very deceiving.

The analogous formulas for LS coupling can be found simply, but they are of considerably greater complexity since the submatrices cannot be expressed in terms of A_f and a_l even for the diagonal elements. These formulas are likely to be applied only in atomic beam studies of those rare earths that contain d-electrons in their ground state. We leave the derivation of the formulas as an exercise for the interested reader.

The calculation of the matrix elements of the electric quadrupole contribution to the hyperfine splittings in the $f^N l$ configuration parallels that of the magnetic hyperfine splittings. In $J_1 j$ coupling we replace the matrix element $(\alpha J \| C^{(2)}_e \| \alpha' J)$ of Eq. 5-28a by the matrix element

$$
\left(f^N \alpha_1 J_1 j J \| \sum_{i=1}^{N+1} r_i^{-3} \, \mathbf{C}_i^{(2)} \| f^N \alpha_1' J_1' j' J \right)
$$

$$
= (-1)^{J_1 + J}(2J + 1)\left[(-1)^j \begin{Bmatrix} J & J & 2 \\ J_1' & J_1 & j \end{Bmatrix} \left(\alpha_1 J_1 \| \sum_{i=1}^{N} \mathbf{C}_i^{(2)} \| \alpha_1' J_1' \right) b_f \right.
$$

$$
\left. + (-1)^{j''} \begin{Bmatrix} J & J & 2 \\ j' & j & J_1 \end{Bmatrix} (j \| \mathbf{C}^{(2)} \| j') b_l \delta(J_1, J_1') \right]. \tag{5-39}
$$

Using Eq. 5-28 we may write the diagonal matrix element as

$$
= (-1)^{J_1 + J + j}(2J + 1)\left[\begin{Bmatrix} J & J & 2 \\ J_1 & J_1 & j \end{Bmatrix} \left(\frac{(J_1 + 1)(2J_1 + 1)(2J_1 + 3)}{4J_1(2J_1 - 1)} \right)^{1/2} B_f \right.
$$

$$
\left. + \begin{Bmatrix} J & J & 2 \\ j & j & J_1 \end{Bmatrix} \left(\frac{(j + 1)(2j + 1)(2j + 3)}{4j(2j - 1)} \right)^{1/2} b_l \right], \tag{5-40}
$$

where B_f and b_l are the electric quadrupole hyperfine-structure constants associated with the f^N core and the added electron l respectively. Again we must remember that Eq. 5-40 will be subject to correction for departures from pure $J_1 j$ coupling. For s- or $p_{1/2}$-electrons the second term in Eq. 5-40 vanishes although not the matrix element of Eq. 5-39 between $p_{1/2}$ and $p_{3/2}$ or the matrix elements associated with the f^N core.

The analogous formulas for LS coupling are, like those of the magnetic hyperfine interaction, rather cumbersome.

5-5 Hyperfine Splittings in the $f^N s$ Configurations

Fermi[170] has shown that when unpaired s-electrons are present in a configuration, N_i, as defined in Eq. 5-7, must be augmented by the term $8\pi|\Psi_s(0)|^2 s_i/3$, where $\Psi_s(0)$ is the value at the nucleus of the normalized Schrödinger eigenfunction of the s-electron. A simplified derivation of Fermi's formula has been given by Nierenberg[171] among others.

For configurations containing s-electrons Eq. 5-7 becomes

$$N_i' = N_i + \tfrac{8}{3}\pi|\Psi_s(0)|^2 s_i. \tag{5-41}$$

N_i will be nonzero only for $l > 0$, and the second term is nonzero only for s-electrons. Following Eqs. 5-36 and 5-37, we may express the matrix elements of the magnetic hyperfine interaction in $J_1 j$ coupling for the $f^N s$ configuration as

$$(f^N \alpha_1 J_1 s; JIFM|H_{\text{hfs}}|f^N \alpha_1' J_1' s; JIFM)$$

$$= \frac{K}{2}\Bigg[(-1)^{J_1+J-1/2}\frac{(2J+1)}{[J(J+1)(2J+1)]^{1/2}}\begin{Bmatrix} J & J & 1 \\ J_1' & J_1 & \tfrac{1}{2} \end{Bmatrix}$$

$$\times \left(f^N \alpha_1 J_1 \Big\| \sum_{i=1}^N N_i \Big\| f^N \alpha_1' J_1'\right)a_f$$

$$+ \frac{J(J+1)+s(s+1)-J_1(J_1+1)}{2J(J+1)}a_s\Bigg], \tag{5-42}$$

where

$$a_s = \frac{16}{3}\pi\beta\beta_N\frac{\mu_I}{I}|\Psi_s(0)|^2. \tag{5-43}$$

The matrix element diagonal in J_1 may be simplified to yield

$$(f^N \alpha_1 J_1 s; JIFM|H_{\text{hfs}}|f^N \alpha_1' J_1 s; JIFM)$$

$$= \frac{K}{2}[\{J(J+1)+J_1(J_1+1)-s(s+1)\}A_f$$

$$+ \{J(J+1)+s(s+1)-J_1(J_1+1)\}a_s]/2J(J+1). \tag{5-44}$$

This formula must be used with some caution where there are departures from pure $J_1 j$ coupling.

Atomic beam measurements yield very accurate values of A_f for the low-lying levels of the neutral rare earth atoms. The change in A_f in going from the neutral to singly ionized rare earths should be quite small; therefore to a very good approximation we could replace A_f in Eq. 5-44 by its experimental value and then derive a_s from the observed hyperfine structure of the $f^N s$ configuration.

It has been stated frequently that since s-electrons are penetrating electrons, and hence have a large a_s value, the contribution of the f^N core to the hyperfine structure may be ignored. This assertion is usually invalid in the rare earths where the states possess high angular momentum.

For example, the ground state of Pm II $(4f^5\ {}^6H_{5/2}6s)_2$ should be almost perfectly J_1j coupled. From Eq. 5-44 the magnetic hyperfine-structure constant for the ground state will be given by

$$A(4f^5\ {}^6H_{5/2}6s)_2 = \frac{[7A(4f^5\ {}^6H_{5/2}) - a_{6s}]}{6}. \tag{5-45}$$

Budick and Marrus[172] have measured for Pm I

$$\begin{aligned} A(4f^5\ {}^6H_{7/2}) &= 447\ \text{Mc/sec} \\ &= 0.0149\ \text{cm}^{-1}. \end{aligned} \tag{5-46}$$

Using Eq. 5-21, we obtain (assuming the ${}^6H_{5/2}$ and ${}^6H_{7/2}$ states are pure)

$$A(4f^5\ {}^6H_{5/2}) = 0.0216\ \text{cm}^{-1}.$$

Reader and Davis[173] have measured the hyperfine structure of the ground state of Pm II under high resolution and found

$$A(4f^5\ {}^6H_{5/2}6s)_2 = 0.01\ \text{cm}^{-1}.$$

Using this value in Eq. 5-45 together with Eq. 5-46, we deduce that

$$a_{6s} = 0.213\ \text{cm}^{-1}.$$

Thus we may conclude that in this particular case the contribution of the f^N core is approximately half that produced by the interaction of the $6s$-electron with the nuclear magnetic moment, and it would indeed be a bad approximation to neglect the core contribution.

Having obtained a value of a_{6s}, it might be expected that the nuclear magnetic moment could be deduced readily. Unfortunately, the calculation of the contact of the $6s$-eigenfunction at the nucleus is subject to several relativistic corrections which are of considerable importance and cannot be neglected in elements as heavy as the rare earths.

5-6   Relativistic Corrections and Hyperfine Structure

In any calculation of nuclear moments from hyperfine structure it is necessary to know the radial parts of the hyperfine-structure constants a_l and a_s as defined in Eqs. 5-10 and 5-43 respectively. Relativistic modifications to these quantities become very important as $\alpha^2 Z^2$ approaches unity. For Gd we find $\alpha^2 Z^2 \sim 0.22$, and for Cm, $\alpha^2 Z^2 \sim 0.50$. Thus relativistic effects will play an appreciable role in the actinides and a lesser, although still quite important, role in the lanthanides.

In this discussion we shall limit ourselves to the general results that have been obtained for the relativistic corrections to the hyperfine a-factors and refer to the literature for the detailed derivations.*

---

* An extensive review of relativistic corrections to the hyperfine-structure formulas has been given by Kopfermann.[160]

The relativistic treatment of hyperfine structure commences with the consideration of the properties of Dirac's equation for a single electron.[174,175] For a single electron in a central field the electronic wave function Ψ obeys the Dirac equation

$$[\boldsymbol{\alpha} \cdot (c\mathbf{p} + e\mathbf{A}) + \beta(mc^2 - eV)]\Psi = E\Psi. \tag{5-47}$$

The solutions to Dirac's equation may be written as[126]

$$\psi_j(r, \theta, \phi) = \begin{bmatrix} u_1 \\ u_2 \\ u_3 \\ u_4 \end{bmatrix} = \begin{bmatrix} g(r)\sqrt{\dfrac{l+m+\frac{1}{2}}{2l+1}}\, Y_{l,\,m-1/2}(\theta, \phi) \\ -g(r)\sqrt{\dfrac{l-m+\frac{1}{2}}{2l+1}}\, Y_{l,\,m+1/2}(\theta, \phi) \\ -if(r)\sqrt{\dfrac{l-m+\frac{3}{2}}{2l+3}}\, Y_{l+1,\,m-1/2}(\theta, \phi) \\ -if(r)\sqrt{\dfrac{l+m+\frac{3}{2}}{2l+3}}\, Y_{l+1,\,m+1/2}(\theta, \phi) \end{bmatrix} \tag{5-48a}$$

for $j = l + \frac{1}{2}$ and

$$\psi_j(r, \theta, \phi) = \begin{bmatrix} u_1 \\ u_2 \\ u_3 \\ u_4 \end{bmatrix} = \begin{bmatrix} g(r)\sqrt{\dfrac{l-m+\frac{1}{2}}{2l+1}}\, Y_{l,\,m-1/2}(\theta, \phi) \\ g(r)\sqrt{\dfrac{l+m+\frac{1}{2}}{2l+1}}\, Y_{l,\,m+1/2}(\theta, \phi) \\ -if(r)\sqrt{\dfrac{l+m-\frac{1}{2}}{2l-1}}\, Y_{l-1,\,m-1/2}(\theta, \phi) \\ -if(r)\sqrt{\dfrac{l-m-\frac{1}{2}}{2l-1}}\, Y_{l-1,\,m+1/2}(\theta, \phi) \end{bmatrix} \tag{5-48b}$$

for $j = l - \frac{1}{2}$. $g(r)$ and $f(r)$ are functions of r only and represent the small and large components of the wave function respectively. In the relativistic wave equation there are two radial functions for an electron in a central field and for the same l but different j these functions satisfy different radial equations. The behavior of the functions at the origin is also different, the value of j having more to do with the nature of the singularity at the origin than the value of l. Thus any attempt to treat hyperfine structure with relativistic wave functions should be made by way of j-j coupling.[176]

We shall consider first the relativistic hyperfine-structure formulas for a single electron outside a core of closed shells and then examine some of the difficulties that arise in two or more electron configurations.

The relativistic matrix elements of the hyperfine interaction for a single electron are well known from the early work of Fermi,[170] Segre,[177] Breit,[178,179] Casimir,[168] and Racah.[180] More recently Schwartz[156,181] and Stone[182,183] have considered these calculations in detail. The central problem in determining the relativistic hyperfine formulas is in the evaluation of the characteristic radial integrals associated with the magnetic-dipole and electric-quadrupole interactions. The difference between the Dirac and Schrödinger equation with spin is appreciable only in a small region about the nucleus. This is in marked contrast to the Slater radial integrals which are quite insensitive to effects near the nucleus. Whereas in the nonrelativistic treatment of hyperfine structure the electron density of all electrons, except s-electrons, vanishes at the nucleus, in the relativistic treatment the small components of the $p_{1/2}$-electrons have the character of s electron eigenfunctions and do not have zero electron density at the nucleus.

We consider first the solution of Dirac's equation for small r and then the actual evaluation of the characteristic integrals. If we put

$$\chi_1 = rf(r) \quad \text{and} \quad \chi_2 = rg(r),$$

we may write the radial differential equations as

$$\frac{d\chi_1}{dr} + \frac{k\chi_1}{r} = \frac{mc}{h}\left(1 - \frac{E - \Phi}{E_0}\right)\chi_2, \tag{5-49a}$$

$$\frac{d\chi_2}{dr} - \frac{k\chi_2}{r} = \frac{mc}{h}\left(1 + \frac{E - \Phi}{E_0}\right)\chi_1, \tag{5-49b}$$

where $k = l + 1$ for $j = l + \frac{1}{2}$ and $k = -l$ for $j = l - \frac{1}{2}$, $E_0 = mc^2$, and Φ is the potential energy of the electron. In atomic units we may put $h/mc = 1$ and write the potential energy (neglecting for the moment screening effects) as

$$V = -\frac{\Phi}{E_0} = \frac{Z\alpha}{r}. \tag{5-50}$$

E/E_0 will be of the order of unity and hence we may write Eq. 5-49 as

$$\frac{d\chi_1}{dr} + \frac{k\chi_1}{r} = \frac{-Z\alpha}{r}\chi_2, \tag{5-51a}$$

$$\frac{d\chi_2}{dr} - \frac{k\chi_2}{r} = \left(2 + \frac{Z\alpha}{r}\right)\chi_1. \tag{5-51b}$$

These two equations are now in the form of the Bessel differential equations[184,185] and may be solved in terms of the Bessel functions to yield

$$\chi_1 = C\alpha Z J_{2\rho}(x) \tag{5-52a}$$

$$\chi_2 = \frac{C[xJ_{2\rho+1}(x) - 2(\rho + k)J_{2\rho}(x)]}{2}, \tag{5-52b}$$

where

$$x = (8Z\alpha r)^{1/2} \quad \text{and} \quad \rho = (k^2 - Z^2\alpha^2)^{1/2}.$$

C is a normalization constant which gives the density at the nucleus of the wave function for the valence electron.

For s-electrons the normalization constant is best deduced from the Rydberg-Ritz formula[160] for an electron series. Casimir[168] has determined C by normalizing for large r the nonrelativistic Schrödinger equation for an effective charge Z_0, where for neutral atoms $Z_0 = 1$, for singly ionized atoms $Z_0 = 2$, etc. In this way Casimir finds

$$C^2 = \frac{\alpha}{2Z}\frac{dE}{dn} = \frac{\alpha Z_0^2}{Zn^*}, \tag{5-53}$$

where n^* is the effective quantum number whose value may be deduced from the Rydberg-Ritz formula

$$E = -\frac{RhcZ_0^2}{n^{*2}} = -\frac{RhcZ_0^2}{(n - \sigma)^2}$$

$$= -\frac{Z_0^2}{2(n - \sigma)^2} \quad \text{(in atomic units),} \tag{5-54}$$

where R is the Rydberg constant and σ is the quantum defect.[169] On differentiating Eq. 5-54 with respect to E, we obtain

$$C^2 = \frac{\alpha Z_0^2}{2Zn^{*2}}\left(1 - \frac{d\sigma}{dn}\right). \tag{5-55}$$

For non-s-electrons C is most conveniently evaluated in terms of the fine-structure separation δ of the states $j = l + \frac{1}{2}$ and $j = l - \frac{1}{2}$ which will have almost identical wave functions for large r. For convenience let us identify quantities associated with $j = l + \frac{1}{2}$ by a single prime and those for $j = l - \frac{1}{2}$ by a double prime. The doublet splitting (in atomic units) may be approximated by[168,186]

$$\delta = 2(\rho' - \rho'' - 1)\frac{dE}{dn}, \tag{5-56}$$

where

$$\rho' = \sqrt{(l + 1)^2 - Z^2\alpha^2} \quad \text{and} \quad \rho'' = \sqrt{l^2 - Z^2\alpha^2}.$$

Comparing Eqs. 5-53 and 5-56, we obtain for non-s-electrons

$$C^2 = \frac{\delta\alpha}{4Z(\rho' - \rho'' - 1)}. \tag{5-57}$$

We note that the fine-structure separation δ may also be written in terms of the nonrelativistic expectation value of $\langle r^{-3}\rangle$ to give[186]

$$\delta = \alpha^2(2l + 1)\frac{HZ\langle r^{-3}\rangle}{4}, \tag{5-58}$$

where

$$H = \frac{2l(l + 1)(\rho' - \rho'' - 1)}{\alpha^2 Z^2}. \tag{5-59}$$

The absolute magnitude of the normalization integrals C' and C'' associated with the states j' and j'' will be slightly different because of the energy difference of the two states. Casimir[168] has made the identification

$$C' \cong -C'',$$

and estimates the difference in magnitude of these quantities by the expression

$$\left|\frac{C''}{C'}\right|^2 = 1 + \frac{3\alpha^2 Z^2}{2l(l + 1)n^*}. \tag{5-60}$$

For heavy atoms this formula may be substantially in error. An explicit calculation by Breit[179] for thallium ($Z = 81$) yields a value of $|C''/C'|^2 = 1.65$ as compared with the value of 1.18 obtained from Casimir's formula.

Having determined the normalization integrals, we may then proceed to evaluate the characteristic radial integrals associated with the magnetic-dipole and electric-quadrupole hyperfine interactions, making use of Eq. 5-52 to express χ_1 and χ_2 in terms of the Bessel functions. On integration over r, we obtain

$$\int_0^\infty r^{-2}\chi_1\chi_2\, dr = -\frac{2\alpha C^2 Z^2 F_r(j, Z)}{a(2l + 1)[\pm(2l + 1) + 1]}, \qquad \pm \text{ as } j = l \pm \tfrac{1}{2} \tag{5-61}$$

for the magnetic dipole integral and

$$\int_0^\infty r^{-3}(\chi_1^2 + \chi_2^2)\, dr = \frac{2\alpha^2 C^2 Z^2 R_r(j, Z)}{a^2 l(l + 1)(2l + 1)} \tag{5-62}$$

for the electric quadrupole integral, where

$$F_r(j, Z) = \frac{2j(j + 1)(2j + 1)}{\rho(4\rho^2 - 1)} \tag{5-63}$$

and

$$R_r(j, Z) = l(l + 1)(2l + 1) \frac{3k(k + 1) - \rho^2 + 1}{\rho(\rho^2 - 1)(4\rho^2 - 1)}. \quad (5\text{-}64)$$

Thus far we have ignored the effects of screening. These effects may be taken into account by replacing the atomic number Z in the preceding formulas by an effective atomic number Z_i. Empirically, we have $Z_i = Z$ for s-electrons, $Z_i = Z - 4$ for p-electrons, $Z_i \cong Z - 11$ for d-electrons, and $Z_i \cong Z - 35$ for $4f$-electrons.

On inserting the explicit forms of the radial integrals into the electronic matrix elements for the magnetic-dipole and electric-quadrupole interactions of a single electron, we obtain the hyperfine-structure constants in cm^{-1} as

1. For s-electrons the magnetic hyperfine constant is given by

$$a_{s_{1/2}} = \frac{8hcR}{3} \frac{\alpha^2 Z_i Z_0^2}{n^{*3}} \left(1 - \frac{d\sigma}{dn}\right) F_r(\tfrac{1}{2}, Z_i) g_I \frac{m}{M_p}. \quad (5\text{-}65)$$

2. For non-s-electrons the magnetic hyperfine constant is given by

$$a_j = a_{l \pm 1/2} = a_{n_l} \frac{l(l + 1)}{j(j + 1)} F_r(j, Z_i), \quad (5\text{-}66)$$

where

$$a_{n_l} = 2\beta\beta_N g_I \langle r^{-3} \rangle$$

and from Eq. 5-58

$$\langle r^{-3} \rangle = \frac{\delta}{\beta^2(2l + 1)Z_i H_r(l, Z_i)}. \quad (5\text{-}67)$$

The electric-quadrupole hyperfine constant is given by

$$b_j = e^2 Q \left(\frac{2j + 1}{2j + 2}\right) \langle r^{-3} \rangle R_r(j, Z_i), \quad (5\text{-}68)$$

where $j = \tfrac{3}{2}$.

Kopfermann[160] has given an extensive tabulation of the numerical values of the relativistic factors $F_r(j, Z_i)$, $R_r(j, Z_i)$, and $H_r(l, Z_i)$. In general, these corrections are close to unity for f-electrons and may be ignored, whereas for $s_{1/2}$ and $p_{1/2}$-electrons the corrections are appreciable and cannot be ignored. Using Kopfermann's tables, we find for $Z_i = 90$, $F_r(\tfrac{1}{2}, 90)/F_r(\tfrac{3}{2}, 90) = 2.62$, leading to $(a_{p1/2}/a_{p3/2}) = 12$, which shows that $p_{1/2}$-electrons should play a far more important role than $p_{3/2}$-electrons in the hyperfine structure of the rare earths.

To estimate the magnetic hyperfine constant a_s for a single s-electron it is necessary to derive a value for n^* and $(1 - d\sigma/dn)$. These values may be calculated from the Rydberg-Ritz formula for an electron series (assuming the series is unperturbed [187]) if the *absolute* term values T of at least three terms in the series are known. We may write the Rydberg-Ritz formula as

$$T = \frac{RZ_0^2}{n^{*2}}, \qquad (5\text{-}69a)$$

putting

$$n^* = n - \sigma = n - \alpha + \beta T, \qquad (5\text{-}69b)$$

where α and β are numerical constants to be determined. We normally do not measure the absolute term values, but rather the term values relative to the ground state. If we know the relative term values of the first three members of the series, we may derive two values for β:

$$\beta = \frac{n_1^* - n_2^* + 1}{T_1 - T_2} \quad \text{and} \quad \beta = \frac{n_2^* - n_3^* + 1}{T_2 - T_3}. \qquad (5\text{-}70)$$

We may now adjust the series limit until the two intervals $T_1 - T_2$ and $T_2 - T_3$ yield the same value of β. This gives the appropriate values of n_1^*, n_2^*, and n_3^*. On differentiating Eq. 5-69a, we establish the identity

$$\frac{d\sigma}{dn} = \frac{d\sigma/dT}{d\sigma/dT - n^*/2T}, \qquad (5\text{-}71)$$

and from Eq. 5-69b

$$\frac{d\sigma}{dT} = -\beta. \qquad (5\text{-}72)$$

Using the value of β deduced from Eq. 5-70 as well as n^* in Eq. 5-71 then yields $d\sigma/dn$. Alternatively, $d\sigma/dn$ may be deduced from just two terms in the series *if* the ionization potential [169] is known. Knowing the ionization potential allows us to convert the term values relative to the ground state into absolute term values; then using Eq. 5-69 we may obtain n_1^* and n_2^*. Inserting these values, together with the observed interval $T_1 - T_2$, into Eq. 5-70 then gives a value of β. We may then calculate $d\sigma/dn$ from Eq. 5-71.

Lang [69] has located the positions of the 6s, 7s, and 8s terms of the one-electron spectrum of Ce IV. Their term values, T_r relative to the ground state $4f(^2F_{5/2})$, are given in the second column of Table 5-2. Using Eqs. 5-69 and 5-70, we deduce from the measured term intervals $7s - 6s$ and $8s - 7s$ a value of

$$\beta = -5.46 \times 10^{-7}.$$

TABLE 5-2   Term values and effective quantum numbers for the s terms of Ce IV

Term	Relative Term Value (cm^{-1})	Effective Quantum Number n^*	Absolute Term Value (cm^{-1})	Quantum Defect σ
6s	86,602	2.894	209,595	3.106
7s	183,502	3.947	112,695	3.053
8s	225,128	4.970	71,069	3.030

The resulting effective quantum numbers n^* and the absolute term values are given in the third and fourth columns of the table respectively. The quantum defect σ may then be found by using Eq. 5-69 to yield the values in the fifth column of the table. Inserting β in Eq. 5-71 together with n^* and T for the 6s term, we find for Ce IV (ns)

$$1 - \frac{d\sigma}{dn} = 1.086.$$

Klinkenberg and Lang[11] have studied the energy levels of the actinide analogue (Th IV) of Ce IV and determined the energies of the 7s and 8s terms relative to the ground state as

$$T_{r7s} = 23,130 \text{ cm}^{-1} \quad \text{and} \quad T_{r8s} = 119,621 \text{ cm}^{-1}.$$

They were also able to deduce the ionization potential as 28.6 eV. This result then allows the absolute term values to be calculated to yield

$$T_{7s} = 208,770 \text{ cm}^{-1} \quad \text{and} \quad T_{8s} = 112,279 \text{ cm}^{-1}.$$

Using Eq. 5-68, we find

$$n^*_{7s} = 2.900 \quad \text{and} \quad n^*_{8s} = 3.954.$$

Putting these values into Eq. 5-70 and then the result into Eq. 5-70 gives for Th IV (ns)

$$1 - \frac{d\sigma}{dn} = 1.088.$$

In both examples we find the correction factor to be very close to unity. A similar examination of the spectra of other rare earths shows that these values are representative of all the rare earths.

Knowing the magnitude of the quantum defect correction factor allows us to calculate the magnitude of the magnetic hyperfine constant for the s-electron using Eq. 5-65. It is of interest to compare these values with the corresponding constants for p-, d-, and f-electrons. Lang[69] has determined the fine structure splittings of the 6p, 5d, and 4f terms of

Ce IV, and Klinkenberg and Lang[11] have given the corresponding splittings for the $7p$, $6d$, and $5f$ terms of Th IV. Their results are summarized in Table 5-3. Using the measured fine-structure separations

TABLE 5-3   Fine-structure splittings in Ce IV and Th IV*

slj	Ce IV	T_r	δ	Th IV	T_r	δ
$^2F_{5/2}$		0			0	
	$4f$		2,253	$5f$		4,325
$^2F_{7/2}$		2,253			4,325	
$^2D_{3/2}$		49,737			9,193	
	$5d$		2,489	$6d$		5,293
$^2D_{5/2}$		52,226			14,486	
$^2P_{1/2}$		122,585			60,239	
	$6p$		4,707	$7p$		12,817
$^2P_{3/2}$		127,292			73,056	

* T_r and δ are given in cm^{-1}.

and Kopfermann's tables[160] for making the relativistic corrections, we have calculated the magnetic hyperfine-structure constants (in atomic units) in terms of $g_l m/M_p$. The results are given in Table 5-4. The magnitude

TABLE 5-4   Magnetic hyperfine a_j factors for Ce IV and Th IV*

Ce IV nlj	$\frac{1}{2}$	$\frac{3}{2}$	$\frac{5}{2}$	$\frac{7}{2}$
^a6s_j	4.254			
^a6p_j	0.902	0.139		
^a5d_j		0.176	0.074	
^a4f_j			0.175	0.097
Th IV				
^a7s_j	14.240			
^a7p_j	2.668	0.232		
^a6d_j		0.212	0.084	
^a5f_j			0.140	0.078

* "a_j" factors are all in atomic units.

of the magnetic hyperfine-structure constants for the s- and $p_{1/2}$-electrons is found to be substantially greater in the actinide (Th) than in the corresponding lanthanide (Ce). This result is a direct consequence of the increasing importance of the relativistic effects as Z increases. Furthermore, we note that in these ions the $p_{3/2}$-electron as well as the d- and f-electrons play only a minor role in the production of the hyperfine splittings. However, as we have already noted, this does not allow us to neglect their contribution in the N-electron problem since in some cases the multiplicative factors that express the dependence of the interactions on the SLJ quantum numbers may be considerable.

Thus far we have considered only the relativistic contributions to the hyperfine structure for a single electron. For f-electrons the relativistic effects are very small and may be neglected to a reasonable order of approximation. Thus in f^N configurations we shall choose to ignore the relativistic effects which will only be of importance if an accuracy of better than approximately 1% is desired. This accuracy is, however, not to be expected to be reached.*

When there is only a single electron outside the f^N configuration it is most convenient to work in the J_1j coupling scheme. For the $f^N s$ configuration we need only replace a_s as defined in Eq. 5-43 by its relativistic equivalent given in Eq. 5-65.

For p-electrons the problem is not as simple because we must consider both the $j = \frac{1}{2}$ and $j = \frac{3}{2}$ states of the p-electron. If J_1j are good quantum numbers, then A_l, as given in Eq. 5-38, may be replaced by its relativistic equivalent given in Eq. 5-66. If, however, J_1j are not good quantum numbers, Eq. 5-37 must be used to calculate the hyperfine interaction matrix element between the $p_{1/2}$ and $p_{3/2}$ states.

For the radial part we have [168]

$$\int_0^\infty r^{-2}(\chi_1'\chi_2'' + \chi_1''\chi_2') \, dr = -\frac{C'C''Z^2}{a} \frac{G_r(l, Z)}{l(l + 1)(2l + 1)}. \quad (5\text{-}73)$$

Making the approximation that $C'C'' \cong -C^2$ and using Eqs. 5-57 and 5-59, we obtain the integral as

$$= \frac{\delta G_r(l, Z)}{4\alpha a Z H_r(l, Z)(2l + 1)}, \quad (5\text{-}74)$$

where

$$G_r(l, Z) = \frac{2l(l + 1)\sin \pi(\rho' - \rho'' - 1)}{\pi\alpha^2 Z^2}. \quad (5\text{-}75)$$

Hence for the relativistically corrected off-diagonal matrix element in Eq. 5-37 we replace a_l by

$$a_l' = 2\beta\beta_N g_I \frac{\delta G_r(l, Z_i)}{4\alpha a Z H_r(l, Z_i)(2l + 1)}. \quad (5\text{-}76)$$

---

* An important exception is found in the ^8S ground state of the f^7 configuration. The diagonal nonrelativistic matrix elements are zero. However, relativistically there are different radial functions associated with $f_{5/2}$ and $f_{7/2}$ single electron states and hence there will be a nonzero relativistic contribution to the ground-state hyperfine structure. This contribution cannot be neglected in the ground states of Eu I or Am I.

In the electric-quadrupole hyperfine interaction we may use Eq. 5-40 to calculate the diagonal matrix elements by replacing B by b_j as defined in Eq. 5-68. The radial integral appropriate to the off-diagonal matrix element is given by[168]

$$\int_0^\infty r^{-3}(\chi_1'\chi_1'' + \chi_2'\chi_2'')\, dr = \frac{\alpha\, \delta S_r(l, Z)}{2a^2 Z H_r(l, Z)(2l + 1)}, \tag{5-77}$$

where

$$S_r(l, Z) = \frac{2l(l + 1)}{\pi\alpha^2 Z^2}\sin \pi(\rho' - \rho'' - 1)$$

$$\times \left\{ \frac{3(\rho' + k')}{8(1 + \rho'') - 4l - 2} + \frac{3(\rho'' + k'')}{8(1 + \rho') + 4l + 2} - \frac{1}{2}\left(\frac{\rho' + \rho'' - 1}{\rho' + \rho'' + 2}\right) \right.$$

$$\left. - \frac{6[\alpha^2 Z^2 + (\rho' + k')(\rho'' + k'')]}{3(2l + 3)(2l - 1) - 16\alpha^2 Z^2} \right\}. \tag{5-78}$$

Kopfermann[160] has made an extensive tabulation of both $S_r(l, Z)$ and $G_r(l, Z)$. To calculate the off-diagonal electric-quadrupole interaction matrix element we simply replace b_l in Eq. 5-39 by

$$b_l' = \frac{e^2 Q\alpha\, \delta S_r(l, Z_i)}{2a^2 Z_i H_r(l, Z_i)(2l + 1)}. \tag{5-79}$$

This completes the general outline of the relativistic modifications to the hyperfine structure formulas that must be considered when the hyperfine structure of elements as heavy as the rare earths are studied. However, the treatment as just outlined is open to several important objections which up to now have not been fully met.

It is clearly inadequate to consider the field for a single electron as being simply the Coulomb field of the nucleus.[188] The shielding produced by the other electrons of the atom must be considered. This we have attempted to treat by introducing a screening constant s defined by $Z_i = Z - s$, which amounts to a change of scale and is undoubtedly an oversimplification. Furthermore, the screening constant is not readily calculable and has consequently been deduced empirically. The normalization constants C' and C'' have been treated as having equal absolute magnitudes, which is contradicted by actual numerical solutions of the Dirac radial equations for specific cases.[179]

The principal effect of the introduction of relativity to the treatment of hyperfine structure is to modify the radial part of the hyperfine interactions.

Casimir has used analytical eigenfunctions for a Dirac electron in a pure Coulomb field. Were relativistic Hartree-Fock wave functions available for the rare earths it would be possible to evaluate the radial integrals numerically and avoid many of the inadequacies of the treatment just outlined. Such a calculation is, however, fraught with serious difficulties and even if it could be done, it would not necessarily lead to exact radial integrals.

Schwartz[181] has attempted to improve Casimir's treatment and overcome some of the objections to it. He has modified the pure Coulomb field by estimating the shielding potential produced by all the other electrons from the Thomas-Fermi statistical model. It is then possible to evaluate the necessary normalized integrals numerically from the screened Dirac radial equations. Schwartz has found that the Casimir formulas overestimate the factors $F_r(j, Z_i)$ and underestimate the factors $|(C'/C'')|^2$ by amounts that are fortuitously compensating. He also finds that $H_r(l, Z_i)$ and Z_i are underestimated. Schwartz's approach should lead to appreciably better radial integrals than Casimir's analytical formulas; however, they have not as yet been evaluated for the rare earth elements.

It is evident that the relativistic corrections are considerable for s- and $p_{1/2}$-electrons and almost negligible for f-electrons. In optical spectroscopy it has been normal to deduce the nuclear moments from the study of the hyperfine structure of the $f^N s$ configurations. These nuclear moments will naturally be subject to the inaccuracies of the treatment of the relativistic corrections for the s-electron and affected by the difficulties associated with the establishment of the f^N core contribution to the hyperfine structure. Atomic beam measurements of the hyperfine structure of the $f^N s^2$ configurations yield very precise magnetic hyperfine constants. The deduction of nuclear moments from these measurements should be relatively insensitive to the effects of the relativistic corrections, but they will, unfortunately, be limited by inaccuracies in calculating the expectation values $\langle r^{-3} \rangle$.

5-7 Nuclear Volume Effects

Thus far we have represented the nucleus as a point charge and a point magnet ignoring the finite extension of the nucleus. Crawford and Schawlow,[189] extending the earlier work of Rosenthal and Breit[190] and of Racah,[191] have considered the effect of a point magnetic dipole situated at the center of gravity of a finite-size nucleus. They considered two cases: (1) where the nuclear charge is distributed uniformly over the surface of a sphere and (2) where the charge is distributed uniformly throughout the volume of a sphere. The magnitude of the interaction of the electron with the nuclear magnetic moment is directly proportional to the integral

$$I = \int_0^\infty r^{-2} \chi_1 \chi_2 \, dr. \tag{5-80}$$

The values of the product $\chi_1 \chi_2$ are weighted most heavily for small values of r, where, for a nucleus of finite size, χ_1 and χ_2 depart most from their values for a pure Coulomb field. Crawford and Schawlow wrote the integral of Eq. 5-80 as

$$I = I_0 - \int_0^{r_1} r^{-2} \chi_1 \chi_2 \, dr, \tag{5-81}$$

where r_1 is the radial distance over which there are deviations from the Coulomb potential and I_0 is the integral as evaluated without regard to the finite nuclear size. The second integral in Eq. 5-81 represents the contribution to the integral I produced within the nuclear volume. On evaluating this integral, assuming a uniform charge distribution within the nucleus, we find

$$I = I_0(1 - \delta), \tag{5-82}$$

where

$$\delta = \frac{2(k + \rho)\rho(2\rho + 1)r^{2\rho - 1}}{(2k + 1)\Gamma^2(2\rho + 1)} \tag{5-83}$$

and as before $\rho = \sqrt{k^2 - \alpha^2 Z^2}$ and $k = -l$ for $j = l - \frac{1}{2}$, and $l + 1$ for $j = l + \frac{1}{2}$. The values of the gamma function may be found from the tables of Davis.[192] The quantity $(1 - \delta)$ represents the correction factor that must be applied to the integral I_0, as evaluated on the hypothesis of the inverse square law, to yield the integral I corrected for the nuclear charge volume effect. Crawford and Schawlow concluded that for a uniformly charged nucleus

$$r_1 \cong \frac{2Zr_0}{a_0}, \tag{5-84}$$

where r_0 is the nuclear radius and a_0 the Bohr radius. The nuclear radius may be approximated by the formula[193,194]

$$r_0 = 1.2 \times 10^{-13} A^{1/3} \text{ cm}, \tag{5-85}$$

where A is the nuclear mass number.

For $^{241}_{95}$Am we find for s-electrons

$$(1 - \delta)_s = 0.75,$$

and for $p_{1/2}$-electrons

$$(1 - \delta)p_{1/2} = 0.88.$$

For all other electrons the correction is wholly negligible, which is as expected since even in the relativistic treatment only s- and $p_{1/2}$-electrons have a nonvanishing electron density at the nucleus.

Bohr and Weisskopf[195] have considered the effect on the magnetic hyperfine structure of the distribution of the nuclear magnetic moment over the nuclear volume assuming the distribution to be spherically symmetric. They show that if the nuclear magnetic moment is regarded as a smeared-out dipole distribution, the hyperfine structure for an s-electron would be expected to differ from the value calculated for a point dipole at the nuclear center by a factor $(1 + \epsilon)$, where

$$\epsilon \simeq - \left(\frac{Zr_0}{a_0}\right)\left(\frac{a_0}{2Zr_0}\right)^{2(1-\rho)}\left(\frac{r^2}{r_0^2}\right)_{av}, \qquad (5\text{-}86)$$

and $r_0 \geq r \geq 0$.

If the nuclear magnetic moment is distributed uniformly through the nuclear volume, $(r^2/r_0^2)_{av} = \frac{3}{5}$, whereas for a uniform surface distribution $(r^2/r_0^2)_{av} = 1$. For $p_{1/2}$-electrons ϵ is approximately $\alpha^2 Z^2$ of that for an s-electron.

For $^{241}_{95}$Am we find for a uniform surface distribution $(1 + \epsilon)_s = 0.90$ and $(1 + \epsilon)_{p1/2} = 0.95$. Again the effects are negligible for other than s- and $p_{1/2}$-electrons.

Bohr[196] and Bohr and Weisskopf[195] have pointed out that the distribution of the magnetic dipole density over the nuclear volume may vary greatly from nucleus to nucleus, depending on the relative contributions of the spin and orbital nuclear magnetic moments.

The net effect of the nuclear volume corrections is to multiply the magnetic hyperfine structure constants given by Eqs. 5-65 and 5-66 by a factor $(1 - \delta)(1 + \epsilon)$. This correction is only significant for s- and $p_{1/2}$-electrons.

5-8   *Isotope Shifts and Hyperfine-Structure Anomalies*

We have already seen that for s- and $p_{1/2}$-electrons there is an appreciable contribution to the hyperfine structure from the part of the electronic wave function that penetrates the nuclear volume. Since the radius of the nucleus varies as $A^{1/3}$, these contributions will be different for different isotopes of the same element. Isotope dependent effects show up in the form of *isotope shifts* and *hyperfine-structure anomalies*.

The *isotope shift* observed in a spectral line can be regarded as the *difference* in the displacements of the lines of each isotope from some fictitious position it would have had if the cause of the shifts were to vanish. To choose a reference position to measure the relative displacements we may take the series limit of the atom or ion. However, in many rare earths the series limit has not been established and some other reference position must be adopted. One possibility is to measure the shifts relative to that of a level that is expected to have a negligible isotope shift (for example, a level of a configuration not involving s- or p-electrons). In ^{241}Am and ^{243}Am, Fred and Tompkins[99] were unable to establish such a level and measured their isotope shifts relative to an assumed shift for the ground states of Am I and Am II respectively. They have observed many of the spectral lines of ^{241}Am and ^{243}Am to be displaced by 0.5 cm^{-1} from each other. These displacements are of the order of the hyperfine splittings and hence unless separated isotopes are used, the hyperfine patterns will overlap leading to hyperfine spectra of great complexity.

The isotope shift may be attributed to two distinct effects,* the mass effect and the nuclear volume effect. The mass effect arises directly out of the difference in the masses of the isotopes and is the sum of two parts. The first is known as the Bohr reduced-mass correction and the second as the Hughes-Eckart effect[197] which depends on the presence of cross-product terms in the momenta of different electrons. Both these effects are entirely negligible in elements as heavy as the rare earths. Thus we shall consider only the nuclear volume effects here.

The importance of the nuclear volume effect in explaining the isotope shifts of the heavy elements was pointed out by Pauli and Peierls[202] and

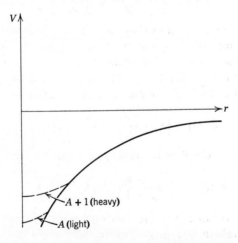

Fig. 5-1 Potential energy V of an electron in the field of the nucleus. The heavy curve is for a point charge nucleus, and the light curves are the modifications produced by the finite radii of the nuclei.

---

* For general reviews of properties of isotope shifts see References 160 and 198–201.

Bartlett.[203]   The nuclear volume effect is illustrated by Fig. 5-1, where we have plotted the potential energy V between the electron and the nucleus against their relative distance r.   The heavy curve represents V for a point nucleus.   The deviation from this curve for the heavier isotope of mass $A + 1$ is *larger* than that for the lighter isotope of mass A, and hence the position of the energy level is expected to be higher for the *heavier* isotope.   The *observed* isotope shift, which will be only a small fraction of the *actual* isotope shift, corresponds to the difference between the effects of the two potential energy curves for the nuclei A and $A + 1$.

Following Racah [191] we may write the change in energy of a spectroscopic term as

$$\delta W = \int_0^{r_0} 4\pi r^2 e\tau(r) \, \delta V(r) \, dr, \tag{5-87}$$

where $e\tau(r)$ is the electric charge density of the electron at the nucleus and $\delta V(r)$ is the difference between the potentials for the two isotopes. Clearly, it is not possible to evaluate the integral without adopting a specific model for the potential within the nuclear volume.   In most models the *grain structure* of the nuclear charge distribution is ignored, being replaced by some smoothed-out average distribution.

Let us write the nuclear potential as [201]

$$V(r) = \left[-\frac{x + 1}{x} + \frac{1}{x}\left(\frac{r}{r_0}\right)^x \right] \frac{Ze^2}{r}. \tag{5-88}$$

If the nuclear charge is uniformly distributed throughout the nuclear volume (assuming the distribution to be spherical), we have $x = 2$, whereas if all the charge is concentrated on the surface of the sphere, $x = \infty$.   The potential for the point charge model has $x = -1$.   On differentiating, Eq. 5-88 with respect to r_0, the nuclear radius, yields

$$\delta V(r) = \left[1 - \left(\frac{r}{r_0}\right)^x \frac{x + 1}{x} Ze^2 \right] \frac{\delta r_0}{r_0^2}. \tag{5-89}$$

For an s-electron the electron density near the nucleus is given by [191]

$$e\tau(r) = \frac{2(1 + \rho)}{[\Gamma(2\rho + 1)]^2} |\psi_s(0)|^2 \left(\frac{2Zr}{a_0}\right)^{2\rho - 2} \tag{5-90}$$

If we neglect the distortion of the electronic wave function by the nuclear field, we may evaluate the integral in Eq. 5-87 using Eqs. 5-89 and 5-90. Integration yields the change in the energy of a spectroscopic term because of a small change δr_0 in the nuclear radius as

$$\delta W_s = \frac{8\pi(x + 1)(\rho + 1)|\psi_s(0)|^2 Ze^2}{(2\rho + 1)(2\rho + x + 1)[\Gamma(2\rho + 1)]^2} \left(\frac{2Z}{a_0}\right)^{2\rho - 2} r_0^{2\rho} \frac{\delta r_0}{r_0}. \tag{5-91}$$

We may replace $|\psi_s(0)|^2$ by its nonrelativistic value

$$|\psi_s(0)|^2 = \frac{ZZ^{*2}\left(1 - \dfrac{d\sigma}{dn}\right)}{a_0^3 n^{*3}}. \tag{5-92}$$

Putting Eq. 5-92 into Eq. 5-91 and converting to wave numbers gives the isotope shift of the spectral lines as

$$\delta T_s = \frac{Z^{*2}}{n^{*3}}\left(1 - \frac{d\sigma}{dn}\right)\frac{4(x + 1)(\rho + 1)R}{(2\rho + 1)(2\rho + x + 1)[\Gamma(2\rho + 1)]^2}\left(\frac{2Zr_0}{a_0}\right)^{2\rho}\frac{\delta r_0}{r_0}\ \text{cm}^{-1}. \tag{5-93}$$

For non-s-electrons the corresponding isotope shift is

$$\delta T_{l>0} = \frac{8Rhck(k + \rho)(x + 1)l(l + 1)\delta'(2Zr_0/a_0)^2}{(2\rho + 1)(2\rho + x + 1)[\Gamma(2\rho + 1)]^2\alpha^2 Z^2 H_r(l, Z)} \tag{5-94}$$

where δ' is the doublet splitting for the particular l.

This grossly simplified model of isotope shifts, although inadequate to explain the magnitudes of the observed isotope shifts in detail, does serve to indicate results of importance in making analyses of rare earth spectra. For $k^2 > 1$ the value of ρ is approximately $|k|$ and thus the isotope shift is non-negligible only for s- and $p_{1/2}$-electrons. The shift for the $p_{1/2}$-electron is approximately $\alpha^2 Z^2$ of that of the s-electron. A p-electron state will, however, usually be an admixture of $p_{1/2}$ and $p_{3/2}$ states and will contribute to the isotope shift in proportion to the amount of $p_{1/2}$-state present. Appreciable isotope shifts are to be expected only if the number of s- or $p_{1/2}$-electrons differs in the two terms of the transition. In this way the isotope shifts can serve as a useful tool in making assignments of electron configurations to observed energy levels. In the transitions $f^N s - f^N p$ an appreciable isotope shift is to be expected, whereas no appreciable shift would be anticipated for the $f^N - f^{N-1}d$ transitions.

In contrast to hyperfine structure the isotope shifts for several electrons are additive apart from the mutual screening of the electrons.[189] Thus, whereas there is no contribution to the hyperfine structure by closed s-shells the isotope shift of the terms of $f^N s^2$ are, apart from a slight reduction due to screening, just twice those of the terms of the $f^N s$ configuration. The *direction* of the isotope shift may be correlated with the fact that the s- or $p_{1/2}$-electron *raises* the level of the *heavier* isotope relative to the lighter one. Thus in $p \rightarrow s$ transitions we anticipate *negative* isotope shifts, whereas for $s \rightarrow p$ transitions we anticipate *positive* isotope shifts.

Wilets and Bradley,[204] and more recently Davis and Marquet,[205] have made an extensive study of the isotope shifts of erbium ($Z = 68$) in an attempt to make assignments of electron configurations to the observed transitions. Natural erbium contains six isotopes with the relative abundances:

A	Relative abundance, %
162	0.136
164	1.56
166	33.4
167	22.9
168	27.1
170	14.9

Apart from [167]Er all these isotopes are even-even and hence do not show hyperfine structure. [167]Er has a nuclear spin of $I = \frac{7}{2}$, and consequently, the intensity of its spectrum is distributed among the hyperfine components of each level. Thus the intensity of the [167]Er spectrum is so diminished that most of the transitions are too weak to be observed. Usually Wilets and Bradley were able to observe only transitions associated with [166]Er, [168]Er, and [170]Er. The lines corresponding to these three isotopes could be distinguished from one another on the basis of their relative intensities, which should be proportional to their relative isotopic abundances.

Most of the isotope shifts observed by Wilets and Bradley occurred in the spectrum of Er II. The anticipated low-lying configurations are

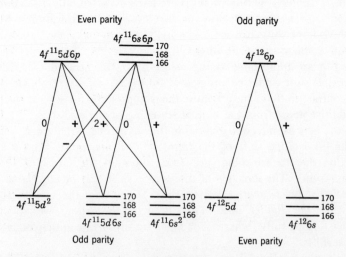

Fig. 5-2 A schematic representation of the isotope shifts for the low-lying configurations of Er II.

given schematically in Fig. 5-2. The isotope shifts associated with the $6p$-electrons should be 20% of the $6s$-electron isotope shifts and in many cases considerably less than this value. The transitions $4f^{11}5d6p - 4f^{11}5d^2$ and $4f^{12}6p - 4f^{12}5d$ should show negligible shifts. Any isotope shifts associated with the transitions $4f^{11}6s6p - 4f^{11}6s5d$ will arise only if there is a difference in the screening of the $6s$-electron by the $5d$- and $6p$-electrons and hence should be quite small. Positive isotope shifts should be associated with the transitions $4f^{12}6p - 4f^{12}6s$, $4f^{11}5d6p - 4f^{11}5d6s$, and $4f^{11}6s6p - 4f^{11}6s^2$. These shifts should be approximately equal in magnitude. If there is weak configuration interaction between the $4f^{11}5d6p$ and $4f^{11}6s6p$ configurations, as there almost certainly will be, transitions $4f^{11}5d6p - 4f^{11}6s^2$ showing approximately twice the positive shift should be possible. Wilets and Bradley observed some shifts to be approximately twice the normal value and identified them with this transition array. Finally, the transitions $4f^{11}6s6p - 4f^{11}5d^2$, which will similarly become allowed in the presence of configuration interaction, should give rise to negative shifts. Wilets and Bradley found many lines with negative isotope shifts.

Thus isotope shifts can be used to group transitions into rather broad categories according to the configurations involved in the transitions. Although this will not lead to unequivocal configuration designations, it can be useful in eliminating many possible configurations. Where there is appreciable configuration interaction, the value of the method is probably very limited. For odd isotopes where there is appreciable hyperfine structure it becomes almost essential to use separated or enriched isotopes such as has been done in the work of Fred and Tomkins[99] on ^{241}Am and ^{243}Am.

The theory we have outlined for the explanation of the isotope shift fails on three specific points.

1. It fails to take into account adequately the large distortion of the electron wave function by the nuclear field, with the result that the magnitude of the isotope shifts are overestimated by approximately a factor of two.

2. The theory fails to predict the anomalously large isotope shifts observed for many of the rare earths.

3. The theory cannot account for the observed odd-even staggering that exists between the odd and even isotopes of the same element. If the nuclear radius is as given simply by Eq. 5-85, we would expect on our model to have

$$\frac{\delta r_0}{r_0} = \frac{\delta A}{3A}. \tag{5-95}$$

However, successive isotopes do not have equidistant positions; rather the odd isotopes lie appreciably nearer to the next lighter isotope than to the heavier isotope.

The complete treatment of these anomalies would take us far into the theory of nuclear structure, which is outside our present scope. We shall restrict ourselves merely to a brief review of some of the salient features of the present-day theories, which are by no means in their final form.

Bodmer[206-208] has taken into account the distortion of the electronic wave function by the nuclear charge distribution using a nonperturbation method due to Broch[209] and has avoided the explicit use of electron wave functions in estimating the isotope shift. He finds that the distortion of the wave function decreases the isotope shift below its value as calculated by the simple perturbation method and that this difference increases with Z as expected. The effect of the distortion, although appreciable and in the right direction, is inadequate, by itself, to account for the discrepancies in the calculated and observed shifts. It should be noted that Bodmer's method is very general and permits the calculation of isotope shifts for any form of nuclear charge distribution.

Meligy[210] has calculated the isotope shift by solving Dirac's equations for an electron in the static field of a nuclear charge of the trapezoidal shape,[211] which closely resembles the charge distribution observed in electron scattering experiments.[212] Again the agreement between the theoretical and experimental shifts is appreciable, but still inadequate. As noted by Bodmer,[208] Meligy's result represents a special case of Bodmer's general result for any charge distribution and cannot ameliorate the discrepancy. Furthermore, these methods which assume a spherically symmetric nuclear charge distribution still cannot account for the anomalous isotope shifts observed for many of the rare earths.

Brix and Kopfermann[213] have conveniently defined an experimental isotope shift constant C_{exp} by putting

$$C_{exp} = \frac{\delta T_s}{Z^{*2}(1 - d\sigma/dn)/n^{*3}},\tag{5-96}$$

which should be independent of the multiplet term under consideration. If odd isotopes with a magnetic splitting factor a_s exist, we can rewrite Eq. 5-96 as

$$C_{exp} = \frac{\delta T_s}{a_s/G},\tag{5-97}$$

where

$$G = \frac{8R\alpha^2 Zmg_I F_r(\tfrac{1}{2}, Z)(1 - \delta)(1 - \epsilon)}{3M_p}.\tag{5-98}$$

The value of C_{exp} as deduced from the experimentally determined isotope shifts may then be compared with the calculated isotope shifts C_{th} by assuming some particular nuclear model.

Brix and Kopfermann[213–214] plotted the ratio C_{exp}/C_{th} as a function of neutron number assuming the uniform charge density model for the nuclear potential, the relationships of Eq. 5-85 for the nuclear radii, and Eq. 5-95 for the relative change in the nuclear radius. The resulting plot for the lanthanides is shown in Fig. 5-3. The theory based on spherical nuclei and the volume effect predicts that all the points should lie on a horizontal line of ordinate one. Even when allowance is made for possible screening effects it is found that the isotope shifts of the lanthanides, especially those of Sm, Eu, and Gd, lie considerably above this ordinate. Clearly, the volume effect is quite inadequate in explaining the anomalously large isotope shifts of the lanthanides.

Brix and Kopfermann suggested that if two isotopes are considered as deformed so as to be *nonspherical* there will, in addition to the normal volume effect, be a contribution due to the difference in shape of the isotopes. The theory of nuclear deformation has been developed in considerable detail by Bohr, Mottelson[215] and Nilsson.[216]

Whenever nuclear configurations occur with sufficiently many particles outside closed shells, it is found that the nuclear shape deviates from spherical symmetry and may be regarded as possessing an intrinsic quadrupole moment Q_0, being related to the spectroscopic quadrupole moment Q by

$$Q_0 = \frac{(I + 1)(2I + 3)}{I(2I - 1)} Q. \tag{5-99}$$

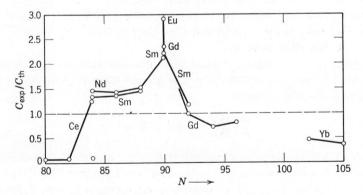

Fig. 5-3   Ratio C_{exp}/C_{th} of the experimental to theoretical isotope shifts as a function of the neutron number N in the lanthanide region.

The intrinsic moment Q_0 precesses together with the axis of symmetry around the total angular momentum I. The nucleus may have an intrinsic moment even if $I = 0$ since the projection on the spin axis vanishes. For closed shells, spherical symmetry exists and there is no nuclear deformation. This should occur at the magic neutron numbers of 82 and 126 with the nuclear deformation reaching a maximum in between.

The additional isotope shift produced by the nuclear deformation effect may be calculated by assuming that the deformed nucleus can be approximated by a uniformly charged ellipsoid of revolution with a generating ellipse given by

$$r(\phi) = r_0\left[1 + \frac{\alpha(3\cos^2\phi - 1)}{2}\right].$$ (5-100)

α will be a direct measure of the extent of the nuclear deformation away from spherical symmetry and may be related to the intrinsic quadrupole moment by

$$\alpha = \frac{5Q_0}{3Zr_0^2}.$$ (5-101)

Then if the isotope shift constant of the deformation is denoted by C_α and that of the volume effect C_v,[216,217]

$$\frac{C_\alpha}{C_v} = \frac{5(2\rho + 3)A}{24Z^2 r_0^4}\frac{\delta(Q_0^2)}{\delta A}\left(1 - \frac{0.09Ze^2}{\hbar c}\right),$$ (5-102)

where the last factor is a relativistic correction.[215] This ratio depends clearly on the change in the intrinsic quadrupole moment in going from one isotope to another. For the odd nuclei we may calculate the intrinsic moment Q_0 from the spectroscopically determined electric-quadrupole moment using Eq. 5-99, whereas for even-even nuclei and nuclei with $I = \frac{1}{2}$ they must be deduced from nuclear data such as γ-ray lifetimes and Coulomb excitation methods.[217]

Sandars and Woodgate[218] have measured the ratio of the electric-quadrupole hyperfine constants for the ground state $4f^7(^8S_{7/2})6s^2$ of the isotopes ^{151}Eu and ^{153}Eu as

$$\frac{B(151)}{B(153)} = 0.393 \pm 0.003,$$

which should be essentially equivalent to the ratio of Q_0 for the two isotopes since both have spin $I = \frac{5}{2}$. Thus on the basis of Eq. 5-102 we would expect the ^{153}Eu isotope to show a much greater isotope shift than the ^{151}Eu isotope because of the large difference in their quadrupole moments.

Meligy et al.,[219] Bodmer,[207,208] and Ionesco-Pallas[220] have made detailed calculations, covering the rare earth regions, of the isotope shifts produced by the nuclear deformation effect and have found a surprisingly good correlation between the measured and calculated isotope shifts using the experimentally deduced values of Q and Q_0. Their calculations would seem to explain the greater part of the anomalously large isotope shifts of the rare earths, although as Bodmer[208] has noted there still remain some discrepancies that cannot be resolved simply in terms of the nuclear volume and deformation effects. Part of these discrepancies can probably be associated with the effects of nuclear compressibility and polarization of the nucleus by the electrons.[217,221] Nevertheless, the interpretation of the isotope effect is by no means in its final form. Thus far the nucleus has been treated as being made of nuclear matter and little attempt has been made to discuss the isotope shift effects in terms of the actual nuclear wave functions. A truly satisfactory theory of the odd-even staggering of isotope shifts has yet to be formulated. A partial explanation of this effect in terms of the nuclear deformation effect has been advanced by Wilets et al.[217] and in terms of polarization effects by Breit et al.[221]

As noted earlier, isotope dependent effects also show up as hyperfine-structure anomalies. Sandars and Woodgate[218] have measured the ratio of the magnetic hyperfine-structure constants of the ground states of ^{151}Eu to that of ^{153}Eu as

$$\frac{A(151)}{A(153)} = 2.26498 \pm 0.00008,$$

and Pichanick et al.[222] have measured the ratio of the nuclear magnetic moment of ^{151}Eu to that of ^{153}Eu as

$$\frac{\mu_N(151)}{\mu_N(153)} = 2.2686 \pm 0.0015.$$

We may write

$$\frac{A(151)}{A(153)} = \frac{\mu_N(151)}{\mu_N(153) \, [1 + \Delta]}, \tag{5-103}$$

where Δ is known as the hyperfine-structure anomaly ($\Delta = -0.16 \pm 0.07\%$). This anomaly arises directly from the difference in the distribution of the magnetic-dipole density over the nuclear volume for the two isotopes.[195,196] The anomaly is associated only with s- and $p_{1/2}$-electrons and thus gives a direct indication that these electrons are contributing to the hyperfine structure. Note, however, the presence of a hyperfine anomaly reveals only a *difference* in the contact of the s and $p_{1/2}$ wave functions at the nucleus and not the total magnitudes of the contributions of the s- and $p_{1/2}$-electrons to the hyperfine structure. The anomaly would be expected to vanish in the ground state of Eu I. The fact that an anomaly exists is a clear indication that s-electrons, and possibly $p_{1/2}$-electrons, do contribute to the magnetic-dipole interaction. Baker and Williams[223] have determined the corresponding anomaly for divalent Eu $4f^7(^8S_{7/2})$ by an electron nuclear double resonance (ENDOR) technique to be $-0.63 \pm 0.07\%$; this figure suggests that the contribution of the s- and $p_{1/2}$-electrons to the hyperfine structure is substantially greater in the third spectra than in the first spectra.

Still more striking evidence for the role of s- and $p_{1/2}$-electrons in the hyperfine structure of the lanthanides is found in the comparison of the A and B factors measured for Eu I and Eu III. In the absence of contributions to the hyperfine structure by s- and $p_{1/2}$-electrons the entire hyperfine structure should be attributable to the $4f^7$ electrons, and hence the ratios of the A factors and the B factors for the atom with respect to those of the ion should be close to unity. It is apparent from Table 5-5

TABLE 5-5 A and B factors (Mc sec) for the ground states of Eu I and Eu III

Isotope	A(Eu I)	A(Eu III)	A(Eu III)/A(Eu I)	
^{151}Eu	$-20.0523(3)$	$-102.9069(13)$	$5.13193(8)$	
^{153}Eu	$-8.8543(2)$	$-45.6730(25)$	$5.15893(30)$	
	B(Eu I)[224]	B(Eu III)[225]	B(Eu III)/B(Eu I)	Isotope
	$-0.7012(35)$	$-0.7855(52)$	1.125	^{151}Eu
	$-1.7852(35)$	$-2.0294(68)$	1.125	^{153}Eu

that the ratio of the A factors departs markedly from unity, whereas the B factors are relatively close to unity. This is just as would be expected if s- and $p_{1/2}$-electrons were contributing to the hyperfine structure. These electrons will be able to contribute to the magnetic-dipole hyperfine structure but not to the electric-quadrupole hyperfine structure except as a cross-term between $p_{1/2}$ and $p_{3/2}$.

Thus it would appear that the effects of configuration interaction are certainly not negligible and probably arise out of the excitation of s- and p-electrons from inner closed shells to higher unfilled s- and p-shells.[226,227]

5-9   Configuration Interaction and Hyperfine Structure

The presence of a hyperfine-structure anomaly in Eu provides direct evidence for the existence of configuration interaction. The effects of configuration interaction should also be reflected in the magnetic-dipole and electric-quadrupole hyperfine structure constants. Only interaction with configurations that differ by the excitation of a single electron are likely to affect the hyperfine structure to any appreciable extent since the operators representing the hyperfine interactions are all one-electron type operators. Judd et al.[228] have shown that single-electron excitations from closed shells are of particular importance. Some of the qualitative properties of these types of excitations may be deduced readily from second-order perturbation theory.

Following Rajnak and Wybourne[49] we can write the correction to the matrix $(nl^N \alpha SLJ | H_{hfs} | nl^N \alpha' S'L'J')$ due to the effect of closed-shell excitations as

$$C = \frac{-2}{\Delta E} \sum_{\sigma, t} (nl^N \alpha SL, n'l'^{4l'+2} {}^1S; SLJ | H_{hfs} | nl^N \alpha SL,$$
$$\times (n'l'^{4l'+1} n''l'')\sigma t; S'L'J')(nl^N SL(n'l'^{4l'+1} n''l'')\sigma t; S'L'J'$$
$$\times |G| nl^N \alpha' S'L'n'l'^{4l'+2} {}^1S, S'L'J'), \quad (5\text{-}104)$$

where G is the Coulombic interaction operator, H_{hfs} that of the hyperfine interaction being considered, and ΔE is the mean excitation energy. The $s \to s$ excitations will play no role in the electric-quadrupole interactions although they may in the magnetic-dipole interactions.

On evaluating the matrix elements and performing the summation over σ and t in Eq. 5-104, we find that the electric-quadrupole matrix element

$$\left(nl^N \alpha SLJ \middle\| \sum_{i=1}^{N} r_i^{-3} \mathbf{C}_i^{(2)} \middle\| nl^N \alpha' SL'J' \right)$$

must be multiplied by a factor $(1 - \gamma_q)$, where

$$\gamma_q = \frac{2(l'\|\mathbf{C}^{(2)}\|l'')\langle n'l'|r^{-3}|nl''\rangle}{\Delta E(l\|\mathbf{C}^{(2)}\|l)\langle nl|r^{-3}|nl\rangle} \left[\frac{2X(2; l''l, l'l)}{5} \right.$$
$$\left. - \sum_k (-1)^k \begin{Bmatrix} l' & l'' & 2 \\ l & l & k \end{Bmatrix} X(k; ll'', l'l) \right], \quad (5\text{-}105)$$

and the quantities $X(k; ab, cd)$ are defined by

$$X(k; ab, cd) = (a\|\mathbf{C}^{(k)}\|c)(b\|\mathbf{C}^{(k)}\|d)R^k(ab, cd), \quad (5\text{-}106)$$

the $R^k(ab, cd)$ being the Slater radial integral defined in Eq. 2-58.

The correction factor $(1 - \gamma_q)$ is directly akin to the correction factors considered by Sternheimer.[229–233] In practice, many configurations contribute to the magnitude of γ_q, some negatively and some positively. If γ_q is negative, we have an example of "antishielding" and the electric-quadrupole moment felt by the electrons will be enhanced; if γ_q is positive, we have "shielding" and the effect of the quadrupole moment is either decreased or increased according to whether $\gamma_q < 1$ or $\gamma_q > 1$. The absolute magnitude of γ_q may exceed unity considerably. Thus the electric-quadrupole hyperfine-structure constant B calculated by assuming no configuration interaction may be found to be different from the measured B value not only in magnitude but also in sign. Judd et al.[228] have found very convincing evidence for the occurrence of antishielding in europium ethylsulfate.

The magnetic-dipole hyperfine interactions will also be affected by the presence of configuration interaction. When the summation in Eq. 5-104 is performed, we find that the magnetic hyperfine-structure constant defined in Eq. 5-20 must be replaced by

$$A = a_l[\mathscr{L}(1 - \gamma_m) + \mathscr{S}(1 - \gamma_m') + (g - 1)\gamma_s], \qquad (5\text{-}107)$$

where

$$\gamma_m = \frac{2\langle n'l'|r^{-3}|n''l''\rangle}{\Delta E\langle nl|r^{-3}|nl\rangle} \left(\frac{l'(l' + 1)(2l' + 1)}{l(l + 1)(2l + 1)}\right)^{1/2} \sum_k \begin{Bmatrix} l' & l' & 1 \\ l & l & k \end{Bmatrix}$$

$$\times X(k; ln''l', n'l'l)\delta(l', l'') \quad (5\text{-}108a)$$

$$\gamma_m' = \frac{2\langle n'l'|r^{-3}|n''l''\rangle(l'\|\mathbf{C}^{(2)}\|l'')}{\Delta E\langle nl|r^{-3}|nl\rangle(l\|\mathbf{C}^{(2)}\|l)} \sum_k (-1)^k \begin{Bmatrix} l' & l'' & 2 \\ l & l & k \end{Bmatrix}$$

$$\times X(k; ll'', l'l), \quad (5\text{-}108b)$$

and

$$\gamma_s = \frac{2(-1)^l X(l; ln's, nsl)8\pi\langle ns|\psi(0)|n's\rangle^2}{\Delta E[l]3\langle nl|r^{-3}|nl\rangle}. \qquad (5\text{-}108c)$$

γ_s takes into account the effects of the $ns \to n's$ one-electron excitations and γ_m and γ_m' the effects of all the other one-electron excitations. Each of these factors is independent of the state of the configuration being studied. Unlike the electric quadrupole interaction, the effects of configuration interaction cannot be represented by a simple scaling of the magnetic hyperfine-structure constant. Each A value will be represented by a different linear combination of the γ-factors. This affords a direct test for the presence of configuration interaction. In the absence of configuration interaction the ratio of the magnetic hyperfine-structure constants for two states belonging to the same configuration should be given by

$$\frac{A}{A'} = \frac{\mathscr{L} + \mathscr{S}}{\mathscr{L}' + \mathscr{S}'}. \qquad (5\text{-}109)$$

It is evident from the form of Eq. 5-107 that this relation will be invalidated in the presence of configuration interaction. If four different A values are known for four states of the same configuration, it should be possible to set up three equations in γ_m, γ_m' and γ_s and deduce their actual magnitudes.

Unfortunately, there are few cases in the rare earths where the validity of Eq. 5-109 can be tested. Ritter[234] has measured the A and B values for the two levels of the $5d6s^2$ configuration of ^{175}Lu ($Z = 71$) and found the ratios

$$\frac{A(^2D_{3/2})}{A(^2D_{5/2})} = 1.32397(1)$$

and

$$\frac{B(^2D_{3/2})}{B(^2D_{5/2})} = 0.812298(5),$$

which may be compared with the values calculated, assuming a pure configuration and making the appropriate relativistic corrections of

$$\frac{A(^2D_{3/2})}{A(^2D_{5/2})} = 2.4306$$

and

$$\frac{B(^2D_{3/2})}{B(^2D_{5/2})} = 0.7976.$$

The relatively good agreement found for the electric-quadrupole constants is to be expected since the individual B values should be scaled in the same proportion. The calculated and experimental ratios for the A factors show a considerable disagreement. A similar discrepancy is found in the magnetic hyperfine constants of these two levels in lanthanum[236] ($Z = 57$). It can only be concluded that these two elements are affected considerably by the presence of configuration interaction. Configuration interaction, which may be of little consequence as far as the energy levels are concerned, may have quite drastic consequences for hyperfine structure. Both La I and Lu I have the $5d6s^2$ type configuration lowest, and the configuration interaction probably involves interactions with the higher $5d6sns$ ($n \geq 7$) and $5d^26s$ configurations as well as with the one-electron excitations from the inner closed shells. These two elements occur at the commencement and end of the lanthanide series, respectively and, although probably not typical of the rare earths, do indicate the large-scale effects that can arise from configuration interaction.

The nuclear moments for many isotopes of the rare earths have been determined from atomic beam measurements of the hyperfine structure of the $f^N s^2$ and $f^N d s^2$ configurations.   The derivation of the nuclear moments from these measurements has usually assumed that the effects of configuration interaction are negligible.   Spalding[235] has measured the ratio of the A factors for the $^5 I_4$ and $^5 I_5$ states of ^{143}Nd and ^{145}Nd and found satisfactory agreement with the ratios predicted by Eq. 5-109.   Similar measurements by Woodgate et al.[237] on the $^7 F_1$ to $^7 F_4$ states of Sm I has similarly been found to be in reasonable agreement with Eq. 5-109. These results would seem to indicate that the effects of configuration interaction with the low-lying states of the lanthanides are indeed very small.   However, they cannot always be neglected.

A particularly striking example of the importance of configuration interaction is found in the hyperfine structure of the ground state, $5f^7(^8 S_{7/2})7s^2$, of Am I.   The isotope ^{241}Am has a nuclear spin of $\frac{5}{2}$ and Marrus et al.[238] have measured the magnetic- and electric-quadrupole splitting factors as

$$A = \pm 0.571 \times 10^{-3} \text{cm}^{-1} \quad \text{and} \quad B = \mp 4.13 \times 10^{-3} \text{cm}^{-1},$$

giving the ratio

$$\frac{B}{A} = -7.23.$$

By including the effects of intermediate coupling, they calculate

$$A = +0.55 \times 10^{-3} \text{cm}^{-1} \quad \text{and} \quad B = +4.8 \times 10^{-3} \text{cm}^{-1},$$

leading to the theoretical ratio of

$$\frac{B}{A} = +8.73.$$

Thus, although the absolute magnitudes are in good agreement with the experimental results, the phase of the ratio B/A is opposite to that observed. Marrus et al. examined the effect of contributions to the A factor that would arise from the excitation of a $7s$-electron to the $8s$-shell, only to find the discrepancy was *increased*.

Bauche and Judd[239] have examined the effects of the excitation of s-electrons from the inner closed shells into the unfilled ns-shells ($n > 7$). In particular, they have considered the excitation of a $3s$-electron into the continuum and have shown that these excitations lead to *negative* values of the γ_s defined by Eq. 5-108c.   Thus the result of Marrus et al. becomes plausible only when these excitations are considered.

Freeman and Watson[240–242] have treated the effects of antishielding on the electric-quadrupole interactions in rare earths within the framework of the unrestricted Hartree-Fock formalism.[117]   By relaxing the normal constraints of the Hartree-Fock method that (1) the spatial part of the one-electron functions be separable into a radial function times an angular function, and (2) that electrons of the same shell but of different m_l have the same radial wave function, they have endeavored to calculate the antishielding factors of the quadrupole moment for Ce^{3+}. Relaxing (1) results in "angular" distortions of the electron shells, whereas relaxing (2) yields "radial" distortions. This leads to a value of $\langle r^{-3} \rangle_Q$ different from that determined from the usual Hartree-Fock wave function. The resultant value of $\langle r^{-3} \rangle_Q$ contains contributions, both positive and negative, from the closed shells as is evident from Table 5-6. In treating

TABLE 5-6   Contributions from closed shells to $\langle r^{-3} \rangle_Q$ for Ce^{3+}

Shell	$\langle r^{-3} \rangle_Q$
$2p$	1.09
$3p$	2.25
$4p$	-0.23
$5p$	-1.26
$3d$	0.20
$4d$	-0.03
$4f$	4.71
Total	6.72 atomic units

magnetic hyperfine interactions they would associate different values of $\langle r^{-3} \rangle$ with the interaction of the orbital and spin moments of the electrons. As yet little application has been made to the rare earths. Studies of ions of other elements do, however, show that the resultant values of $\langle r^{-3} \rangle$ may differ from one another by ten or more per cent and may differ substantially from the usual $\langle r^{-3} \rangle$ integral. These results cast further doubt on the usual methods of deducing nuclear moments from hyperfine-structure measurements.

5-10   Relative Intensities and Hyperfine Patterns

The relative intensities of the electric-dipole transitions between two hyperfine-structure multiplets may be calculated readily in the JIF scheme by following the same procedure for calculating the relative intensities of transitions between two LS coupled multiplets if the correspondence.

$$S \rightarrow I, \quad L \rightarrow J, \quad J \rightarrow F$$

is made. In the absence of external fields the selection rules are:

$$\Delta I = 0, \quad \Delta J = 0, \pm 1, \quad \text{and} \quad \Delta F = 0, \pm 1, \quad \text{but not } 0 \leftrightarrow 0.$$

The relative intensities are given by:

$$J \to J$$

$F \to F + 1$

$$\frac{A[(F + J + I + 2)(F + J - I + 1)(F + I - J + 1)(J + I - F)]}{4(F + 1)}.$$

$$(5\text{-}109a)$$

$F \to F$

$$\frac{A(2F + 1)[F(F + 1) + J(J + 1) + I(I + 1)]^2}{4F(F + 1)}.$$

$$(5\text{-}109b)$$

$F \to F - 1$

$$\frac{A[(F + J + I + 1)(F + J - I)(F + I - J)(J + I - F)]}{4(F + 1)}.$$

$$(5\text{-}109c)$$

$$J \to J - 1$$

$F \to F + 1$

$$\frac{A'[(F + I - J + 1)(F + I - J + 2)(I + J - F)(I + J - F - 1)]}{4(F + 1)}.$$

$$(5\text{-}110a)$$

$F \to F$

$$\frac{A'[(F + J + I + 1)(F + I - J + 1)(F + J - I)(J + I - F)(2F + 1)]}{4F(F + 1)}.$$

$$(5\text{-}110b)$$

$F \to F - 1$

$$\frac{A'[(F + J + I)(F + J + I + 1)(F + J - I)(F + J - I - 1)]}{4F},$$

$$(5\text{-}110c)$$

where

$$A = |(\alpha J \|\mathbf{P}\| \alpha' J)|^2 J(J + 1)(2J + 1) \qquad (5\text{-}111a)$$

and

$$A' = \frac{|(\alpha J \|\mathbf{P}\| \alpha' J - 1)|^2}{J(2J - 1)(2J + 1)}. \qquad (5\text{-}111b)$$

A and A' depend on the particular configurations being considered and the coupling of their electronic states. These quantities would be evaluated only if absolute intensities were to be calculated, which is rarely, if ever, the case. The selection rules and the formulas for the *relative* intensities hold independently of the configuration or couplings of the electronic states provided there are no perturbations from nearby hyperfine multiplets. Furthermore, they are independent of the magnetic-dipole or electric-quadrupole origin of the hyperfine structure. Kopfermann[160] has given a convenient table of the relative intensities for $I = \frac{1}{2}$ to $I = \frac{9}{2}$.

In general, the relative intensities given by Eqs. 5-109 and 5-110 are found to reproduce the observed intensities closely enough to allow the assigning of F-values to the levels to be made on the basis of intensity. Departures of the intensities from their calculated values will, however, occur if there is self-reversal of the spectral line.

5-11   Zeeman Effect and Hyperfine Structure

In the presence of an external magnetic field H_0, the hyperfine-structure Hamiltonian must be supplemented by two terms that arise from the interaction of the nuclear magnetic moment μ_I and the electronic-dipole moment μ_e to give the resultant Hamiltonian

$$\mathcal{H} = \mathcal{H}_{hfs} + \mu_e H_0 - \mu_I H_0 = \mathcal{H}_{hfs} + \mathcal{H}_{mag}. \quad (5\text{-}112)$$

For weak fields where the Zeeman interactions are small compared with the hyperfine interactions, the levels may be most appropriately characterized in the $JIFM$ scheme of quantum numbers. In this scheme the matrix elements of $\mathcal{H}_{mag}$, which follow from Eqs. 2-30, 2-48, and 2-49, become

$$(\alpha JIFM |\mathcal{H}_{mag}| \alpha' JIF'M)$$

$$= (-1)^{F-M} \begin{pmatrix} F & 1 & F' \\ -M & 0 & M \end{pmatrix} [(F, F')]^{1/2}$$

$$\times \left[(-1)^{J+I+F'+1} \begin{Bmatrix} F & F' & 1 \\ J & J & I \end{Bmatrix} (\alpha J \|\mu_e\| \alpha' J) - (-1)^{J+I+F+1} \begin{Bmatrix} F & F' & 1 \\ I & I & J \end{Bmatrix} \right.$$

$$\left. \times (I\|\mu_I\|I) \right]. \quad (5\text{-}113)$$

The 3-j and 6-j symbols may be evaluated explicitly to give the matrix elements diagonal in F as

$$(\alpha JIFM |\mathcal{H}_{mag}| \alpha' JIFM)$$

$$= \frac{MH_0}{2F(F+1)} [[F(F+1) + J(J+1) - I(I+1)]\beta g_J$$

$$- [F(F+1) + I(I+1) - J(J+1)]\beta_N g_I], \quad (5\text{-}114)$$

where g_J and g_I are respectively the electronic and nuclear Landé factors. If we set

$$g_I' = \frac{\beta_N}{\beta} g_I, \quad (5\text{-}115)$$

and

$$g_F = \left\{ \frac{[F(F+1)+J(J+1)-I(I+1)]g_J - [F(F+1)+I(I+1)-J(J+1)]g_I'}{2F(F+1)} \right\},$$

$$(5\text{-}116)$$

we obtain Eq. 5-114 as

$$(\alpha JIFM | \mathscr{H}_{\text{mag}} | \alpha JIFM) = \beta g_F M H_0. \tag{5-117}$$

For the matrix elements with $F' = F - 1$ we find

$$(\alpha JIFM | \mathscr{H}_{\text{mag}} | \alpha JIF-1M) = \beta H_0 (F^2 - M^2)^{1/2} [(F + J + I + 1)$$
$$\times (F + I - J)(F + J - I)(J + I - F + 1)]^{1/2} (g_J + g_I'). \tag{5-118}$$

In a very weak magnetic field (approximately 10 gauss) the off-diagonal matrix elements may be ignored as a first approximation. Within this approximation each hyperfine-structure level splits into $2F + 1$ equally spaced levels. These splittings are usually not resolvable by the techniques of optical spectroscopy. They may, however, be determined by atomic beam resonance techniques with considerable accuracy.

For strong magnetic fields (usually approximately 10^4 gauss) the coupling between the nuclear and electronic moments is broken and it becomes more appropriate to characterize the levels in the $JJ_z II_z M$ scheme of quantum numbers. In both the strong field and the weak field, M remains a good quantum number. The diagonal matrix elements in the strong field scheme become

$$(\alpha JJ_z II_z M | \mathscr{H}_{\text{mag}} | \alpha JJ_z II_z M) = \beta H_0 (J_z g_J - I_z g_I'), \tag{5-119}$$

and the off-diagonal elements are given by

$$(\alpha JJ_z II_z M | \mathscr{H}_{\text{mag}} | \alpha JJ_z \pm 1 II_z \mp 1M) = \frac{\beta H_0}{2} \{ g_J [(J \mp J_z)(J \pm J_z + 1)]^{1/2}$$
$$- g_I' [(I \pm I_z)(I \mp I_z + 1)]^{1/2} \}. \tag{5-120}$$

The off-diagonal elements become negligible compared to the diagonal elements at high fields and may be neglected to a first approximation. In this case each Zeeman level is observed to split into $2I + 1$ equally spaced sublevels due to the hyperfine interactions. In contrast to the weak field, the levels form a symmetric pattern about the center of gravity of the hyperfine-structure multiplet.

At intermediate field strengths the off-diagonal matrix elements can no longer be ignored and neither of the coupling schemes adequately represents the levels. In this case only M remains as a good quantum number. The transition from the weak field limit to the strong field limit is shown schematically for a level with $J = 2$ and nuclear spin $I = 1$ in Fig. 5-4. In the weak field limit the splittings resulting from the combined effects of hyperfine and Zeeman interactions will be given by the diagonal element of the Hamiltonian Eq. 5-112

$$(\alpha JIFM | \mathscr{H} | \alpha JIFM) = \frac{AK}{2} + B \left(\frac{\frac{3}{4} K(K + 1) - I(I + 1)J(J + 1)}{2I(2I - 1)J(2J - 1)} \right)$$
$$+ \beta g_F M H_0, \tag{5-121}$$

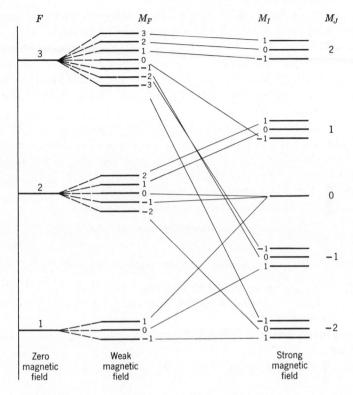

Fig. 5-4   Transition from the weak magnetic field limit to the strong field limit for a level with $J = 2$ and nuclear spin $I = 1$.

and in the strong field limit we have

$$(\alpha J J_z I I_z M | \mathscr{H} | \alpha J J_z I I_z M) = J_z I_z A + B \left\{ \frac{[3I_z^2 - I(I + 1)]}{4IJ(2J - 1)(2I - 1)} \right.$$

$$\left. \times [3J_z^2 - J(J + 1)] \right\} + \beta H_0 (J_z g_J - I_z g_I'). \quad (5\text{-}122)$$

In practice, the weak or strong field limits are seldom attained. The splittings may, however, be traced out over a range of magnetic field strengths and the limits obtained by extrapolation for atomic beam resonance measurements.

5-12 Atomic Beam Resonance Measurements

Atomic beam resonance techniques are capable of yielding extremely precise measurements of the hyperfine structure-constants and the electronic and nuclear g-values.   Their application is, however, usually limited to the low-lying levels of neutral atoms because only these states can have an appreciable population at the normal operating temperatures of atomic beams.   In brief,* the method of atomic beam resonances consists of passing a beam of atoms through a steady magnetic field H_0 on which is superimposed a radio-frequency magnetic field.   The r-f field can induce magnetic-dipole transitions between the hyperfine-structure levels. When there is resonance between the inducing frequency and the induced radiation, the induced transitions occur in sufficient number to produce an observable effect.   At the resonance the frequency ν_0 of the inducing field, which may be measured very accurately, equals the frequency separation of the two levels involved in the transition.

In a weak field the magnetic-dipole selection rules are

$$\Delta M = 0 \quad (\sigma \text{ components}) \quad \text{only if} \quad \Delta F = \pm 1$$

and

$$\Delta M = \pm 1 \quad (\pi \text{ components}) \quad \text{only if} \quad \Delta F = 0, \pm 1.$$

The σ transitions will be produced by components of the r-f field parallel to H_0, and the π transitions will be produced by components of the r-f field perpendicular to H_0.

For a strong magnetic field the corresponding magnetic-dipole selection rules are

$$\Delta J_z = 0, \qquad \Delta I_z = \pm 1$$

and

$$\Delta I_z = 0, \qquad \Delta J_z = \pm 1.$$

These selection rules limit greatly the number of possible transitions. For large values of J and I the number of allowed transitions may still be fairly large which results in many observable resonances, thus making the assignment of quantum numbers to the levels both difficult and confusing.   By suitable design of the magnetic fields used to focus the atomic beam before and after its passage through the uniform field H_0, it is possible to limit the observation of resonances to those that involve a change in the sign of J_z.[171,243]   This limits the transitions for half-integer J to $J_z = \frac{1}{2}$ to $J_z = -\frac{1}{2}$.   For integer J the double transition $J_z = 1$ to $J_z = -1$ is usually possible.   Frequently higher multiple transitions are observed, although still with the restriction that the sign of J_z changes.

By studying different types of allowed transitions it is possible to determine with considerable accuracy the quantum numbers, g-factors, and

---

* Detailed accounts of the experimental techniques are contained in References 25 and 158–160 and in the many atomic beam research reports of the Lawrence Radiation Laboratory, University of California, Berkeley.

hyperfine-structure constants. Thus in the weak field limit it follows from Eq. 5-121 that the resonance frequencies of the $\Delta F = 0$ transitions will occur at

$$\nu_0 = \frac{\beta g_F H_0}{h},$$

(5-123)

where h is Planck's constant. Measurement of these frequencies can lead to the determination of the quantities g_J, J, I, and F.

By knowing J, I, and F, it is then possible to deduce the hyperfine-structure constants A and B from observations of the resonances involving $\Delta F = \pm 1$ transitions. For the σ-components $\Delta M = 0$ and the resonance frequencies in the weak field limit are given by

$$\nu_0 = \left\{ AF_> + \frac{3BF_>[F_>^2 - J(J+1) - I(I+1) + \frac{1}{2}]}{2IJ(2J-1)(2I-1)} - \frac{\beta(g_J - g_I')MH_0[J(J+1) - I(I+1)]}{2F_>(F_>-1)(F_>+1)} \right\} \bigg/ h,$$

(5-124)

where $F_>$ is the greater of F and F'. Thus, by measuring several resonances and extrapolating to the weak field limit, it is possible to deduce A and B.

In the strong field limit the $\Delta J_z = \pm 1$ transitions will give resonances at the frequencies

$$\nu_0 = \left\{ I_z A + \frac{3B[3I_z^2 - I(I+1)](2J_{z>} - 1)}{4IJ(2J-1)(2I-1)} + \beta H_0 g_J \right\} \bigg/ h,$$

(5-125)

and the $\Delta I_z = \pm 1$ transitions will give resonances at

$$\nu_0 = \left\{ J_z A + \frac{3B[3J_z^2 - J(J+1)](2I_{z>} - 1)}{4IJ(2J-1)(2I-1)} - \beta H_0 g_I' \right\} \bigg/ h,$$

(5-126)

where $J_{z>}$ and $I_{z>}$, are, respectively the greater of J_z and J_z' and of I_z and I_z'.

Measurement of the resonance frequencies of the $\Delta J_z = \pm 1$ transitions allows A, B, and g_J to be determined with considerable precision. Similarly, g_I' may be determined from the resonance frequencies of the $\Delta I_z = \pm 1$ transitions. g_I' is normally approximately $g_J/2000$, and hence A and B must be known to a very high accuracy if g_I' is to be determined with even moderate precision.

The weak field transitions normally yield A, B, and g_J but not g_I'. The nuclear moments μ_I and Q may be derived from the measured values of A and B as have those of most of the rare earths.* This, however, represents an indirect determination of the nuclear moments since it

---

* An extensive tabulation of nuclear moments has been given by Lindgren.[244]

requires a detailed knowledge of the electronic wave function. Measurement of the strong field transitions yields the nuclear magnetic moments directly without requiring any knowledge of the electronic wave function. The comparison of the directly measured moments with those deduced by the electronic wave function can be used as a test for the validity of the wave functions.[111,138] Knowing A and the directly determined nuclear magnetic moment allows $\langle r^{-3} \rangle$ to be found if it can be assumed that a single value of $\langle r^{-3} \rangle$ can be associated with the relationship between A and μ_I. The validity of this assumption is questionable, and as a result the values of $\langle r^{-3} \rangle$ that are found may not correspond to those that would follow from the "true" electronic wave function.

Although the nuclear magnetic moments may be measured directly, the electric-quadrupole moments cannot. If the value of $\langle r^{-3} \rangle$ is supposed to be the same for both the electric-quadrupole and magnetic-dipole moments, it is possible to measure the magnetic-dipole moment directly and deduce an effective value of $\langle r^{-3} \rangle$. This value can then be used to calculate the magnitude of the electric-quadrupole moment from the measured value of B. If configuration interaction is involved, the identification of the same $\langle r^{-3} \rangle$ value for both types of hyperfine interactions has little validity.

The external field H_0 used to determine the nuclear magnetic moments induces directly a diamagnetic electron-current density in the electron cloud which gives rise to an opposing magnetic field. Thus a small diamagnetic shielding correction must be made to the measured moments. Kopfermann[160] has given a convenient table for making these corrections.

5-13 Optical Hyperfine Structure Measurements

Atomic beam resonance measurements have several distinct advantages over the corresponding optical spectroscopic measurements. They are particularly well adapted to measuring the spins and hyperfine-structure constants of even quite short-lived isotopes (approximately 2 hours) with a precision far surpassing the most sophisticated optical spectroscopic techniques. There are, however, important areas where optical techniques are superior. For example, because of the peculiar physical properties of uranium, it has not as yet been possible to form atomic beams of uranium to allow their nuclear spin determination. In optical spectroscopy the nuclear spins of both ^{233}U and ^{235}U were determined readily from their atomic spectra.[244] Similarly, the spins of the stable isotopes until quite recently posed special difficulties for atomic beam measurements and were first determined from optical spectroscopy.

If $I \geq J$, each level splits into $(2J + 1)$-components, whereas if $I \leq J$, each level splits into $(2I + 1)$-components. If the hyperfine splittings in the combining levels are sufficiently different, the nuclear spin determination reduces to a simple counting of the components of the hyperfine-structure multiplets for large J-values. For example, in $^{141}Pr\,II$ spectra many hyperfine patterns with six components are observed from which the nuclear spin $I = \frac{5}{2}$ has been deduced.[169]

The observed hyperfine patterns originate from the difference in the hyperfine splittings of the two combining levels of the transition. Thus, to derive reliable values of the hyperfine-structure constants A and B, it is essential to separate out from the observed patterns the individual structure of the two combining levels. It cannot be safely assumed that the hyperfine structure of one of the levels is negligible. As we have seen, appreciable hyperfine structure can be associated even with non-s-electrons. The complete analysis of the hyperfine-structure patterns into the individual hyperfine-structure multiplets of the two combining levels is usually a task of considerable complexity because of the difficulty of resolving all the components of the pattern. This is particularly the case where there is an appreciable contribution to the hyperfine structure by the electric-quadrupole interaction.

Where it is possible to determine the levels of a hyperfine-structure multiplet, we are able to deduce A and B from the energy differences of the components if I and J are known. The separation of two levels F_1 and F_2 will be given by

$$\Delta E_{12} = \frac{A(K_1 - K_2)}{2} + \frac{3B[K_1(K_1 + 1) - K_2(K_2 + 1)]}{8IJ(2J - 1)(2I - 1)}, \quad (5\text{-}127)$$

where K_1 and K_2 are as defined in Eq. 5-14. For $I = \frac{1}{2}$ the quadrupole term vanishes, leaving

$$\Delta E = A(J + \tfrac{1}{2}). \quad (5\text{-}128)$$

Optical transitions between hyperfine-structure multiplets are normally observed as electric-dipole transitions and in a strong magnetic field the selection rules become

$$\Delta I_z = 0 \qquad \Delta J_z = 0 \qquad \pi\text{-components polarized parallel to the field,}$$

and

$$\Delta J_z = \pm 1 \quad \sigma\text{-components polarized perpendicular to the field.}$$

Thus the selection rule on J_z is the same as for the Zeeman effect without hyperfine structure. As a result the normal Zeeman effect is observed, but with each J_z-component being split into $2I + 1$ sublevels. If the electric-quadrupole interaction is small, these sublevels will be equally spaced. Because of the selection rule on I_z, only $2I + 1$ sublevels will be observed even when there are hyperfine splittings in both the combining levels. The nuclear spin may be unequivocally identified if the sublevels can, in fact, be resolved into the full $2I + 1$ sublevels. The relative intensities of the J_z-components, when integrated over the hyperfine-structure sublevels, are just the same as would be found if there had been no hyperfine structure.

Hyperfine-structure studies are particularly important in deducing energy levels from spectral lines. In the rare earths a given spectrum for a single stage of ionization will have 15,000 or more spectral lines. The energy levels may be deduced from these data by searching for repeating differences in the energies of the transitions. With such a number of spectral lines many accidental coincidences may be expected and the problem of distinguishing these accidental coincidences from real coincidences becomes acute. Here observations of the hyperfine structure of the combining levels can be of considerable assistance since each level involved in combination possesses its own unique hyperfine structure splittings. Examples may be found in the work of Sugar[32] on Pr III and of Fred and Tomkins[99] on Am I and Am II.

5-14 Concluding Remarks on Hyperfine Structure

The last decade has seen considerable attention to the hyperfine structure and isotope shifts of rare earth spectra by both the techniques of atomic beam resonances and of optical spectroscopy. Much more work remains. The nuclear spins of many of the rare earth isotopes remain unknown. Some have half-lives of only a few hours or even less, and yet many should be amenable to examination by atomic beam resonances. As more direct measurements of the nuclear magnetic moments are made, it should be possible to use these moments in conjunction with hyperfine-structure studies to probe the electronic wave functions of the rare earths near the nucleus. These results should provide extremely delicate tests for theoretically calculated wave functions. The extension of the techniques of electron nuclear double resonance (ENDOR) and nuclear magnetic resonance should make possible similar observations for ionized rare earths. With the development of optical pumping techniques it may well be possible to make very precise hyperfine-structure studies of the excited states of both atoms and ions. Optical studies of hyperfine structure are likely to continue to be used as a tool for making spectral terms analyses. Optical methods will also continue to be of considerable importance in studying isotope shifts in the rare earths. Interferometric methods are providing very precise measurements of hyperfine interactions and isotope shifts.

CHAPTER 6

Spectra of Rare Earth Salts

6-1 Crystal Field Splitting of Energy Levels

The lanthanides normally occur as tripositive ions in the salts and solutions of their compounds. Their optical spectra have been studied extensively in both absorption and fluorescence.[245-248] At low temperatures the absorption spectra are usually found to consist of groups of sharp lines. The lines within a group may have separations approximately 100 cm^{-1}. The positions of the groups of lines are relatively unaffected by the environment of the lanthanide ion and may be correlated with the positions of the energy levels of the $4f^N$ configuration of the free, tripositive ion.

For a free atom or ion spherical symmetry exists, and each level is $(2J + 1)$fold degenerate. On placing the ion in a crystal, the spherical symmetry is destroyed and each level splits under the influence of the electric field produced by the environment. Usually, the environment about the rare earth ion will possess a well-defined symmetry (of lower symmetry than spherical) and the degree to which the $(2J + 1)$fold degeneracy is removed will depend on the point symmetry about the rare earth ion.

Kramers' theorem[249] shows that for odd-electron systems there is a twofold degeneracy in the energy states that cannot be removed by any electric fields. This remaining degeneracy can be removed only by the application of a magnetic field or by exchange interactions between paramagnetic ions. It is interesting to note that at temperatures approaching absolute zero this degeneracy must necessarily be removed by some mechanism if Nernst's theorem is to retain its validity.[250]

The Hamiltonian H for an ion placed in a crystal field may be written as

$$H = H_F + V, \tag{6-1}$$

where H_F is the Hamiltonian of the free ion and V is the potential provided by the crystal environment about the ion of interest.   In general, we shall suppose that the eigenvalues and eigenfunctions of H_F are known and regard the potential V as a perturbation.   The unperturbed eigenfunctions will have complete spherical symmetry, and hence we may try to expand V in terms of spherical harmonics or operators that transform like spherical harmonics.   Thus we may expand the potential in terms of the tensor operators $\mathbf{C}_q^{(k)}$ to give

$$V = \sum_{k,q,i} B_q^k (\mathbf{C}_q^{(k)})_i, \tag{6-2}$$

where the summation involving i is over all the electrons of the ion of interest.   For the moment we shall regard the quantities B_q^k as simply coefficients of the expansion* to be determined empirically from the experimental data without assuming any details of the model.   These parameters differ by a numerical factor from those commonly found in the literature.   The author feels that B_q^k's defined in Eq. 6-2 enter most naturally into the theory as developed in terms of tensor operators.   It seems that future crystal field calculations will be made in terms of the matrix elements of tensor operators rather than the older operator equivalent technique.[251-255]   The relationship between the B_q^k's and the commoner $A_k^q \langle r^k \rangle$ parameters are given in Table 6-1.

The first term in the expansion has $k = q = 0$ and is thus spherically symmetric.   This term is by far the largest term in the expansion and is responsible for the greater part of the lattice energy or heat of solution.[256,257]   In the first approximation this term gives a uniform shift of all the levels of the configuration and may be ignored as far as the crystal field splittings of the levels is concerned.   Its influence will be felt only in the presence of second-order interactions with other configurations.[258]

If only f-electrons are involved, the terms in the expansion with $k \le 6$ are nonzero.   Furthermore, all the terms with k-odd vanish for configurations containing solely equivalent electrons.   Thus for the f^N configuration the matrix elements of V will be given by

$$(f^N \alpha SLJJ_z | V | f^N \alpha' SL'J'J'_z) = \sum_{k,q} B_q^k (f^N \alpha SLJJ_z | \mathbf{U}_q^{(k)} | f^N \alpha' SL'J'J'_z)$$
$$(f \| \mathbf{C}^{(k)} \| f). \tag{6-3}$$

The matrix elements of the tensor operator $\mathbf{U}_q^{(k)}$ are diagonal in the spin S

---

* Note that although the B_q^k's will be real functions of the radial distance, the non-cylindrical terms (that is, terms with $|q| > 0$) will not necessarily be real functions of the angular coordinates.

TABLE 6-1 Relationship of the B_q^k parameters to those of the $A_q^k \langle r^k \rangle$ parameters

$$B_0^2 = 2A_2^0 \langle r^2 \rangle$$

$$B_2^2 = \frac{\sqrt{42}}{21} A_2^2 \langle r^2 \rangle$$

$$B_0^4 = 8A_4^0 \langle r^4 \rangle$$

$$B_2^4 = \frac{-2\sqrt{10}}{55} A_4^2 \langle r^4 \rangle$$

$$B_3^4 = -\frac{2\sqrt{35}}{35} A_4^3 \langle r^4 \rangle$$

$$B_4^4 = \frac{8\sqrt{70}}{55} A_4^4 \langle r^4 \rangle$$

$$B_0^6 = 16 \, A_6^0 \langle r^6 \rangle$$

$$B_2^6 = \frac{2\sqrt{105}}{10,395} A_6^2 \langle r^6 \rangle$$

$$B_3^6 = -\frac{8\sqrt{105}}{105} A_6^3 \langle r^6 \rangle$$

$$B_4^6 = \frac{\sqrt{14}}{21} A_6^4 \langle r^6 \rangle$$

$$B_6^6 = \frac{16\sqrt{231}}{231} A_6^6 \langle r^6 \rangle$$

and may be readily evaluated by using first Eq. 2-30 and then Eq. 2-49 to yield

$$(f^N \alpha S L J J_z | U_q^{(k)} | f^N \alpha' S L' J' J'_z) = (-1)^{J - J_z} \begin{pmatrix} J & k & J' \\ -J_z & q & J_z' \end{pmatrix}$$
$$\times (f^N \alpha S L J \| U^{(k)} \| f^N \alpha' S L' J'), \quad (6\text{-}4)$$

where

$$(f^N \alpha S L J \| U^{(k)} \| f^N \alpha' S L' J') = (-1)^{S + L + J' + k} ([J, J'])^{1/2}$$
$$\times \begin{Bmatrix} J & J' & k \\ L' & L & S \end{Bmatrix} (f^N \alpha S L \| U^{(k)} \| f^N \alpha' S L'). \quad (6\text{-}5)$$

The doubly reduced matrix elements of $U^{(k)}$ may be calculated from Eq. 2-92 or obtained directly from the tables of Nielson and Koster.[43] A convenient tabulation for f^3 has been given by Judd,[259] who has also discussed in some detail the group-theoretical properties of these operators.[260]

The axial terms $U_0^{(k)}$ will lead to a splitting of levels with differing J_z, whereas the terms $U_q^{(k)}$ will mix states for which $J_z - J_z' = q$. As a result of this mixing, J and J_z will cease to be good quantum numbers.

The values of k and q will be limited by the point symmetry of the rare earth ion site, since the Hamiltonian must be invariant under the operations of the point symmetry group. If we restrict our attention to the states of the same parity, k will assume only even values. Consider now D_{3h} symmetry, where there is a threefold axis of rotational symmetry with a reflection plane perpendicular to it. The electric field must exhibit this symmetry and hence if a $2\pi/3$ rotation is made, followed by a reflection, on the potential V, the new potential may be equated with the original potential only if $q = 0$ or ± 6. Thus within a pure f^N configuration the potential V for D_{3h} symmetry may be written as

$$D_{3h}: \quad V = B_0^2 \mathbf{C}_0^{(2)} + B_0^4 \mathbf{C}_0^{(4)} + B_0^6 \mathbf{C}_0^{(6)} + B_6^6 (\mathbf{C}_6^{(6)} + \mathbf{C}_{-6}^{(6)}), \quad (6\text{-}6)$$

where we make use of the fact that the potential is real and Hermitian, that is,

$$B_q^k = (-1)^q B_q^{k*}, \quad (6\text{-}7)$$

and we understand that the $\mathbf{C}_q^{(k)}$'s are to be summed over all the electrons of the configuration as in Eq. 6-2. We note that Eq. 6-6 is invariant under D_{6h} symmetry. The difference between D_{3h} and D_{6h} symmetry comes from the fact that the complete potential for D_{3h} also contains terms with k-odd, but these have been suppressed since we have limited ourselves to matrix elements within a configuration.

C_{3h} symmetry occurs in all the rare earth ethylsulfates $[R(C_2H_5SO_4)_3 \cdot 9H_2O)$, where R stands for a rare earth]. This symmetry is also found in the trichlorides (RCl_3) and tribromides (RBr_3) of the lanthanides from lanthanum to gadolinium. Lanthanum trichloride is frequently used as a host for rare earth ions since it is free of absorption over a wide wavelength range. C_{3h} symmetry is also common to the trichlorides and tribromides of the actinides at least as far as americium. The potential for C_{3h} symmetry differs from that of Eq. 6-6 by an imaginary noncylindrical term, $iB_6'^6(\mathbf{C}_6^{(6)} - \mathbf{C}_{-6}^{(6)})$. In most practical cases the crystal field has been found to exhibit an effective potential appropriate to D_{3h} symmetry because of the additional terms in the C_{3h} potential being negligibly small.

C_{3v} symmetry occurs in the rare earth bromates $[R(BrO_3)_3 \cdot 9H_2O]$ and the rare earth magnesium and zinc double nitrates $[RMg_3(NO_3)_2 \cdot 24H_2O$ and $RZn_3(NO_3)_2 \cdot 24H_2O]$. For this symmetry the crystal field potential has the form

$$C_{3v}: \quad V = B_0^2 \mathbf{C}_0^{(2)} + B_0^4 \mathbf{C}_0^{(4)} + B_3^4 (\mathbf{C}_{-3}^{(4)} - \mathbf{C}_3^{(4)}) + B_0^6 \mathbf{C}_0^{(6)}$$
$$+ B_3^6 (\mathbf{C}_{-3}^{(6)} - \mathbf{C}_3^{(6)}) + B_6^6 (\mathbf{C}_{-6}^{(6)} + \mathbf{C}_6^{(6)}). \quad (6\text{-}8)$$

The rare earth double nitrates are of special interest since the oxygen atoms, at least in cerium magnesium double nitrates, lie approximately at the vertices of an icosahedron, a result first inferred from crystal spectra by Judd[262] and later by an actual x-ray structure determination by Templeton et al.[263]

C_{3h}, and to a lesser extent C_{3v}, symmetries have long been favorites for those who have studied the crystal spectra of the rare earths, partly because of the large amount of experimental data that has been amassed on the rare earth trichlorides and the rare earth double nitrates and to the relatively simple form of the crystal field potential. Nevertheless, an appreciable amount of data has been collected on rare earth salts of lower symmetry. The crystal field potential for these lower symmetries requires the inclusion of still further terms in the expansion. Thus C_{2v} symmetry which is frequently encountered requires that nine terms in the expansion be retained, namely,

$$C_{2v}: \quad V = B_0^2 C_0^{(2)} + B_2^2(C_{-2}^{(2)} + C_2^{(2)}) + B_0^4 C_0^{(4)} + B_2^4(C_{-2}^{(4)} + C_2^{(4)})$$
$$+ B_4^4(C_{-4}^{(4)} + C_4^{(4)}) + B_0^6 C_0^{(6)} + B_2^6(C_{-2}^{(6)} + C_2^{(6)})$$
$$+ B_4^6(C_{-4}^{(6)} + C_4^{(6)}) + B_6^6(C_{-6}^{(6)} + C_6^{(6)}). \tag{6-9}$$

It is clear that the unequivocal determination of the nine different B_q^k coefficients will only be possible by fitting very extensive experimental data.

Once the point symmetry and the appropriate form of the crystal field potential have been decided on it becomes possible to construct the crystal field energy matrix by a simple, but tedious, calculation. By introducing suitable crystal quantum numbers we are able to divide the states of the free ion into classes so that all the states within a given class may interact with one another but not with states belonging to another class. Or in the language of group theory, we may reduce the crystal field energy matrix into a set of irreducible submatrices.

We have already noted that the crystal field matrix elements must satisfy the selection rule $J_z - J_z' = q$ to be nonvanishing. Following Hellwege,[264] we may conveniently introduce a set of crystal quantum numbers μ such that

$$J_z = \mu(\bmod q). \tag{6-10}$$

For example, consider D_{3h} symmetry. The values of q will be limited to 0 and ± 6. For an odd number of electrons, remembering, of course, the Kramers' degeneracy, the states of the free ion may be divided into three distinct classes characterized by the crystal quantum numbers $\mu = \pm\frac{1}{2}, \pm\frac{3}{2}$, and $\pm\frac{5}{2}$, and for an even number of electrons there will be four classes characterized by the crystal quantum numbers $\mu = 0, \pm 1, \pm 2$, and 3. These crystal quantum numbers may be used to classify the crystal field energy levels even when J and J_z cease to be good quantum numbers. States where μ is double-valued (for example, $\mu = \pm 1$) will be doubly degenerate, whereas states for which μ is single-valued (for example, $\mu = 0$) will be nondegenerate apart from the occasional occurrence of accidental degeneracy.

The crystal quantum number classification of the different JJ_z states of the free ion are given for C_{3h} symmetry in Table 6-2. The analogous

TABLE 6-2   Crystal quantum numbers for C_{3h} and D_{3h} symmetry

Even Number of Electrons

μ	0	± 1	± 2	3	*No. Levels*
J	J_z	J_z	J_z	J_z	
0	0				1
1	0	± 1			2
2	0	± 1	± 2		3
3	0	± 1	± 2	$-3, +3$	5
4	0	± 1	$\pm 2, \mp 4$	$-3, +3$	6
5	0	$\pm 1, \mp 5$	$\pm 2, \mp 4$	$-3, +3$	7
6	$-6, 0, +6$	$\pm 1, \mp 5$	$\pm 2, \mp 4$	$-3, +3$	9
7	$-6, 0, +6$	$\mp 7, \pm 1, \mp 5$	$\pm 2, \mp 4$	$-3, +3$	10
8	$-6, 0, +6$	$\mp 7, \pm 1, \mp 5$	$\pm 8, \pm 2, \mp 4$	$-3, +3$	11
9	$-6, 0, +6$	$\mp 7, \pm 1, \mp 5$	$\pm 8, \pm 2, \mp 4$	$+9, -3, +3, -9$	13

Odd Number of Electrons

μ	$\pm \frac{1}{2}$	$\pm \frac{3}{2}$	$\pm \frac{5}{2}$	*No. Levels*
J	J_z	J_z	J_z	
$\frac{1}{2}$	$\pm \frac{1}{2}$			1
$\frac{3}{2}$	$\pm \frac{1}{2}$	$\pm \frac{3}{2}$		2
$\frac{5}{2}$	$\pm \frac{1}{2}$	$\pm \frac{3}{2}$	$\pm \frac{5}{2}$	3
$\frac{7}{2}$	$\pm \frac{1}{2}$	$\pm \frac{3}{2}$	$\pm \frac{5}{2}, \mp \frac{7}{2}$	5
$\frac{9}{2}$	$\pm \frac{1}{2}$	$\pm \frac{3}{2}, \mp \frac{9}{2}$	$\pm \frac{5}{2}, \mp \frac{7}{2}$	6
$\frac{11}{2}$	$\pm \frac{1}{2}, \mp \frac{11}{2}$	$\pm \frac{3}{2}, \mp \frac{9}{2}$	$\pm \frac{5}{2}, \mp \frac{7}{2}$	7
$\frac{13}{2}$	$\pm \frac{13}{2}, \pm \frac{1}{2}, \mp \frac{11}{2}$	$\pm \frac{3}{2}, \mp \frac{9}{2}$	$\pm \frac{5}{2}, \mp \frac{7}{2}$	8
$\frac{15}{2}$	$\pm \frac{13}{2}, \pm \frac{1}{2}, \mp \frac{11}{2}$	$\pm \frac{15}{2}, \pm \frac{3}{2}, \mp \frac{9}{2}$	$\pm \frac{5}{2}, \mp \frac{7}{2}$	9

tables for C_{3v} and C_{2v} symmetry are given in Tables 6-3 and 6-4 respectively. The J-value of the free ion state is given in the first column of the tables, and the succeeding columns give the J_z states that may be associated with the indicated crystal quantum number. The total number of levels that a state of given J splits into under the influence of the crystal field of the given symmetry is given in the last column.

For C_{3h} symmetry (and for D_{3h} symmetry) a $J = 6$ state of the free ion will split into nine distinct levels. Three of these levels will be nondegen-

TABLE 6-3   Crystal quantum numbers for C_{3v} symmetry

Even Number of Electrons

μ	0	± 1	No. Levels
J	J_z	J_z	
0	0		1
1	0	± 1	2
2	0	$\pm 1, \mp 2$	3
3	$-3, 0, +3$	$\pm 1, \mp 2$	5
4	$-3, 0, +3$	$\pm 4, \pm 1, \mp 2$	6
5	$-3, 0, +3$	$\pm 4, \pm 1, \mp 2, \mp 5$	7
6	$-6, -3, 0, +3, +6$	$\pm 4, \pm 1, \mp 2, \mp 5$	9
7	$-6, -3, 0, +3, +6$	$\pm 7, \pm 4, \pm 1, \mp 2, \mp 5$	10
8	$-6, -3, 0, +3, +6$	$\pm 7, \pm 4, \pm 1, \mp 2, \mp 5, \mp 8$	11
9	$-9, -6, -3, 0, +3, +6, +9$	$\pm 7, \pm 4, \pm 1, \mp 2, \mp 5, \mp 8$	13

Odd Number of Electrons

μ	$\pm \frac{1}{2}$	$\pm \frac{3}{2}$	No. Levels
J	J_z	J_z	
$\frac{1}{2}$	$\pm \frac{1}{2}$		1
$\frac{3}{2}$	$\pm \frac{1}{2}$	$\pm \frac{3}{2}$	2
$\frac{5}{2}$	$\mp \frac{5}{2}, \pm \frac{1}{2}$	$\pm \frac{3}{2}$	3
$\frac{7}{2}$	$\mp \frac{5}{2}, \pm \frac{1}{2}, \pm \frac{7}{2}$	$\pm \frac{3}{2}$	4
$\frac{9}{2}$	$\mp \frac{5}{2}, \pm \frac{1}{2}, \pm \frac{7}{2}$	$\pm \frac{3}{2}, \pm \frac{9}{2}$	5
$\frac{11}{2}$	$\mp \frac{11}{2}, \mp \frac{5}{2}, \pm \frac{1}{2}, \pm \frac{7}{2}$	$\pm \frac{3}{2}, \pm \frac{9}{2}$	6
$\frac{13}{2}$	$\mp \frac{11}{2}, \mp \frac{5}{2}, \pm \frac{1}{2}, \pm \frac{7}{2}, \pm \frac{13}{2}$	$\pm \frac{3}{2}, \pm \frac{9}{2}$	7
$\frac{15}{2}$	$\mp \frac{11}{2}, \mp \frac{5}{2}, \pm \frac{1}{2}, \pm \frac{7}{2}, \pm \frac{13}{2}$	$\pm \frac{3}{2}, \pm \frac{9}{2}, \pm \frac{15}{2}$	8

erate and classified as $\mu = 0$, two pairs of the levels will be doubly degenerate and classified by the numbers $\mu = \pm 1$, and $\mu = \pm 2$. In addition to these seven levels there will be two more nondegenerate levels with $\mu = 3$. Thus the 13×13 crystal field energy matrix for a pure $J = 6$ state may be reduced to a 3×3 matrix ($\mu = 0$) and five 2×2 matrices. However, the two matrices for $\mu = \pm 1$ are equivalent as are the two matrices for $\mu = \pm 2$. Hence we are left with only a 3×3 matrix and three distinct 2×2 matrices to be solved. The eigenvectors of these matrices will indicate the linear combination of the J_z states from which each level originated. In principle, we could solve these matrices in terms of the four parameters B_0^2, B_0^4, B_0^6, and B_6^6, deriving their magnitudes by a least-squares fit to the observed energy levels. These levels may then be labeled with the appropriate crystal quantum numbers.

Since D_{3h} and C_{3h} point symmetries yield equivalent crystal quantum numbers, our calculation does not indicate any way of distinguishing

TABLE 6-4   Crystal quantum numbers for C_{2v} symmetry

Even Number of Electrons

μ	0	± 1	No.
J	J_z	J_z	Levels
0			1
1	0	$-1, +1$	3
2	$-2, 0, +2$	$-1, +1$	5
3	$-2, 0, +2$	$-3, -1, +1, +3$	7
4	$-4, -2, 0, +2, +4$	$-3, -1, +1, +3$	9
5	$-4, -2, 0, +2, +4$	$-5, -3, -1, +1, +3, +5$	11
6	$-6, -4, -2, 0, +2, +4, +6$	$-5, -3, -1, +1, +3, +5$	13
7	$-6, -4, -2, 0, +2, +4, +6$	$-7, -5, -3, -1, +1, +3, +5, +7$	15
8	$-8, -6, -4, -2, 0, +2, +4, +6, +8$	$-7, -5, -3, -1, +1, +3, +5, +7$	17
9	$-8, -6, -4, -2, 0, +2, +4, +6, +8$	$-9, -7, -5, -3, -1, +1, +3, +5, +7, +9$	19

Odd Number of Electrons

μ	$\pm\frac{1}{2}$	No.
J	J_z	Levels
$\frac{1}{2}$	$\pm\frac{1}{2}$	1
$\frac{3}{2}$	$\pm\frac{1}{2}, \mp\frac{3}{2}$	2
$\frac{5}{2}$	$\pm\frac{5}{2}, \pm\frac{1}{2}, \mp\frac{3}{2}$	3
$\frac{7}{2}$	$\pm\frac{5}{2}, \pm\frac{1}{2}, \mp\frac{3}{2}, \mp\frac{7}{2}$	4
$\frac{9}{2}$	$\pm\frac{9}{2}, \pm\frac{5}{2}, \pm\frac{1}{2}, \mp\frac{3}{2}, \mp\frac{7}{2}$	5
$\frac{11}{2}$	$\pm\frac{9}{2}, \pm\frac{5}{2}, \pm\frac{1}{2}, \mp\frac{3}{2}, \mp\frac{7}{2}, \mp\frac{11}{2}$	6
$\frac{13}{2}$	$\pm\frac{13}{2}, \pm\frac{9}{2}, \pm\frac{5}{2}, \pm\frac{1}{2}, \mp\frac{3}{2}, \mp\frac{7}{2}, \mp\frac{11}{2}$	7
$\frac{15}{2}$	$\pm\frac{13}{2}, \pm\frac{9}{2}, \pm\frac{5}{2}, \pm\frac{1}{2}, \mp\frac{3}{2}, \mp\frac{7}{2}, \mp\frac{11}{2}, \mp\frac{15}{2}$	8

these two point symmetries.   The question naturally arises, "Has the maximum possible information been deduced from the symmetry properties of the D_{3h} and C_{3h} point symmetries?"   To examine this question in detail we turn to the methods of group theory.

6-2   Applications of Group Theory of Crystal Spectra

A knowledge of group theory can be of considerable assistance in studying the crystal field splittings of energy levels from the point of view of the symmetry properties of the crystal fields.   We shall limit ourselves to but a sketch of the basic results of group theory that are of direct application to the interpretation of crystal spectra.   Many excellent texts on group theory are available to which the reader is referred for greater detail.[265-274]*

---

* Readers unfamiliar with the theory of groups should profit by studying the books by Hamermesh[268] and Heine.[267]   A good nonspecialized account of the applications of group theory is given by Eyring et al.[271]   The paper by Bethe[270] represents the first detailed application of group theory to the study of crystal field splittings and should be read by all.

We may regard a symmetry operation as any operation that sends a symmetrical figure into itself. We shall symbolize these operations as follows:

E = the identity operation which leaves the figure in its original position

C_n = rotation about an axis of symmetry through an angle $2\pi/n$

σ_h = reflection in a plane of symmetry perpendicular to the principal axis (that is, the axis with the largest value of n)

σ_v = reflection in a plane of symmetry that contains the principal axis

i = inversion through a center of symmetry

S_n = rotation about a symmetry axis by $2\pi/n$ followed by a reflection in a plane perpendicular to the axis of rotation

A finite group G is a set of h distinct elements $P_1, P_2, \ldots, P_h$ that satisfy the following group postulates:

1. The product of any two elements in the set is itself an element of the set.

2. The set contains an identity element E such that $P_\alpha E = EP_\alpha = P_\alpha$ for all elements of the group.

3. For each element of the group there exists an inverse element belonging to the set such that

$$P_\alpha P_\alpha^{-1} = P_\alpha^{-1} P_\alpha = E$$

4. The associative law of multiplication is valid, that is,

$$P_r(P_s P_t) = (P_r P_s)P_t.$$

The commutative law of multiplication does not necessarily hold. If all the elements of the set do commute among themselves, they are said to form an *Abelian* group.

The set of operators that send a symmetrical figure into itself form a group. For every group we may construct a multiplication table. Consider the equilateral triangle shown in Fig. 6-1. There will be six distinct symmetry operations that may be performed on the triangle. These are as follows:

1. E, the identity operation.

2. C_3, clockwise rotation through $2\pi/3$ about the principal axis.

3. C_3^2, clockwise rotation through $4\pi/3$ or anticlockwise through $2\pi/3$ about the principal axis.

4. $C_2(1)$, rotation through π about the axis OA.

5. $C_2(2)$, rotation through π about the axis OB.

6. $C_2(3)$, rotation through π about the axis OC.

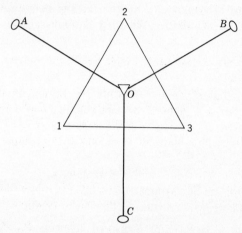

Fig. 6-1   The symmetries of an equilateral triangle (D_3).

These six symmetry operators may be shown to satisfy all the four group postulates. The successive application of any two of these operations to

TABLE 6-5   Multiplication table for D_3 symmetry

	E	C_3	C_3^2	$C_2(1)$	$C_2(2)$	$C_2(3)$
E	E	C_3	C_3^2	$C_2(1)$	$C_2(2)$	$C_2(3)$
C_3	C_3	C_3^2	E	$C_2(3)$	$C_2(1)$	$C_2(2)$
C_3^2	C_3^2	E	C_3	$C_2(2)$	$C_2(3)$	$C_2(1)$
$C_2(1)$	$C_2(1)$	$C_2(2)$	$C_2(3)$	E	C_3	C_3^2
$C_2(2)$	$C_2(2)$	$C_2(3)$	$C_2(1)$	C_3^2	E	C_3
$C_2(3)$	$C_3(3)$	$C_2(1)$	$C_2(2)$	C_3	C_3^2	E

the triangle is equivalent to some single operation among the six. For example, the operation C_3 followed by the operation $C_2(3)$ is equivalent to the operation $C_2(1)$. In this way we may construct a multiplication

TABLE 6-6   The irreducible representations of the group D_3

	E	C_3	C_3^2
$^1\Gamma_1$	1	1	1
$^1\Gamma_2$	1	1	1
$^2\Gamma_3$	$\begin{pmatrix} 1 & 0 \\ 0 & 1 \end{pmatrix}$	$\begin{pmatrix} -\dfrac{1}{2} & -\dfrac{\sqrt{3}}{2} \\ \dfrac{\sqrt{3}}{2} & -\dfrac{1}{2} \end{pmatrix}$	$\begin{pmatrix} -\dfrac{1}{2} & \dfrac{\sqrt{3}}{2} \\ -\dfrac{\sqrt{3}}{2} & -\dfrac{1}{2} \end{pmatrix}$

table as in Table 6-5. This symmetry is known as D_3 point symmetry. Inspection of the multiplication table for D_3 point symmetry shows that the three symmetry operators E, C_3, and C_3^2 satisfy all the group postulates among themselves and may be said to form a *subgroup* of D_3. This subgroup actually corresponds to the case of C_3 symmetry. C_3 symmetry occurs if the twofold axes of rotation do not carry the triangle into a position indistinguishable from its original position, for example, if we were to paint the one side of the triangle so that the twofold rotations could be distinguished.

The C_{3h} point symmetry which is frequently found in rare earth salts is formed by applying the operation σ_h to each of the symmetry elements of the purely rotation-point symmetry group C_3. The reader may show that the C_{3h} point symmetry group will contain six distinct elements: E, C_3, C_3^2, σ_h, S_3, and $\sigma_h S_3^2$. Similarly, D_{3h} symmetry is formed by applying σ_h to each of the symmetry elements of the point symmetry group D_3 to give in addition to the elements of D_3 the elements $\sigma_v(1)$, $\sigma_v(2)$, $\sigma_v(3)$, σ_h, S_3, and S_3^2. The C_{3v} point symmetry which is found in the rare earth bromates and double nitrates is formed by applying the operation σ_v to each of the elements of C_3. The C_{3v} point symmetry group contains the elements E, C_3, C_3^2, $\sigma_v(1)$, $\sigma_v(2)$, and $\sigma_v(3)$.

A symmetry operator P_σ is said to belong to the same *class* as another symmetry operator $P_\sigma{}'$ if the condition

$$P_\alpha^{-1} P_\sigma P_\alpha = P_\sigma{}'$$

is satisfied where P_α^{-1} is the inverse of the symmetry operator P_α, both of which belong to the group. Inspection of Table 6-5 shows that for D_3 point symmetry there are three classes: E, (C_3, C_3^2), and $(C_2(1), C_2(2), C_2(3))$. For our purposes a class may be regarded as a set of symmetry operators having the same physical function. The identity operator E always forms a class by itself.

We can construct a set of numbers or matrices which have the same multiplication table as the operators of the group. These we may say form a *representation* of the group. Any set of elements that multiply

$C_2(1)$	$C_2(2)$	$C_2(3)$
1	1	1
-1	-1	-1
$\begin{pmatrix} -1 & 0 \\ 0 & 1 \end{pmatrix}$	$\begin{pmatrix} \dfrac{1}{2} & \dfrac{\sqrt{3}}{2} \\ \dfrac{\sqrt{3}}{2} & -\dfrac{1}{2} \end{pmatrix}$	$\begin{pmatrix} \dfrac{1}{2} & -\dfrac{\sqrt{3}}{2} \\ -\dfrac{\sqrt{3}}{2} & -\dfrac{1}{2} \end{pmatrix}$

according to the group multiplication table will form a representation Γ of the group. A particular representation for the group D_3 is given in Table 6-6. An n-dimensional representation will be said to be *reducible* if a linear transformation exists that will decompose all the matrices of the representation into block form. If the representation cannot be reduced to a block form by a linear transformation, it is said to be *irreducible*. Calling the irreducible representations $\Gamma_1, \Gamma_2, \Gamma_3, \ldots, \Gamma_n$, we may say that the reducible representation Γ is composed of the irreducible representations $\Gamma_1 + \Gamma_2 + \Gamma_3 + \cdots + \Gamma_n$. Two irreducible representations will be said to be *equivalent* if they differ from one another by only a similarity transformation. The number of nonequivalent irreducible representations of a group may be shown to equal the number of classes. Thus for D_3 there will be just three irreducible representations. For D_{3h} there will be six irreducible representations corresponding to the six classes of the elements of the group D_{3h}.

The dimensions of the irreducible representations may be found as follows: with c classes we get c irreducible representations, each of dimension f_n; then

$$f_1^2 + f_2^2 + \cdots + f_c^2 = h, \tag{6-11}$$

where h is the order of the group. The *order* of a group is the number of distinct elements in the group. Thus for D_{3h} symmetry we have $c = 6$ and $h = 12$; therefore

$$1^2 + 1^2 + 1^2 + 1^2 + 2^2 + 2^2 = 12. \tag{6-12}$$

Hence for D_{3h} there will be four one-dimensional representations $^1\Gamma_1$, $^1\Gamma_2$, $^1\Gamma_3$, $^1\Gamma_4$, and two two-dimensional representations $^2\Gamma_5$ and $^2\Gamma_6$. The number of irreducible representations, and their dimensions, may be determined without constructing a multiplication table or determining the structure of the representation.

The *character* $\chi_s(P)$ of the matrix $\Gamma_s(P)$ is defined as the trace of the matrix, that is,

$$\chi_s(P) = \sum_i \Gamma_s(P)_{ii}. \tag{6-13}$$

The character of a matrix is invariant under any similarity transformation and hence the characters of all the matrices Γ_s belonging to a particular class are equivalent, and we need not distinguish the elements of a class in constructing character tables, only indicate the number of elements in the class. We may thus characterize a representation by its character system.

TABLE 6-7　Character table for the group D_3

	E	$2C_3$	$3C_2$
$^1\Gamma_1$	1	1	1
$^1\Gamma_2$	1	1	-1
$^2\Gamma_3$	2	-1	0

The character table for D_3 point symmetry is shown in Table 6-7.*

The character χ_w of a reducible representation is equal to the sum of the characters of the irreducible representations into which it decomposes. It is frequently necessary to find the number of times n_s that a given irreducible representation Γ_s occurs in the decomposition of a reducible representation. This may be shown to be given by

$$n_s = \frac{1}{h} \sum_P \chi_s(P) \cdot \chi_w(P), \tag{6-14}$$

where h is the order of the group and the summation is over all the h operations of the group. Thus, to determine n_s, we need know only the characters of the reducible and the irreducible representations. In many cases we may simply determine n_s by adding the characters of the irreducible representations together in such a way as to reproduce the characters of the reducible representation. We may now consider the application of group theory to the problem of determining the number of levels, and their degeneracies, that a state of a given value of J will split into if placed in a crystal field of a definite point symmetry.

6-3　Symmetry and Crystal Field Splittings

The Hamiltonian H_0 of a free atom or ion is invariant under all the operations of the three-dimensional rotation group R_3. On placing the atom in a crystal field, the symmetry about the atom will be reduced from spherical symmetry to the symmetry of the position the atom occupies in the crystal. The perturbed Hamiltonian $H = H_0 + V$ will no longer be invariant under the operations of R_3, but rather of those of the subgroup of R_3 that is associated with the point symmetry of the atom in the crystal. The free ion levels will split into a number of sublevels that may be characterized by the irreducible representations of the subgroup. To calculate the number of sublevels, and their degeneracies, we have merely

---

* Throughout this chapter we follow the systematic Γ notation of Koster et al.[272] except for indicating the dimensionality of the representations by a superscript to the left of Γ. It is important for the reader to note that the subscripts to the right of Γ do not always follow those given earlier by Bethe[270] and others. For a discussion of the advantages of the present notation in crystal field theory see Koster et al.[272]

to determine the number of times the irreducible representations of the subgroup occur in the reducible representations of R_3.

Each J-value of the free atom will span a $(2J + 1)$-dimensional representation of R_3. These representations may be decomposed readily into the irreducible representations of the subgroup associated with a particular point symmetry if we know the characters of every symmetry operator that is common to both R_3 and its subgroup.

For a rotation through an angle ϕ about an arbitrary axis, the character of the irreducible representation D_J of R_3 is given by[270]

$$\chi(\phi) = \frac{\sin (2J + 1)\phi/2}{\sin \phi/2}.$$ (6-15)

For integral J,

$$\chi(\phi) = \chi(\phi + 2\pi),$$ (6-16)

that is, the character is, as it should be, single-valued under rotation of 2π. However, for half-integral J

$$\chi(\phi) = - \chi(\phi + 2\pi),$$ (6-17)

that is, the character is double-valued under rotations of 2π. Furthermore, the character of the identity operation can be either

$$\chi(0) = 2J + 1$$ (6-18)

or

$$\chi(2\pi) = -(2J + 1).$$ (6-19)

We note that for half-integral J a unique character is obtained only in the case of rotations by π about an arbitrary axis, since then

$$\chi(\pi) = \chi(3\pi) = 0.$$ (6-20)

Clearly, a double-valued representation of R_3 can contain only double-valued representations of the crystallographic point groups as irreducible components. To obtain double-valued representations of the crystallographic point groups Bethe[270]* has introduced the fiction that the crystal goes into itself under rotations of 4π rather than rotations of 2π. A new group element, R, rotation by 2π, is introduced and applied to each of the elements of the single-valued point group. These new elements are designated by the placing of a bar over the group elements on which R operates. The double group contains twice as many elements as the single group and thus has more classes than the single group, although not necessarily twice as many, since rotations by π will be unique.

---

* Several important extensions and corrections to Bethe's[270] original discussion of double groups have been given by Opechowski.[275]

Consider now C_{3v} symmetry. For the single group there are just three classes (E, $2C_3$ and $3\sigma_v$) and three irreducible representations ($^1\Gamma_1$, $^1\Gamma_2$, and $^2\Gamma_3$). For the double group there will be six classes (E, $2C_3$, $3\sigma_v$, $\overline{E}$, $2\overline{C}_3$, and $3\overline{\sigma}_v$). The double group will have order 12 and from Eq. 6-12 we deduce that it will have six irreducible representations ($^1\Gamma_1$, $^1\Gamma_2$, $^2\Gamma_3$, $^2\Gamma_4$, $^1\Gamma_5$, and $^1\Gamma_6$). The double groups are usually distinguished from the single groups by adding a prime as a superscript to the point group designation (for example, C'_{3v}). The character table for the double group C'_{3v} is given in Table 6-8. The character table for C_{3v} is enclosed by dashed lines.

TABLE 6-8   Character table for the double group C'_{3v}

	E	$2C_3$	$3\sigma_v$	$\overline{E}$	$2\overline{C}_3$	$3\overline{\sigma}_v$
$^1\Gamma_1$	1	1	1	1	1	1
$^1\Gamma_2$	1	1	-1	1	1	-1
$^2\Gamma_3$	2	-1	0	2	-1	0
$^2\Gamma_4$	2	1	0	-2	-1	0
$^1\Gamma_5$	1	-1	i	-1	1	$-i$
$^1\Gamma_6$	1	-1	$-i$	-1	1	i

Let us first consider the case of integral J. The symmetry operations of each class of C_{3v} may be regarded as pure rotations in R_3 with the following identifications:

E = the identity operations, $\phi = 0$

C_3 = the operation of rotation through $\phi = \pm 2\pi/3$ about the principal axis

σ_v = the operation of rotation through $\phi = \pi$ perpendicular to the principal axis

TABLE 6-9   Characters of the classes of C_{3v} contained in the representations D_J of R_3

J	E	$2C_3$	$3\sigma_v$
0	1	1	1
1	3	0	-1
2	5	-1	1
3	7	1	-1
4	9	0	1
5	11	-1	-1
6	13	1	1
7	15	0	-1
8	17	-1	1

We may now construct a table of the characters of the classes of C_{3v} contained in each of the representations D_J of R_3 using Eq. 6-15. The resulting character table is shown in Table 6-9. The representations D_J of R_3 may then be decomposed into the irreducible representations of C_{3v} for integral values of J using Eq. 6-14 together with the characters from Table 6-8 to give the results of Table 6-10.

TABLE 6-10   Reduction of $R_3 \to C_{3v}$ for integral J

J	$R_3 \to C_{3v}$	Number of Levels
0	$^1\Gamma_1$	1
1	$^1\Gamma_2 + {}^2\Gamma_3$	2
2	$^1\Gamma_1 + 2{}^2\Gamma_3$	3
3	$^1\Gamma_1 + 2{}^1\Gamma_2 + 2{}^2\Gamma_3$	5
4	$2{}^1\Gamma_1 + {}^1\Gamma_2 + 3{}^2\Gamma_3$	6
5	$^1\Gamma_1 + 2{}^1\Gamma_2 + 4{}^2\Gamma_3$	7
6	$3{}^1\Gamma_1 + 2{}^1\Gamma_2 + 4{}^2\Gamma_3$	9
7	$2{}^1\Gamma_1 + 3{}^1\Gamma_2 + 5{}^2\Gamma_3$	10
8	$3{}^1\Gamma_1 + 2{}^1\Gamma_2 + 6{}^2\Gamma_3$	11

For half-integer J the characters of the classes of the double group C'_{3v} contained in each of the representations D_J of R_3 are found again using Eq. 6-15. The characters associated with the classes σ_v and $\bar{\sigma}_v$ are all zero, and those associated with the classes $\bar{E}$ and $\bar{C}_3$ have the same magnitude, but have opposite sign to that of the classes E and C_3 respectively. It is left to the reader to verify that for integer J the representations D_J of R_3 decompose into the irreducible representations of the double group C'_{3v} as shown in Table 6-11. In the absence of magnetic fields or

TABLE 6-11   Reduction of $R_3 \to C'_{3v}$ for half-integral J

J	$R_3 \to C'_{3v}$	Number of Levels
$\frac{1}{2}$	$^2\Gamma_4$	1
$\frac{3}{2}$	$({}^1\Gamma_5 + {}^1\Gamma_6) + {}^2\Gamma_4$	2
$\frac{5}{2}$	$({}^1\Gamma_5 + {}^1\Gamma_6) + 2{}^2\Gamma_4$	3
$\frac{7}{2}$	$({}^1\Gamma_5 + {}^1\Gamma_6) + 3{}^2\Gamma_4$	4
$\frac{9}{2}$	$2({}^1\Gamma_5 + {}^1\Gamma_6) + 3{}^2\Gamma_4$	5
$\frac{11}{2}$	$2({}^1\Gamma_5 + {}^1\Gamma_6) + 4{}^2\Gamma_4$	6
$\frac{13}{2}$	$2({}^1\Gamma_5 + {}^1\Gamma_6) + 5{}^2\Gamma_4$	7
$\frac{15}{2}$	$3({}^1\Gamma_5 + {}^1\Gamma_6) + 5{}^2\Gamma_4$	8

exchange interactions, the levels that transform according to the irreducible representations $^1\Gamma_5$ and $^1\Gamma_6$ will, according to Kramers' degeneracy theorem, always appear as degenerate pairs. Tables for the reductions of the irreducible representations D_J of R_3 to the irreducible representations of the thirty-two crystallographic point groups have been given by Koster et al.[272]

Runciman[276] has considered the general problem of calculating the number of levels a state of a given J will be split into for each of the thirty-two crystallographic point groups and has shown that the point groups may be classified under four headings as follows:

1. Cubic: O_h, O, T_d, T_h, T.
2. Hexagonal: D_{6h}, D_6, C_{6v}, C_{6h}, C_6, D_{3h}, C_{3h}, D_{3d}, D_3, C_{3v}, S_6, C_3.
3. Tetragonal: D_{4h}, D_4, C_{4v}, C_{4h}, C_4, D_{2d}, S_4.
4. Lower symmetry: D_{2h}, D_2, C_{2v}, C_{2h}, C_2, C_s, S_2, C_1.

Then for integral J all the point groups within one of these classes will give rise to the same number of levels as shown in Table 6-12. For

TABLE 6-12   Splittings for integral J

J	0	1	2	3	4	5	6	7	8
Cubic	1	1	2	3	4	4	6	6	7
Hexagonal	1	2	3	5	6	7	9	10	11
Tetragonal	1	2	4	5	7	8	10	11	13
Lower symmetry	1	3	5	7	9	11	13	15	17

half-integral values of J all the groups other than cubic give rise to $J + \frac{1}{2}$ levels as given in Table 6-13. Thus, knowing the symmetry class at the

TABLE 6-13   Splittings for half-integral J

J	$\frac{1}{2}$	$\frac{3}{2}$	$\frac{5}{2}$	$\frac{7}{2}$	$\frac{9}{2}$	$\frac{11}{2}$	$\frac{13}{2}$	$\frac{15}{2}$
Cubic	1	1	2	3	3	4	5	5
All other symmetries	1	2	3	4	5	6	7	8

site of the rare earth ion in a crystal, we can predict readily the number of levels a state of given J will split into. Alternatively, rare earth ions may be used to probe the symmetry of sites in crystals. An interesting example of use of a rare earth ion as a symmetry probe has been given by Oshima et al.,[277] who used the fluorescence of Sm^{3+} to study the phase transition in barium titanate at $-80°C$.

6-4   Descending Symmetries

It is sometimes useful to regard a crystal field as being made up of components of decreasing symmetry.[278,279] For example, we might consider any crystal field as being made up of a large spherical component which has superimposed on it components of lower symmetry. We occasionally encounter crystal spectra which come quite close to exhibiting a higher symmetry than is apparent from the group designation of the site symmetry of the rare earth ion. This higher symmetry is made apparent by the appearance of groups of nearly degenerate levels.

A particularly intriguing example of the concept of descending symmetry is found in the salts of the rare earth double nitrates. In these salts the rare ion normally occupies a site having C_{3v} point symmetry and the crystal field potential may be written as in Eq. 6-18. Judd[262] made the remarkable observation that if the sixth-order parameters are related by the equations

$$\frac{B_3^6}{B_0^6} = \pm \tfrac{4}{3}(105)^{1/2} \qquad \frac{B_6^6}{B_0^6} = -14(231)^{1/2}, \qquad (6\text{-}21)$$

and all the other parameters are put equal to zero, it is impossible to induce a splitting in levels with $J < 3$ by second-order interactions. Furthermore, he noted that the ratios of the sixth-order crystal field parameters for the rare earth double nitrates[280] did, in fact, correspond closely to those of Eq. 6-21 and the remaining terms in the C_{3v} crystal field potential were small by comparison. This was interpreted to imply that the crystal field was dominated by a symmetry higher than cubic.

Since there is only one point group that possesses higher symmetry than cubic, namely, the icosahedral group P,[281-283] it was proposed that the crystal field possessed an icosahedral symmetry that was slightly distorted to the symmetry of its subgroup C_{3v}. Thus the crystal field potential may be regarded as having two components. The first is a dominating potential function V_P corresponding to icosahedral symmetry, and the second is a much weaker residual C_{3v} symmetry potential function V_R. The effect of V_P is to split up the energy levels of the free ion according to the reduction of $R_3 \to P$ as shown in Table 6-14. It is apparent from

TABLE 6-14   Reduction of R_3 to icosahedral symmetry

J		J	
0	$^1\Gamma_1$	$\tfrac{1}{2}$	$^2\Gamma_6$
1	$^3\Gamma_2$	$\tfrac{3}{2}$	$^4\Gamma_8$
2	$^5\Gamma_5$	$\tfrac{5}{2}$	$^6\Gamma_9$
3	$^3\Gamma_3 + {}^4\Gamma_4$	$\tfrac{7}{2}$	$^2\Gamma_7 + {}^6\Gamma_9$
4	$^4\Gamma_4 + {}^5\Gamma_5$	$\tfrac{9}{2}$	$^4\Gamma_8 + {}^6\Gamma_9$
5	$^3\Gamma_2 + {}^3\Gamma_3 + {}^5\Gamma_5$	$\tfrac{11}{2}$	$^2\Gamma_6 + {}^4\Gamma_8 + {}^6\Gamma_9$
6	$^1\Gamma_1 + {}^3\Gamma_2 + {}^4\Gamma_4 + {}^5\Gamma_5$	$\tfrac{13}{2}$	$^2\Gamma_6 + {}^2\Gamma_7 + {}^4\Gamma_8 + {}^6\Gamma_9$
7	$^3\Gamma_2 + {}^3\Gamma_3 + {}^4\Gamma_4 + {}^5\Gamma_5$	$\tfrac{15}{2}$	$^4\Gamma_8 + 2{}^6\Gamma_9$
8	$^3\Gamma_3 + {}^4\Gamma_4 + 2{}^5\Gamma_5$		

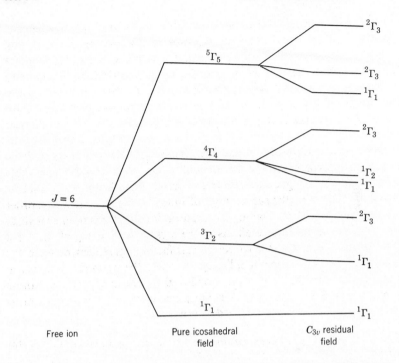

Fig. 6-2   Schematic splitting of a $J = 6$ level in a predominantly icosahedral field.

this table that there can be no splitting in a purely icosahedral field for levels with $J < 3$. It is interesting to note that in an icosahedral field a $J = \frac{15}{2}$ level actually splits into *fewer* levels than one with $J = \frac{13}{2}$. The degeneracy of the levels is extraordinarily high. This degeneracy will, to a large extent, be removed by the weak residual C_{3v} potential V_R, with the result that each of the irreducible representations of P will break up into the irreducible representations of the group C_{3v}. The reduction of $P \rightarrow C_{3v}'$ may be found by comparing $R_3 \rightarrow P$ (Table 6-14) with $R_3 \rightarrow C_{3v}'$ (Tables 6-10 and 6-11). The resulting reduction of $P \rightarrow C_{3v}'$ is shown in Table 6-15. The splitting of a $J = 6$ level in a predominantly icosahedral field is shown schematically in Fig. 6-2.

TABLE 6-15   The reduction $P \rightarrow C_{3v}'$

$^1\Gamma_1 \rightarrow \, ^1\Gamma_1$ or $^1\Gamma_2$	$^2\Gamma_6 \rightarrow \, ^2\Gamma_4$
$^3\Gamma_2 \rightarrow \, ^1\Gamma_1 + \, ^2\Gamma_3$ or $^1\Gamma_2 + \, ^2\Gamma_3$	$^2\Gamma_7 \rightarrow \, ^2\Gamma_4$
$^3\Gamma_3 \rightarrow \, ^1\Gamma_2 + \, ^2\Gamma_3$ or $^1\Gamma_1 + \, ^2\Gamma_3$	$^4\Gamma_8 \rightarrow (^1\Gamma_5 + \, ^1\Gamma_6) + \, ^2\Gamma_4$
$^4\Gamma_4 \rightarrow \, ^1\Gamma_1 + \, ^1\Gamma_2 + \, ^2\Gamma_3$	$^6\Gamma_9 \rightarrow (^1\Gamma_5 + \, ^1\Gamma_6) + 2^2\Gamma_4$
$^5\Gamma_5 \rightarrow \, ^1\Gamma_1 + 2^2\Gamma_3$ or $^1\Gamma_2 + 2^2\Gamma_3$	

Judd and Wong[284] have discussed the application of the special properties of an icosahedral crystal field to the interpretation of the magnetic properties of several rare earth double nitrates, and McLellan[285] has given a very detailed discussion of the eigenfunctions for integer and half-integer values of J symmetrized according to the icosahedral group and the group C_{3v}. McLellan has also given extensive tables to permit the ready calculation of the magnetic splitting factors for the doublet states.

Brochard and Hellwege,[286] and more recently Dieke and Heroux,[287,288] have studied experimentally the absorption spectrum and Zeeman effect of neodymium magnesium double nitrate, $Nd_2Mg_3(NO_3)_{12} \cdot 24H_2O$. Tinsley,[289] following the earlier work of Judd,[262,280] has made a first-order crystal field calculation, making a correction for the effects of intermediate coupling but neglecting the effects of the crystal field mixing of the "free ion" levels. She was able to obtain satisfactory agreement between the calculated and experimental splittings by using the parameters shown in Table 6-16. The ratios of B_q^k/B_0^k are also given and compared with those given by Eq. 6-21. We note that the parameters are indeed quite close to those predicted for the icosahedral symmetry.

TABLE 6-16   Crystal field parameters for neodymium magnesium double nitrate

$B_0^2 = 146$ $B_0^4 = -147$ $B_3^4 = \pm 268$ $B_0^6 = 1954$ $B_3^6 = \pm 2388$
$B_6^6 = -2428$ cm^{-1}

k, q		2, 0	4, 0	4, 3	6, 0	6, 3	6, 6
B_q^k/B_0^6	Icos. symmetry	0	0	0	1	± 1.5275	-0.9211
$B_q^k B/_0^6$	C_{3v} symmetry	0.075	-0.075	0.137	1	± 1.222	-1.243

Koster et al.[272] and Wilson et al.[290] have given extensive tables for obtaining the correlations between the irreducible representations of a point symmetry group and the corresponding irreducible representations of another point group of lower symmetry. We may thus readily construct tables analogous to that of Table 6-15 for any of the point groups.

In some of the rare earth garnets it is useful to consider the crystal field as having a predominantly cubic symmetry O_h with a slight distortion to rhombohedral or orthorhombic symmetry.[291-295] In this case we descend from the high cubic symmetry to a field of very low symmetry. Consider, for example, the descent in symmetry from O_h to C_{2v} symmetry. The crystal field potential for C_{2v} symmetry will involve nine distinct crystal field parameters. In treating a crystal field problem as complex as this it is sometimes advantageous to consider first only those parts of the C_{2v} potential that are common to the potential for the cubic field and then endeavor to fix the parameters for the cubic field to reproduce the broad features of the observed spectra. The effects of the residual C_{2v} field may then be considered as a perturbation on the cubic field.

Another example of descending symmetry arises in the rare earth ethyl-sulfates.[261] The point symmetry at a rare earth ion in the ethylsulfate lattice is C_{3h}.[296] However, the nine waters of crystallization tend to cluster around the rare earth ion exhibiting the slightly higher symmetry D_{3h}. Thus Sayre and Freed[297] have found it more meaningful to label the crystal field levels of europium ethylsulfate nona-hydrate according to the irreducible representations of D_{3h} rather than to those of C_{3h}. In a similar manner Hellwege[298] has found that in europium bromate nona-hydrate the strong field of D_{3h} symmetry from waters predominates over the weak field of C_{3v} symmetry of the rest of the crystal.

6-5   Crystal Quantum Numbers and Irreducible Representations

The irreducible representations of the point symmetry groups can be used clearly as good quantum numbers to label the different crystal field levels since there can be no crystal field interactions between states belonging to different irreducible representations if the point symmetry is well defined. Even when $\alpha SLJJ_z$ cease to be good quantum numbers, the irreducible representations remain as good quantum numbers.

For configurations with an *odd* number of electrons the crystal field levels belonging to the noncubic groups may be equally as well labeled by crystal quantum numbers or by the irreducible representations of the point symmetry group. In this case it is immaterial whether the crystal field energy matrices are constructed in terms of a basis $|\alpha SLJ^{\delta}\Gamma_r)$ involving the irreducible representations $^{\delta}\Gamma_r$ of the point group or the basis $|\alpha SLJJ_z\mu)$ since both the bases and the matrices are necessarily equivalent. We note that for odd electron configurations it is not possible to distinguish between D_{3h} and C_{3h} symmetry either on the basis of crystal field energy level calculations or the selection rules. For the noncubic groups each crystal field level will be a twofold degenerate Kramers' pair. If one state of the Kramers' pair has the eigenfunction[253]

$$a \mid J, J_z) + b \mid J', J_z') + \cdots, \tag{6-22}$$

then the other state will have the eigenfunction

$$(-1)^{J+J_z}a^* \mid J, -J_z) + (-1)^{J'+J_z'}b^* \mid J', -J_z') + \cdots, \tag{6-23}$$

where J_z has everywhere been reversed in sign, the complex conjugate coefficients are used, and the phase factor $(-1)^{J+J_z}$ is inserted in front of each component. This choice ensures the eigenfunctions transform properly under the operation of time-reversal.[266]*

For configurations with an *even* number of electrons the irreducible representations of the point symmetry group usually form a wider class of quantum numbers for labeling the crystal field levels than the corresponding crystal field quantum numbers. Thus for D_{3h} symmetry the states may be labeled by the six irreducible representations of D_{3h} instead of just four crystal quantum numbers. This means that the crystal field energy matrices that are calculated in the basis $|\alpha SLJ^{\delta}\Gamma_r\rangle$ are frequently of smaller dimensions, and more numerous, than those calculated in the basis $|\alpha SLJJ_z\mu\rangle$. In other words, crystal quantum numbers do not always lead to the maximum possible reduction of the crystal field energy matrix into its irreducible submatrices.

The correspondence between the crystal quantum numbers and the irreducible representations of several noncubic point groups is given in Table 6-17 for configurations having an even number of electrons. It

TABLE 6-17   Correspondence between crystal quantum numbers and the irreducible representations of several point groups for an even number of electrons

Point Symmetry	Crystal Quantum Number	Irreducible Representation
D_{3h}	0	$^{1}\Gamma_1, {}^{1}\Gamma_2$
	± 1	$^{2}\Gamma_5$
	± 2	$^{2}\Gamma_6$
	3	$^{1}\Gamma_3, {}^{1}\Gamma_4$
C_{3h}	0	$^{1}\Gamma_1$
	± 1	$(^{1}\Gamma_5 + {}^{1}\Gamma_6)$
	± 2	$(^{1}\Gamma_2 + {}^{1}\Gamma_3)$
	3	$^{1}\Gamma_4$
C_{3v}	0	$^{1}\Gamma_1, {}^{1}\Gamma_2$
	± 1	$^{2}\Gamma_3$
C_{2v}	0	$^{1}\Gamma_1, {}^{1}\Gamma_2$
	1	$^{1}\Gamma_3, {}^{1}\Gamma_4$

is preferable to label the states of ions having an even number of electrons by the irreducible representations of the symmetry group rather than by crystal quantum numbers since then the full use of the properties of the irreducible representations can be exploited.

Consider the f^2 configuration in D_{3h} symmetry.[299] If the crystal field energy matrix (91×91) is constructed in the $|\alpha SLJJ_z\mu\rangle$ basis, it may be

---

* Note in Eqs. 6-22 and 6-23 we follow the phase convention of Elliott and Stevens rather than that of Wigner, his phase being written as $(-1)^{J-J_z}$.

factorized into the following submatrices: a 17×17 ($\mu = 0$), two identical 14×14 ($\mu = \pm 1$), two identical 16×16 ($\mu = \pm 2$), and a further 14×14 ($\mu = 3$). However, by constructing the matrices in a $|\alpha SLJ^{\delta}\Gamma_r\rangle$ basis, we find that the $\mu = 0$ matrix breaks into a 12×12 ($^1\Gamma_1$) matrix and a 5×5 ($^1\Gamma_2$) matrix, and the $\mu = 3$ matrix breaks into two 7×7 matrices ($^1\Gamma_3$ and $^1\Gamma_4$).

To make practical calculations using the irreducible representations of the point symmetry group, it is necessary to determine those linear combinations of the state $|J, J_z\rangle$ that transform irreducibly under all the operations of the symmetry group to form $|J, J_z\rangle$ basis functions for the different irreducible representations.

Several different techniques exist for determining these linear combinations. Wigner[266] has given a general method using projection operators, and Meijer[300] has presented a particularly elegant method using the idempotent elements of the ring of the group. Koster et al.[272] have provided tables for constructing the basis functions for all the thirty-two crystallographic point groups; this problem may therefore be regarded as having been solved completely.

6-6 The Zeeman Effect in Rare Earth Crystals

Many crystal field levels occur as two- or more- fold degenerate states. This degeneracy may be wholly or partially removed by the application of an external magnetic field. The magnetic field is usually applied either in a direction parallel to the optic axis (the parallel Zeeman effect) or perpendicular to the optic axis (the perpendicular Zeeman effect). A study of the behavior of the crystal field levels in a magnetic field can lead to determining the degeneracies of the levels and thus a distinction between different species of levels according to their degeneracies. This information can be of considerable value in assigning quantum numbers to the levels.

The Hamiltonian for an ion in a crystal field to which a magnetic field $\mathscr{H}$ has been applied may be written as

$$H = H_{\text{free ion}} + V_{\text{crys}} + \mathscr{H} \cdot (\mathbf{L} + 2\mathbf{S}). \tag{6-24}$$

In general, the perturbation produced by the magnetic field on the ion will be very much smaller than that produced by the crystal field, and thus it is advantageous to calculate the matrix elements of $(\mathbf{L} + 2\mathbf{S})$ using the basis functions that describe the crystal field levels; that is, we first diagonalize the crystal energy matrix and then use the resulting eigenvectors as the basis functions for calculating the magnetic splittings. In the most general case the quantum numbers $\alpha SLJJ_z$ will cease to be good quantum numbers and only the irreducible representations of the point group (or equally well the crystal quantum numbers μ) will remain as good quantum numbers. The eigenvector of a crystal field state $|f^N\gamma\,{}^\delta\Gamma_r)$ would have the form

$$|f^N\gamma\,{}^\delta\Gamma_r) = a|f^N\alpha SLJJ_z) + b|f^N\alpha'S'L'J'J_z') + \cdots. \qquad (6\text{-}25)$$

For the parallel Zeeman effect the magnetic part of the Hamiltonian of Eq. 6-24 may be written as

$$H_{\text{mag}} = \mathscr{H}_z(L_z + 2S_z), \qquad (6\text{-}26)$$

and for the perpendicular Zeeman effect as

$$H_{\text{mag}} = \mathscr{H}_x(L_x + 2S_x). \qquad (6\text{-}27)$$

Thus the matrix elements of interest will be of the form

$$(f^N\gamma\,{}^\delta\Gamma_r|(L_z + 2S_z)|f^N\gamma'\,{}^\rho\Gamma_s) \qquad (6\text{-}28)$$

for the parallel effect and

$$(f^N\gamma\,{}^\delta\Gamma_r|(L_x + 2S_x)|f^N\gamma'\,{}^\rho\Gamma_s) \qquad (6\text{-}29)$$

for the perpendicular effect.

The first problem is to determine under what conditions will these matrix elements be nonvanishing. The answer to this problem will then tell us immediately which of the crystal field levels will show a first-order splitting in the presence of a magnetic field.

Consider D_{3h} symmetry. $L_z + 2S_z$ transforms as ${}^1\Gamma_2$, whereas $L_x + 2S_x$ transforms as ${}^2\Gamma_5$. For an even number of electrons the representations are all real and we have for the products of the irreducible representations of D_{3h} with ${}^1\Gamma_2$ and ${}^2\Gamma_5$

$$
\begin{array}{ll}
{}^1\Gamma_1 \times {}^1\Gamma_2 = {}^1\Gamma_2 \qquad & {}^1\Gamma_1 \times {}^2\Gamma_5 = {}^2\Gamma_5 \\
{}^1\Gamma_2 \times {}^1\Gamma_2 = {}^1\Gamma_1 \qquad & {}^1\Gamma_2 \times {}^2\Gamma_5 = {}^2\Gamma_5 \\
{}^1\Gamma_3 \times {}^1\Gamma_2 = {}^1\Gamma_4 \qquad & {}^1\Gamma_3 \times {}^2\Gamma_5 = {}^2\Gamma_6 \\
{}^1\Gamma_4 \times {}^1\Gamma_2 = {}^1\Gamma_3 \qquad & {}^1\Gamma_4 \times {}^2\Gamma_5 = {}^2\Gamma_6 \\
{}^2\Gamma_5 \times {}^1\Gamma_2 = {}^2\Gamma_5 \qquad & {}^2\Gamma_5 \times {}^2\Gamma_5 = {}^2\Gamma_6 + {}^1\Gamma_1 + {}^1\Gamma_2 \\
{}^2\Gamma_6 \times {}^1\Gamma_2 = {}^2\Gamma_6 \qquad & {}^2\Gamma_6 \times {}^2\Gamma_5 = {}^2\Gamma_5 + {}^1\Gamma_3 + {}^1\Gamma_4
\end{array}
$$

An inspection of the products involving ${}^1\Gamma_2$ shows that for the parallel effect there will be no matrix elements coupling states belonging to the same one-dimensional representation. There will, however, be off-diagonal matrix elements coupling the states of ${}^1\Gamma_1$ with those of ${}^1\Gamma_2$ and of ${}^1\Gamma_3$ with ${}^1\Gamma_4$. These states will correspond to different crystal field levels, which will normally be well separated from one another, with the result that their mutual perturbation will be negligible. Similarly, there can be no matrix elements coupling states belonging to $^2\Gamma_5$ with those of $^2\Gamma'_6$. The matrix elements between states belonging to the same two-dimensional representation do not necessarily vanish, and therefore the degeneracy of these states will normally be removed and each of the $^2\Gamma_5$ and $^2\Gamma_6$ levels observed to split. This gives a very simple way of distinguishing the $^2\Gamma_5$ and $^2\Gamma_6$ states from the singly degenerate states.

For the perpendicular effect, the diagonal matrix elements all vanish and there can be therefore no first-order splittings of the $^2\Gamma_5$ and $^2\Gamma_6$ states. This result holds for all the symmetry groups when the configuration contains an even number of electrons.

In holmium ethylsulfate crystals the ground state is a $^2\Gamma_5$ ($\mu = \pm 1$) level, and 6.01 cm^{-1} higher there is a $^1\Gamma_1$ ($\mu = 0$) level.[301] It is apparent that for the parallel Zeeman effect the twofold degeneracy of the $^2\Gamma_5$ level will be removed but that there will be no mutual perturbation of the $^1\Gamma_1$ and $^2\Gamma_5$ levels. For the perpendicular effect the $^2\Gamma_5$ level will not be split in the first order; however, it will couple with the $^1\Gamma_1$ level and therefore it would be expected to show a second-order splitting because of the very close proximity of the $^1\Gamma_1$ level.[302]

When the components of the multidimensional representations are not real, we cannot use the simple method just outlined since the products of the components will not necessarily be real.* It may, however, be shown that for single-valued groups if the tensor operator of interest transforms as $^\rho\Gamma_p$, the matrix elements of this operator between a state transforming as $^\delta\Gamma_r$ and another as $^t\Gamma_s$ will be zero unless the triple product $^\rho\Gamma_p \times {}^\delta\Gamma_r \times {}^t\Gamma_s$ contains the identity representation $^1\Gamma_1$. For double groups the product $^\delta\Gamma_r \times {}^t\Gamma_s$ must be antisymmetrized to ensure that the products of the components of the representations are real. Koster and Statz[303,304] have considered these problems in relationship to the Zeeman effect of paramagnetic ions in solids.

To obtain the nonvanishing matrix elements between states as defined in Eq. 6-25 it is necessary to evaluate elements of the type

$$(f^N\alpha SLJJ_z|(L_z + 2S_z)|f^N\alpha SLJ'J_z) \tag{6-30}$$

for the parallel effect and of the type

$$(f^N\alpha SLJJ_z|(L_x + 2S_x)|f^N\alpha SLJ'J_z'). \tag{6-31}$$

for the perpendicular effect.

These matrix elements are necessarily diagonal in the quantum numbers αSL. The matrix elements of Eq. 6-30 are precisely those found in Sec. 4-2 for the free ion (Eqs. 4-3 and 4-5). For the parallel effect the matrix

---

* This point has been discussed in detail by Hamermesh[268] (page 173).

elements are diagonal in J_z but not in J.   States having the same αSLJ_z
quantum numbers may be coupled to states differing in J by up to one unit.

If J is a good quantum number, we obtain for the parallel Zeeman
effect

$$(f^N\alpha J^\delta \Gamma_r|(L_z + 2S_z)|f^N\alpha J^\delta \Gamma_r) = a^2 J_z g(SLJ) + b^2 J_z' g(S'L'J). \quad (6\text{-}32)$$

For the noncubic groups the crystal field levels are never more than twofold degenerate and it is convenient to define a splitting factor,[287] $s_\parallel$ for
the parallel effect such that

$$s_\parallel(f^N\alpha J^\delta \Gamma_r) = 2[a^2 J_z g(SLJ) + b^2 J_z' g(S'L'J) + \cdots,], \quad (6\text{-}33)$$

where $s_\parallel$ is normally given in Lorentz units (1 L.U. $= eH/4\pi mc$).

It must be realized that Eqs. 6-32 and 6-33 specifically assume that there
is no mixing of states of different J either by the magnetic field or the crystal
field.   Axe and Dieke[305] have noted that if J mixing by the crystal field
is neglected, J_z is a good quantum number for all three components of the
$^6H_{5/2}$ ground state of Sm^{3+} in $LaCl_3$ crystals.   The lowest level of $^6H_{5/2}$
has $J_z = \pm\frac{1}{2}$, and hence $s_\parallel = g = 0.284$.   As a result of a 0.31% admixture of $^6H_{7/2}$ in the $J_z = \pm\frac{1}{2}$ states when J mixing is included, they
find that $s_\parallel$ is increased to 0.586 L.U., which is then in excellent agreement
with their measured value of 0.58 L.U.   We now consider the perpendicular Zeeman effect.   The matrix elements of Eq. 6-29 may be determined
readily if we first write $L_x + 2S_x$ in tensor operator form using Eq. 2-29,
and then apply the usual tensor techniques.   In this way we obtain the
matrix elements diagonal in J as

$$(f^N\alpha SLJJ_z|(L_x + 2S_x)|f^N\alpha SLJJ_z \pm 1) = \pm\frac{g}{2}[(J \mp J_z)(J \pm J_z + 1)]^{1/2}$$

$$(6\text{-}34)$$

and for the elements with $J' = J - 1$ we obtain

$$(f^N\alpha SLJJ_z|(L_x + 2S_x)|f^N\alpha SLJ - 1J_z \pm 1) = \pm \sqrt{(J \mp J_z)(J \mp J_z - 1)}$$

$$\times \left(\frac{(S + L + J + 1)(J + L - S)(J - L + S)(L + S - J + 1)}{16J^2(2J + 1)(2J - 1)}\right)^{1/2}.$$

$$(6\text{-}35)$$

Notice that the matrix elements of $L_x + 2S_x$ are only nonvanishing for
states that differ in J_z by ± 1.   This means that for the perpendicular
Zeeman effect it is possible to induce a first-order splitting only for states
containing $J_z = \pm\frac{1}{2}$ and hence only states with $\mu = \pm\frac{1}{2}$ will show a
first-order splitting.   This affords a very simple method of identifying
$\mu = \pm\frac{1}{2}$ levels.   In this particular case, Eq. 6-34 simplifies to

$$(f^N\alpha SLJ, \pm\frac{1}{2}|(L_x + 2S_x)|f^N\alpha SLJ, \mp\frac{1}{2}) = \pm\frac{g}{2}(J + \frac{1}{2}). \quad (6\text{-}36)$$

If J is a good quantum number, it is convenient to define a perpendicular splitting factor $s_\perp$ such that

$$s_\perp = g(J + \tfrac{1}{2}).$$

In the event of intermediate coupling among the states of the J-manifold, we simply replace g by its intermediate coupling value. We note here that in paramagnetic resonance studies the splitting factors are usually written as $g_\parallel$ and $g_\perp$.

In uniaxial crystals the splitting factors in the x- and y-directions are equivalent. If the magnetic field is applied at some angle ϕ with respect to the optic axis, the resultant splitting factor $s(\phi)$ will be given by

$$s(\phi) = s_\parallel{}^2 \cos^2 \phi + s_\perp{}^2 \sin^2 \phi. \qquad (6\text{-}37)$$

If instead of a single crystal we examine a powder in a magnetic field, the splitting factor $s(\phi)$ must be averaged over all possible orientations to yield

$$s(\phi)_{\mathrm{av}}^2 = \frac{s_\parallel{}^2 + 2s_\perp{}^2}{3}. \qquad (6\text{-}38)$$

Chow[306] has attempted to study the Zeeman spectrum of NdF_3 as a powder, but he was only able to obtain a broadening of the lines with no resolvable splittings. Nevertheless, Eq. 6-38 may prove useful in analyzing the spectrum of rare earth compounds such as the anhydrous rare earth nitrates where there is little possibility of obtaining the material in single crystal form.

Crystals of low symmetry, such as the monoclinic, hydrated, rare earth trichlorides, are highly anisotropic and the x- and y-directions are no longer equivalent,[307,308] it then becomes necessary to consider also the matrix elements of $(L_y + 2S_y)$. These matrix elements are related to those of $(L_x + 2S_x)$ by the expression (see Eq. 2-29)

$$(f^N \alpha SLJJ_z | (L_y + 2S_y) | f^N \alpha SLJ'J_z \pm 1) = \mp i(f^N \alpha SLJJ_z | $$
$$\times (L_x + 2S_x) | f^N \alpha SLJ'J_z \pm 1). \qquad (6\text{-}39)$$

Then if J is a good quantum number, we may define a splitting factor s_y for the case where the field is along the y-axis by writing

$$s_y = (J + \tfrac{1}{2})g. \qquad (6\text{-}40)$$

If the magnetic field H makes an angle θ with the z-axis and an angle ϕ with the x-axis, then H may be resolved into the components

$$\begin{aligned} H_x &= H \sin \theta \cos \phi, \\ H_y &= H \sin \theta \cos \phi, \\ H_z &= H \cos \theta. \end{aligned} \qquad (6\text{-}41)$$

The splitting factor s for an arbitrary orientation of the magnetic field may then be expressed in terms of the splitting factors s_x, s_y, and s_z, which are associated with the x-, y-, and z-axes, respectively to yield

$$s^2 = s_x^2 \sin^2 \theta \cos^2 \phi + s_y^2 \sin^2 \theta \sin^2 \phi + s_z^2 \cos^2 \theta. \qquad (6\text{-}42)$$

To obtain the average splitting for a powder we simply average over all the possible orientations to obtain

$$s_{\mathrm{av}}^2 = \frac{s_x^2 + s_y^2 + s_z^2}{3}. \qquad (6\text{-}43)$$

If H lies in the xy-plane, then Eq. 6-42 becomes

$$s^2(\phi) = s_x^2 \cos^2 \phi + s_y^2 \sin^2 \phi. \qquad (6\text{-}44)$$

6-7   Energy Levels of Rare Earth Ions in Crystals and Solutions

Before making detailed analyses of the spectra of rare earth ions in crystals and solutions it is usually desirable, and usually necessary, to establish first the identity of the electronic energy levels of the "free ion" from which the spectra arose. For the $+3$ or higher valencies of the rare earths this generally entails identifying the energy levels of f^N type configurations and for divalent rare earths considering also the levels of the $f^{N-1}d$ and $f^{N-1}s$ configurations.

Considerable progress has been made in the interpretation of the energy levels that have been deduced from the crystal spectra of the trivalent lanthanides. In general, the crystal field splittings are not more than a few hundred wave numbers, and thus the essential structure of the free ion configuration tends to be preserved. If the crystal field patterns do not overlap, the positions of the free ion levels may be taken, to first order, as being at the centers of gravity of the patterns. Detailed experimental analyses of these patterns will indicate frequently the J-value, and in some cases the g-value, of the "free ion" level from which it was derived. Where the patterns overlap there will normally be considerable mixing of the "free ion" levels, so that the resultant pattern can no longer be associated with a particular "free ion" level.

The experimental "free ion" energy levels may be compared with those calculated by diagonalizing the free ion energy matrices for a trial set of parameters. This calculation will usually result in the positive identification and classification of many of the "free ion" levels, and the parameters may then be refined by the method of least squares. The resultant eigenvectors can be used to calculate the magnetic splitting factors.

The most extensive analyses of the "free ion" levels deduced from crystal spectra have been made for systems with not more than four

$4f$-electrons (or holes).   In these cases a sufficient number of levels has been identified to permit the parameters to be refined by least-squares fitting to the data.   The analysis of the crystal spectra of the trivalent ions in the middle of the lanthanide series has not advanced sufficiently, as yet, to permit calculations without some simplifying approximations. Thus the existing analyses of the spectra of the lanthanides Sm^{3+} to Dy^{3+} have all involved the hydrogenic approximation.   The parameters that have been used in interpreting the trivalent lanthanide "free ion" levels are given in Table 6-18.   The spin-orbit coupling constants appear to

TABLE 6-18   Parameters deduced from the crystal spectra of the trivalent lanthanides

Ion	F_2	F_4	F_6	ζ	References*
Ce^{3+}				644	69
Pr^{3+}	305.4	51.88	5.321	729.5	299, 309–311
Nd^{3+}	327.5	48.66	5.356	884.6	312–315
Pm^{3+}	346.2	47.68	5.232	1070	60, 316–320
Sm^{3+}	370	51.08	5.591	1200	57, 321–325
Eu^{3+}	401	55.36	6.059	1320	326, 327
Gd^{3+}	406	56.05	6.135	1583	328, 329
Tb^{3+}	434	59.91	6.558	1705	326, 330
Dy^{3+}	420	57.98	6.346	1900	57, 331–334
Ho^{3+}	414.6	68.80	7.272	2163	60, 335–339
Er^{3+}	433.2	67.13	7.356	2393.3	340–342
Tm^{3+}	451.1	68.07	7.437	2656	343–346
Yb^{3+}				2882.7	70

All values are in cm^{-1}.

* The first reference for each ion refers to the calculation and the succeeding references refer to the sources of experimental data.

increase smoothly with increasing atomic number, whereas the F_k's increase somewhat erratically.   This latter behavior is probably a result of the use of the hydrogenic approximation and of the neglect of configuration interaction.

Runciman and Wybourne,[347] and more recently Margolis,[299] have investigated the effect of adding a configuration interaction correction term† $\alpha L(L + 1)$ to the energy matrices of Pr^{3+} $(4f)^2$ and found a substantial decrease in the mean error (from 200 to 127 cm^{-1}).   Margolis found the parameters then to be

$$F_2 = 308.0, \quad F_4 = 50.92, \quad F_6 = 5.115, \quad \zeta = 753.9, \quad \alpha = 14.77\ cm^{-1}.$$

† Both these papers have misinterpreted this term as an orbit-orbit interaction.

The inclusion of this correction term has an appreciable effect on all the parameters. It would be of considerable interest to examine the effects of the complete correction factor given by Eq. 2-129 for systems with three or more f-electrons (or holes). It is important that the "free ion" levels be fitted as closely as possible since we cannot expect the crystal field parameters to make up for inadequacies in the "free ion" calculation.

Marshall and Stuart[348] have shown that the effect of placing a free ion into a crystal (or a solution) is to expand out the wave function of the ion into the crystal. This expansion (known as the *nephelauxetic effect*[279]) is a direct result of the screening of the $4f$-electrons by the overlapping charge clouds of the surrounding ligands. This in effect leads to a decrease in the effective nuclear charge. Thus the Slater parameters and spin-orbit coupling constants found from crystal spectra can be expected to be *less* than those of the free ion.

Wong and his associates[349-352] have compared the effects of different anions on the energies of the free ion levels of Pr^{3+} and Nd^{3+}, and McLaughlin and Conway[353] have made similar comparisons of the effects of different cations for Pr^{3+}. In both cases systematic shifts of the "free ion" levels, which can be correlated with charges in the Slater parameters due to charges in the overlap of the surrounding ligands, have been observed. A similar observation has been made by Carnall and Wybourne[86] for the shifts of the free ion levels of the actinides in crystals and solutions. The existence of the nephelauxetic effect implies that the Slater parameters determined from crystal or solution spectra are dependent on the environment of the rare earth ion. Wong et al.[352] have studied systems where the changes in the Slater parameters are approximately 2%.

The crystal absorption spectra of the trivalent actinides show a marked resemblance to those of the lanthanides.[354] The observed absorption lines are sharp and weak as would be expected for Laporte-forbidden intra-$5f^N$ transitions, and crystal fields are found to give splittings of the "free ion" levels which are only slightly larger than those found in the lanthanides. Lämmermann and Conway[355] have given a detailed interpretation of the spectrum of Pu^{3+} ($5f^5$) in $LaCl_3$, and Conway[356] has substantially revised an earlier analysis of Gruber[357,358] of the spectrum of Am^{3+} ($5f^6$) in $LaCl_3$.* A preliminary analysis of the spectrum of Np^{3+} ($5f^4$) in $LaCl_3$ has been given by Gruber.[359]

Carnall and Wybourne[86,360] have made a systematic attempt to correlate the theoretical and experimental results for the trivalent actinides U^{3+} ($5f^3$)

---

* See also D. S. Gorbenko-Germanov, *Fiz. Probl. Spektroskopii, Akad. Nauk SSSR, Materialy* 13-go (*Trinadtsaiogo*) *Soveshih.*, **1**, 242 (1960).

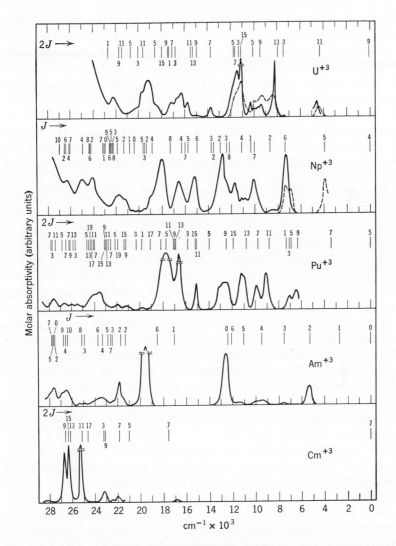

Fig. 6.3 Calculated "free-ion" levels and solution absorption spectra of the trivalent actinides, $5f^3$–$5f^7$. U: --- U^{3+} in molten LiCl–KCl eutectic at 400°, —— U^{3+} in 1.0M $DClO_4$ at 23°; Np: --- Np^{3+} in molten LiCl–KCl eutectic at 400°, —— Np^{3+} in 0.5M $DClO_4$ at 23°; Pu: —— Pu^{3+} in 1.0M $DClO_4$ at 23°; Am: —— Am^{3+} in molten LiNO$_3$–KNO$_3$ eutectic at 150°; Cm: —— Cm^{3+} in 1.0M $HClO_4$ at 23°.

to Cm^{3+} ($5f^7$), supplementing the crystal spectra data with data deduced from studies of the solution spectra. The solution spectra data are particularly important for the highly radioactive actinide ions. The lack of permanent radiation damage permits studies of the spectra in solution to be made at high concentrations of actinides that would be quite impossible in the solid state. This property of solution spectra is particularly advantageous in detecting very weak transitions.[360,361]

Carnall and Wybourne have calculated the energies of the free ion levels of the trivalent actinides and compared them with the energies of the observed absorption hands. The results are shown in Fig. 6-3. The existing data are barely sufficient to permit a meaningful least-squares determination of the parameters and therefore the $5f$-hydrogenic approximation was invoked. The parameters used are given in Table 6-19. The

TABLE 6-19   Parameters for calculation of the energy levels of trivalent actinides

	U^{3+}	Np^{3+}	Pu^{3+}	Am^{3+}	Cm^{3+}	
F_2	196	225	240	260	280	
ζ	1666	2070	2292	2548	2968	cm^{-1}

spin-orbit coupling parameters of the trivalent actinides are approximately twice as large and the electrostatic parameters two-thirds as large as those of the corresponding lanthanides (cf. Table 6-18). Consequently, the energy-level structures of the actinides exhibit considerable departures from Russell-Saunders coupling. Very often the levels are better described in j-j coupling. The quantum numbers L and S no longer have any physical meaning and for the free ion levels only J remains as a good quantum number. However, because of the pronounced tendency toward j-j coupling the levels tend to appear in nearly degenerate groups. These levels should be strongly mixed by the Stark fields due to the surrounding ligands and even J will cease to be a good quantum number. Detailed analyses of these groups of levels will be quite impossible without the complete inclusion of the crystal field interactions.

It should also be possible to study the spectroscopic properties of Bk, Cf, and E ions once usable quantities are produced. However, it appears unlikely that usable quantities of the heavier actinides, fermium to lawrencium, will be produced in the forseeable future.

6-8   Crystal Spectra of Divalent Rare Earths

For a long time the study of the divalent lanthanides in crystalline environments was limited to the ions Sm^{2+}, Eu^{2+}, and Yb^{2+}.[362] The other lanthanides all have large negative reduction potentials with respect to the divalent state and do not normally form divalent compounds. Divalent lanthanide ions can, however, be stabilized in a host crystal whose cations have an even larger negative reduction potential. Trivalent lanthanide ions may be incorporated substitutionally into an alkaline earth dihalide host crystal and then the trivalent ions reduced to the divalent state. The incorporation of the trivalent ions in a divalent lattice will be accompanied by charge compensation, probably by an interstitial halide ion. When the charge compensation is remote from the substitutional site, the lanthanide ion will possess the point symmetry of the divalent host cations.

Hayes and Twidell[22] have irradiated a Tm^{3+}-doped CaF_2 crystal with 50-kV x-rays and found that the Tm^{3+} ions that are at cubic sites can capture an electron to form stable divalent Tm^{2+} ions. Kiss[363] has obtained similar results by irradiating the crystal with γ-rays. The capture of an electron by the Tm^{3+} ion leaves behind a self-trapped hole which is closely related to the F^{2-} center found in LiF.[364] Hayes et al.[364] have studied the formation of Ho^{2+} ions in CaF_2 and obtained clear evidence that only the Ho^{3+} ions that occur at cubic sites are reduced. Kiss and his associates[23] have succeeded in reducing all the lathanides to the divalent state by γ-irradiation of trivalent ions in CaF_2. The reduction may also be made by chemical methods[24] such as heating the trivalent lanthanide-doped crystal in the alkaline earth cation vapor. In this case it is possible to obtain a 100% conversion of the trivalent ions into the divalent state.

Butement[366] has studied the absorption and fluorescence spectra of divalent Sm, Eu, and Yb in aqueous solutions and in the chlorides of barium, sodium, and strontium. The ground state of Yb^{2+} is the closed-shell configuration $4f^{14}$ $(^1S_0)$, and hence there can be no $4f \leftrightarrow 4f$ transitions. Butement has observed a very strong and broad absorption band to commence just below 28,000 cm^{-1} and another similar band at approximately 40,500 cm^{-1}. Strong fluorescence was observed in the ultraviolet.

Bryant[70] has observed the free ion spectrum of Yb^{2+} ion and found the $4f^{13}6s$ and $4f^{13}5d$ configurations to be completely overlapping one another, with their levels commencing at 33,500 cm^{-1} above the $4f^{14}$ $(^1S_0)$ ground state. Transitions from the ground state to the states of the $4f^{13}5d$ configuration will be Laporte-allowed electric-dipole transitions, and those to the $4f^{13}6s$ will be forbidden. The $5d$- and $6s$-electrons will, unlike the $4f$-electrons, be unshielded outer electrons and thus considerably influenced by their environment. The crystal field should strongly mix the states of the $4f^{13}5d$ and $4f^{13}6s$ configurations breaking down the electric-dipole selection rule for the latter configurations. Were the $5d$- and $6s$-electrons to interact only weakly with their environment we would expect to see many narrow, but intense, absorption bands corresponding to transitions from the ground state to the crystal field split levels of the $4f^{13}5d$ and $4f^{13}6s$ configurations. The fact that Butement saw only two widely spaced broad bands indicates that the weak-field description is unphysical. A superior zeroth approximation would seem to be to regard the $5d$-electron as being uncoupled from the $4f^{13}$ core and interacting very strongly with the crystal field to give rise to two $^4\Gamma_8$ and one $^2\Gamma_7$ states (for cubic symmetry). These states should be widely separated since the crystal field is certainly stronger than the spin-orbit coupling of the $4f^{13}$ core and considerably stronger than the relatively weak interaction of the $5d$-electron with the core. The crystal field states could then be regarded as being perturbed by the $4f^{13}$ core. Such a complex calculation as this would be of dubious value unless it were possible to resolve the fine structure of the absorption bands.

The spectra of the divalent lanthanide-doped crystals are, in general, characterized by the appearance of a system of broad and intense absorption bands originating from the $4f^{N-1}5d$ and $4f^{N-1}6s$ configurations. The energy at which the band system is observed to commence varies markedly from ion to ion and to a lesser extent from crystal to crystal. In the free Ce^{2+} ion, Sugar[367] finds the $4f5d$ configuration to commence only 3276.66 cm^{-1} above the $4f^2(^3H_4)$ ground state. In the crystalline state, the crystal field levels will almost certainly extend to energies lower than the lowest crystal field level of the $4f^2(^3H_4)$ state. In Gd^{2+} the $4f^75d$ levels are probably lowest in both the free ion and the crystal. The $4f^9$ configuration is probably lowest in Tb^{2+} free ions, whereas in the crystal the levels of the $4f^85d$ configuration occur almost certainly lowest.[24]

The divalent lanthanide ions in the alkaline earth dihalides are normally at sites of cubic symmetry and hence the $4f \leftrightarrow 4f$ transitions are usually limited to magnetic dipole character. Forced electric-dipole transitions may, however, occur sometimes. These transitions will involve a lattice vibration in such a way that the initial or final state of the transition is a vibrational state of the electronic level. In this case the frequency of the transition will differ from that of a pure electric-dipole transition by one or more vibrational quanta. Axe and Sorokin[368] have observed considerable vibronic structure in the $4f \leftrightarrow 4f$ spectra of Sm^{2+}-doped $SrCl_2$ and SrF_2 crystals. They have shown further that the fine structures of the $4f^{N-1}5d$ bands of the divalent rare earths are due to the vibronic coupling of pure electronic states with states involving multiquantum excitation of even-parity vibrations, and they have discussed the vibronic selection rules appropriate to these transitions.

The absorption and fluorescence spectrum of the Sm^{2+} ion in various crystal hosts has been studied extensively.[368-380] The ground multiplet (^7F) of the Sm^{2+} ion belongs to the $4f^6$ configuration, with the lowest levels of the $4f^55d$ configuration commencing approximately 20,000 cm^{-1} higher. The $^5D_0$ level of the $4f^6$ configuration would be expected to occur at 14,500 cm^{-1} above the ground state. In a crystal field the levels of the $4f^6$ configuration undergo moderate splittings with only a slight change of their centers of gravity from those of the free ion. The levels of the $4f^5 5d$ configuration undergo very large crystal field splittings, with the result that the lowest crystal field components occur quite close to the $^5D_0$ level of $4f^6$.

In CaF_2 the Sm^{2+} ion enters substitutionally into a site of O_h symmetry, and as a result no pure intra-$4f^6$ electric-dipole transitions would be expected. Two narrow absorption lines are observed at 14,110 and 14,482 cm^{-1}, respectively with a broad absorption band starting at 15,000 cm^{-1}. The two lines were first interpreted as being the $^5D_0$ and $^5D_1$ levels of the $4f^6$ configuration.[372] Runciman and Stager,[374] and Kaplyanskii and Przhevuskii,[379] have studied their behavior under a uniaxial stress and shown that they actually correspond to $^1\Gamma_1$ and $^2\Gamma_3$ crystal field levels of the $4f^5 5d$ configuration, respectively. The $^1\Gamma_1$ upper state appears in fluorescence to the $^2\Gamma_3$ state of $^7F_1$, and the upper $^2\Gamma_3$ state appears in absorption from the $^1\Gamma_1$ ground state.

A large strain splitting is observed in the absorption line while the fluorescence line undergoes a considerable shift to lower energies. The $4f$-electrons are well shielded and hence may be expected to be relatively unaffected by the strain, showing neither a splitting nor a shift to lower energies. The $5d$-electron is unshielded and thus could be expected to show considerable strain effects. Since the fluorescing line begins in a singly degenerate $^1\Gamma_1$ state, it should show a shift under strain but no splitting, whereas the absorption line which terminates on the upper $^2\Gamma_3$ state should both split and exhibit a shift of energy, as indeed is observed.[374,379] These assignments have received additional confirmation by the Zeeman effect measurements of Zakharchenya and Ryskin.[380]

In Sm^{2+}-doped BaF_2, SrF_2, and $SrCl_2$ crystals the $^5D_0$ level of the $4f^6$ occurs *below* the edge of the first absorption band of the $4f^5 5d$ system.[368,373,376–379] Again, the Sm^{2+} ion occupies a site of O_h symmetry. The $^5D_0$ level may be identified by its magnetic-dipole fluorescence to the $^7F_1$ level. Wood and Kaiser[376] have been able to "see" several of the symmetry-forbidden intra-$4f^6$ electric-dipole transitions by adding approximately 5% of CaF_2 to the SrF_2 melt to induce a slight distortion of the lattice away from O_h symmetry.

Dieke and Sarup[375] have observed the fluorescence of the Sm^{2+} ion as an impurity in $LaCl_3$. In this system the $4f^5 5d$ absorption system occurs *above* the $^5D_1$ level of $4f^6$, so that they were able to observe fluorescence from both the $^5D_1$ and $^5D_0$ levels to those of the ^7F ground multiplet. The excitation of the fluorescence spectrum occurs by allowed transitions from the ground state into the $4f^5 5d$ band system. Part of this energy is then given up to the lattice by phonon emission, populating the metastable $^5D_1$ and $^5D_0$ levels from which the fluorescence follows. In $LaCl_3$, the Sm^{2+} ion evidently occupies a site of very low symmetry, which suggests that the charge-compensating ion is intimately coupled with the Sm^{2+} site. Dieke and Sarup were able to observe a complete removal of the degeneracy of the ^7F levels by the crystal field. Ofelt[326] has fitted their observed levels to a calculated set of levels assuming $4f$-hydrogenic ratios for the Slater integrals and the values

$$F_2 = 330 \qquad \zeta_{4f} = 1050 \text{ cm}^{-1}.$$

These values are approximately 20% less than those found for the iso-electronic ion Eu^{3+}.

Europium readily forms divalent compounds and has been studied extensively in alkaline earth halide crystals.[366,380–385] Eu^{2+} is iso-electronic with Gd^{3+} and has a $4f^7(^8S_{7/2})$ ground state. The first excited $4f^7$ level ($^6P_{7/2}$) would be expected to occur at approximately 26,000 cm^{-1}. However, the absorption bands of the $4f^65d$ system commence with a sharp line at 24,206 cm^{-1} in CaF_2 followed by a series of intense absorption bands which mask the weak $4f^7$ absorption lines. The upper level at 24,206 cm^{-1} splits into two sublevels in the presence of a magnetic field, whereas the sevenfold degeneracy of the ground state is completely removed.[291,292] The upper level also shows a splitting into two sublevels on the application of a uniaxial stress,[379,382] indicating that the level is a fourfold degenerate $^4\Gamma_8$ state of the $4f^65d$ system and not a level of the $4f^7$ configuration. Eu^{2+}-doped SrF_2 and BaF_2 crystals show a similar spectrum, although shifted progressively to higher energies.[384]

The divalent lanthanides are of particular interest as optical maser materials. The broad $4f^{N-1}5d$ absorption bands allow large quantities of existing radiation to be pumped via the allowed $4f^N \rightarrow 4f^{N-1}5d$ transitions. Part of this energy is transferred to the metastable $4f^N$ levels from which maser action may be initiated. These systems are relatively efficient and may in some cases be operated continuously. Kiss et al. have operated $CaF_2:Dy^{2+}$ maser with solar radiation continuously.[386]

The study of the spectroscopic properties of the divalent lanthanides has only just begun. Their successful preparation now opens up the possibility of preparing crystals that are doped in other unusual valence states. Among the possibilities should be monovalent lanthanides, divalent actinides and trivalent protactinium, and thorium.

6-9   Crystal Field Calculations

Calculations of the crystal field splittings of the "free ion" levels of the rare earth ions have centered largely around the application of crystal field potential expansions of the type given in Eq. 6-2. The terms appearing in these expansions have been limited by considerations of the point symmetry of the rare earth ion in the crystal lattice. In the earliest it was assumed that the f^N configuration followed LS coupling and the crystal field was introduced as a small perturbation on the free ion levels. More recently the emphasis has been on doing complete crystal field calculations where the entire coulomb, spin-orbit, and crystal field interaction matrices have been constructed and diagonalized. These latter calculations allow us to examine closely the validity of expansions like Eq. 6-2.

The spectrum of the Pr^{3+} ion substituted into single crystals of $LaCl_3$ has been studied extensively,[309-311,387-390] and has resulted in the establishment of all the energy levels of the $4f^2$ configuration. Margolis[299,343] has diagonalized the complete crystal field energy matrices for the $4f^2$ configuration in D_{3h} symmetry which is appropriate to this system. His calculation permits the complete inclusion of both the effects of intermediate coupling and the crystal field mixing of the free ion levels.

The contribution of the crystal field potential to the Hamiltonian is usually very much smaller than that of the Coulomb and spin-orbit interaction of the free ion. The complete set of parameters (F_k, ζ_f, and B_q^k) cannot be simultaneously treated as free variables in a least-squares fitting since if they are all allowed to vary simultaneously the crystal field parameters will tend to accommodate the inadequacies of the treatment of the free ion levels, with the result that although the calculation of the free ion levels will be improved, the crystal field splittings of the levels will be badly represented. In other words, the centers of gravity of the empirical levels do not correspond to the calculated levels and the crystal field parameters try to adjust so as to cause these centers of gravity to coincide. Thus it is desirable to perform the calculation in a series of iterative steps. First, the parameters F_k and ζ_f are adjusted to fit the free ion levels and then the crystal field parameters are adjusted to fit the crystal levels.

To obtain the "free ion" levels it is necessary to determine the centers of gravity of the crystal field components of each free ion level. If the degeneracies of all the crystal field components of each free ion levels are known, then a first estimate of the centers of gravities may be found by weighting the crystal field components according to their degeneracies. Where some of the components are missing it may be possible to obtain a good estimate of the centers of gravity by using an intial set of crystal field parameters to estimate the positions of the missing components and obtain improved centers of gravity with each refinement of the crystal field parameters.

The off-diagonal crystal field matrix elements will tend to shift the centers of gravity of the terms from their positions in the "free ion." This shift can be determined only by an iterative method whereby the shift of the centers of gravity is first determined by diagonalizing the free ion matrices and then later the improved crystal field parameters included to get new centers of gravity. Even when this is done we shall find that the centers of gravity of the empirical levels will still not correspond to the calculated positions of the "free ion" levels because of the inadequacies of the "free ion" part of the calculation. These deviations are usually of the order of the magnitude of the crystal field splittings (approximately 150 to 200 cm^{-1}). This discrepancy will seriously prejudice the fit of the crystal field components unless some attempt is made to overcome these deviations. The deviations may, in part, be removed by introducing the configuration-interaction correction parameters α, β, and γ (see Sec. 2-17). However, these parameters will only partially reduce the deviations. One way out of this dilemma has been suggested by Margolis.[299,343] His suggestion is to add along the trace of the free ion matrices small correction terms so that when the matrices are diagonalized they yield energy levels that agree as closely as possible to the empirical levels. This is, of course done only after the "free ion" parameters have been determined. This method will distort the "free ion" eigenfunctions slightly; however, the small decrease in their accuracy will be more than offset by the better description of the crystal field obtained.

Margolis obtained a standard deviation of 7 cm^{-1} for 40 of the observed levels* compared with the standard deviation of 10.3 cm^{-1} for 27 levels found by Judd,[391] who included the effects of intermediate coupling but not those of J-mixing by the crystal field. The worst agreement was found for the levels based on $^1D_2$. When these levels were omitted, the standard deviation was reduced to 4 cm^{-1}. Eisenstein[392] has performed similar calculations and concluded that no single set of crystal field parameters will give good agreement between the calculated and observed levels for all the multiplets. He has also calculated the crystal field splittings of Nd^{3+} and Er^{3+} in $LaCl_3$ by diagonalizing the complete crystal field matrices for the f^3 and f^{11} configurations in D_{3h} symmetry.

The crystal field parameters determined for most of the lanthanides ions in $LaCl_3$ crystal hosts are listed in Table 6-20 and those determined for the lanthanide ethylsulfates are given in Table 6-21. The crystal field parameters given in these tables show a somewhat erratic variation with atomic number. The crystal field calculations are not, however, all of

---

* Note Margolis's calculation does not include experimental energy of the $^1S_0$ level which was found later.[390]

TABLE 6-20   Crystal field parameters for various lanthanide ions in $LaCl_3$

Ion	B_0^2	B_0^4	B_0^6	B_6^6	References
Pr^{3+}	95	−325	−634	427	299
Nd^{3+}	195	−309	−710	466	312
Sm^{3+}	162	−182	−709	448	305
Eu^{3+}	178	−304	−816	521	327
Tb^{3+}	184	−320	−480	305	330
Dy^{3+}	182	−311	−371	271	305
Er^{3+}	188	−298	−424	279	340

All values in cm^{-1}

TABLE 6-21   Crystal field parameters for various lanthanide ethylsulfates

Ion	B_0^2	B_0^4	B_0^6	B_6^6	References*
Pr^{3+}	31	−706	−778	578	393–395
Nd^{3+}	117	−568	−457	456	396, 287, 288
Sm^{3+}	154	−385	−624	580	397, 321
Eu^{3+}	160	−505	−617	537	261, 398
Tb^{3+}	220	−598	−544	488	399, 400
Dy^{3+}	250	−208	−480	515	397, 334
Ho^{3+}	250	−630	−478	412	399, 401, 402
Er^{3+}	252	−650	−496	407	403†–405
Tm^{3+}	195	−568	−457	456	406–408, 346

All values in cm^{-1}

* The first reference for each ion reports the actual calculation, and the succeeding references contain experimental data.

† The values for Er^{3+} differ from those of Reference 403. See E. H. Erath, *J. Chem. Phys.*, **38**, 1787 (1963).

the same reliability. In some cases crystal field interactions between the free ion levels have been completely ignored. This approximation will be very bad where the free ion levels are close together as in the middle of the lanthanide period. In other cases the calculations have included only levels derived from the ground multiplet, whereas in still others no attempt has been made to include intermediate coupling effects. The reader should check very carefully the approximations involved in each of the calculations. Before deciding on the validity, or otherwise, of the crystal field expansion it is important to make sure that all the information content has been used and that the discrepancies are not simply due to only partial treatment of the problem.

Wong and Richman[349–351] have studied the crystal field spectra of Pr^{3+} and Nd^{3+} in $LaBr_3$ which is isomorphic with the $LaCl_3$ structure. While they observed a nephelauxetic effect for the "free ion" levels, the crystal field splittings were almost unchanged, which is a result that is compatible with a simple expansion of the f-electron charge cloud in going from $LaCl_3$ to $LaBr_3$.

The interpretation of the crystal field splittings of the actinides is a particularly complex problem. The breakdown of Russell-Saunders coupling is so extreme as to make impossible any meaningful crystal field calculations without taking the intermediate coupling fully into account. As an added difficulty there is the marked tendency of the free ion levels to occur in groups which will become hopelessly mixed by the crystal field. There would appear to be little possibility of making much progress with actinide crystal spectra without performing very detailed calculations.

In the trivalent actinides the crystal field splittings are comparable with those of the lanthanides. For the higher valence states of the actinides the situation is quite complex. Axe et al.[409] have studied the electronic structure of octahedrally coordinated $Pa^{4+}(5f^1)$ substituted in Cs_2ZrCl_6. For an octahedral field (O_h) we have from Eq. 6-2,

$$V_{O_h} = B_0^4 C_0^{(4)} + B_4^4 (C_{-4}^{(4)} + C_4^{(4)}) + B_0^6 C_0^{(6)} + B_4^6 (C_{-4}^{(6)} + C_4^{(6)}). \quad (6\text{-}45)$$

However, V_{O_h} is necessarily invariant under the twofold axes of rotation of a cube, and hence the parameters may be related to give

$$V_{O_h} = B_0^4 [C_0^{(4)} + \sqrt{\tfrac{5}{14}}\,(C_{-4}^{(4)} + C_4^{(4)})] + B_0^6 [C_0^{(6)} - \sqrt{\tfrac{7}{2}}\,(C_{-4}^{(6)} + C_4^{(6)})]. \quad (6\text{-}46)$$

In Pa^{4+} there is only one $5f$-electron, and it is therefore possible to express the crystal field energy matrices in terms of just three parameters B_0^4, B_0^6, and ζ_{5f}. Axe[410] observed four of the five expected energy levels of Pa^{4+} in an O_h field. These data were supplemented by paramagnetic resonance measurements on the ground state.[409] By requiring that the three parameters fit both the energy levels and the magnetic data, Axe et al. were able to deduce the values

$$B_0^4 = 3552\ cm^{-1}, \qquad B_0^6 = 660\ cm^{-1}, \qquad and \quad \zeta_{5f} = 1490\ cm^{-1}.$$

These values may be compared with the values of

$$B_0^4 = 45{,}904\ cm^{-1}, \qquad B_0^6 = 8648\ cm^{-1}, \qquad and \quad \zeta_{5f} = 2405\ cm^{-1}$$

found by Eisenstein and Pryce[17] for the octahedrally coordinates single $5f$-electron of NpF_6. In both cases the fourth-order potential term is dominating. In NpF_6 the crystal field is quite close to the strong field limit and it is no longer meaningful to associate the crystal field levels with a particular free ion state.[39]

The absorption spectra of the U^{4+} ion in various crystal hosts have probably received more attention than any of the other actinides.[411-415]

Conway[411] has reported the absorption spectrum of U^{4+} in CaF_2 and interpreted the observed levels as being due to the crystal field splittings of the free ion states of the $5f^2$ configuration. The observed levels were compared with those calculated for the free ion assuming a $5f$-hydrogenic eigenfunction and the values

$$F_2 = 206 \text{ cm}^{-1} \quad \text{and} \quad \zeta_{5f} = 1870 \text{ cm}^{-1}.$$

Conway's interpretation was strongly challenged by Satten et al.[412] and by Pollack and Satten,[413] who contended that the magnitude of the crystal field splittings was as large, or larger, than the spin-orbit splittings of the free ion states and no physical meaning could therefore be attached to the free ion levels.

McLaughlin has studied the spectrum of UCl_4, where the U^{4+} ion is known to have D_{2d} point symmetry.[416] He deduced the parameters

$$F_2 = 206.1 \text{ cm}^{-1}, \quad F_4 = 30.09 \text{ cm}^{-1}, \quad F_6 = 4.516 \text{ cm}^{-1},$$
$$\text{and} \quad \zeta_{5f} = 1683 \text{ cm}^{-1}.$$

His value for the spin-orbit constant is approximately 13% smaller than Conway's, suggesting a greater degree of covalency[417-419] than in $CaF_2:U^{4+}$, although part of this decrease may be associated with treating all the Slater integrals as parameters rather than using the $5f$-hydrogenic approximation. McLaughlin was able to give a very satisfactory interpretation of the crystal field splittings in D_{2d} point symmetry using the parameters:

$$B_0^2 = -566 \text{ cm}^{-1}, \quad B_0^4 = 1238 \text{ cm}^{-1}, \quad B_4^4 = -2168 \text{ cm}^{-1},$$
$$B_0^6 = -6048 \text{ cm}^{-1}, \quad \text{and} \quad B_4^6 = -800 \text{ cm}^{-1}.$$

These parameters are considerably larger than those found for the lanthanides. The crystal field splittings were as large as 1900 cm^{-1}. Thus for actinides in valence states of $+4$ or greater it will be absolutely essential to construct the complete crystal field matrices if meaningful results are to be achieved. Here we have a case where the crystal field, Coulomb, and spin-orbit interactions are all large and hence must be considered together.

The interpretation of the spectroscopic properties of the tetravalent actinides pose a particularly fascinating problem in solid-state physics. Their detailed study should shed considerable light on the interaction of ions with the vibrational modes of the entire crystal. Satten and his associates[412,413] have studied the spectra of U^{4+} in several salts where there is a center of inversion and have observed a very rich vibronic spectra. The detailed discussion of their results would take us far from our present course, but it cannot be emphasized too much that future developments in the detailed understanding of the interaction of rare earth ions with the crystal lattice will depend greatly on studies such as these.*

The crystal field splittings of ions having a half-filled shell are of special interest since they can only arise from departures from Russell-Saunders coupling or the crystal field mixing of states of different class.[40,41,85] In particular, the splitting of the $^8S_{7/2}$ ground state of the f^7 configuration has been a subject of great fascination to solid-state spectroscopists. To first order an S state cannot be split by a crystal field. Nevertheless, paramagnetic resonance experiments[425-430] have shown that the ground state of Gd^{3+} splits† in the crystal fields by 0.3 to 1.0 cm^{-1}. Although many mechanisms[431-434] have been proposed to explain the observed splittings, few actual calculations have been attempted. Several mechanisms have been discussed by Hutchison et al.[428] The effect of spin-orbit interaction, Λ, is to mix into the $^8S_{7/2}$ state a small admixture of $^6P_{7/2}$ and $^6D_{7/2}$ character, as can be seen from the following approximate eigenvectors:[86]

$$Gd^{3+}\quad 0.9844|^8S) + 0.1736|^6P) - 0.0140|^6D),$$
$$Cm^{3+}\quad 0.8884|^8S) + 0.4197|^6P) - 0.0909|^6D).$$

This effect suggests the possibility that the ground state splitting may arise from a fourth-order mechanism which can be schematically represented by

$$(^8S_{7/2}|\Lambda|^6P_{7/2})(^6P_{7/2}|\Lambda|^6D_{7/2})(^6D_{7/2}|V_{crys}|^6P_{7/2})(^6P_{7/2}|\Lambda|^8S_{7/2}). \quad (6\text{-}47)$$

For this mechanism the splitting would be proportional to ζ_f^3 and *linear* in the crystal field. The crystal field matrix elements $(^6D_{7/2}|V_{crys}|^6P_{7/2})$ will be nonzero only for the B_0^2 and B_2^2, and therefore for crystals with at least a threefold axis of symmetry the splitting will be simply proportional to B_0^2. Calculations show that this mechanism will indeed give rise to splittings of the observed order. However, as Hutchison et al. have noted, this cannot be the sole mechanism of the ground-state splitting since there is not a simple linear relationship between the splittings observed in different crystals having the same point symmetry. They have proposed an additional fourth-order mechanism which may be represented schematically as follows:

$$(^8S_{7/2}|\Lambda|^6P_{7/2})(^6P_{7/2}|V_{crys}|^6X_J)(^6X_J|V_{crys}|^6P_{7/2})(^6P_{7/2}|\Lambda|^8S_{7/2}), \quad (6\text{-}48)$$

where X may be a D, G, or I state of f^7. The contributions of all these states must be considered in deriving the splitting. This mechanism will

---

* The reader interested in vibronic effects in the lanthanides should find the papers in References 388 and 420 to 424 of particular value.

† Abraham et al.[435] find the splitting in Cm^{3+} to be substantially larger. See also Reference 86.

be quadratic in V_{crys} and hence will lead to no simple relationship between the splittings in different crystals in accord with experimental observation. Hutchison et al. considered this mechanism as dominant. Their conclusion was, however, partly prejudiced by their assumption that B_0^2 was approximately zero for gadolinium ethylsulfate. We know now that B_0^2 is approximately 180 cm^{-1}, and the first mechanism must be therefore considered as dominant, although certainly not the sole source of the splitting.

Pryce[432] has suggested a second-order mechanism that may be represented schematically as

$$(4f^7, {}^8S_{7/2}|V_{s-s}|4f^66p, {}^8D_{7/2})(4f^66p, {}^8D_{7/2}|V_{crys}|4f^7, {}^8S_{7/2}), \quad (6\text{-}49)$$

where V_{s-s} is the spin-spin interaction. This mechanism is also linear in B_0^2 and could not, by itself, explain the observed splittings. Furthermore, the $4f^66p$ configuration is about 140,000 cm^{-1} above the $4f^7$, ${}^8S_{7/2}$ and hence this mechanism would probably lead to a rather smaller splitting than the first. Nevertheless, in explaining the observed splittings which are also very small, no mechanism can be completely ignored for all will give a finite splitting.

6-10   Intensities of Rare Earth Crystal and Solution Spectra

The optical transitions so typical of the spectra of rare earth ions in crystals and solutions usually correspond to intra-f^N transitions of predominantly electric-dipole character. For a free ion, electric-dipole transitions between states of the same configuration are strictly parity forbidden, and thus any explanation of the observed spectra of crystals or solutions must concern itself with noncentro-symmetric interactions that lead to a mixing of states of opposite parity. This mixing may result from several distinct mechanisms.[436,437] One of the most obvious mechanisms is simply the coupling of states of opposite parity by way of the *odd* terms in the crystal field expansion of Eq. 6-2.

Let $(\psi J J_z|$ and $|\psi'J'J_z')$ be two states of a configuration nl^N which become slightly admixed, by the crystal field, with states κ ($\equiv \psi''J''J_z''$) of the configurations $nl^{N-1}n'l'$ and $n'l'^{4l'+1}nl^{N+1}$ to yield two mixed parity states (A and B) such that

$$(A| = (\psi J J_z| - \sum_\kappa \frac{(\psi J J_z|V|\kappa)(\kappa|}{E(\psi J J_z) - E(\kappa)} \qquad (6\text{-}50a)$$

and

$$|B) = |\psi'J'J_z') - \sum_\kappa \frac{|\kappa)(\kappa|V|\psi'J'J_z')}{E(\psi'J'J_z') - E(\kappa)}. \qquad (6\text{-}50b)$$

The symmetry in a crystal is lower than spherical and we may therefore resolve the electric-dipole operator $\mathbf{P}$ into its x-, y-, and z-components by writing

$$\mathscr{P}_{\rho}^{(1)} = -\sum_{i} r_i (\mathbf{C}_{\rho}^{(1)})_i, \tag{6-51}$$

where $\rho = 0$ gives the z-components corresponding to the absorption or emission of π-polarized light and $\rho = \pm 1$ gives the $x \pm iy$ components for σ-polarized light. The nonzero matrix elements of $\mathscr{P}_{\rho}^{(1)}$ between the parity mixed states $(A|$ and $|B)$ will be

$$(A|\mathscr{P}_{\rho}^{(1)}|B) = -\sum_{\kappa} \frac{(\psi J J_z|V|\kappa)(\kappa|\mathscr{P}_{\rho}^{(1)}|\psi' J' J_z')}{E(\psi J J_z) - E(\kappa)}$$
$$-\sum_{\kappa} \frac{(\psi J J_z|\mathscr{P}_{\rho}^{(1)}|\kappa)(\kappa|V|\psi' J' J_z')}{E(\psi' J' J_z') - E(\kappa)} \tag{6-52}$$

where the summations are to be made over all the perturbing states. As it stands this summation is intractable. Following Judd[438] and Ofelt[439] we make the approximation of replacing the energy denominators by a single average denominator E_{av} and then make the closure* over the perturbing states to yield

$$(A|\mathscr{P}_{\rho}^{(1)}|B) = \sum_{\lambda, q} Y(\lambda, q, \rho)(l^N \alpha S L J J_z|U_{\rho+q}^{(\lambda)}|l^N \alpha' S L' J' J_z'), \tag{6-53}$$

where

$$Y(\lambda, q, \rho) = -\frac{2}{E_{\mathrm{av}}} \sum_{k} (-1)^{q+\rho}(2\lambda + 1) \begin{pmatrix} 1 & \lambda & k \\ \rho & -(q+\rho) & q \end{pmatrix} \begin{pmatrix} l & l & \lambda \\ 1 & k & l' \end{pmatrix}$$
$$\times (l\|\mathbf{C}^{(1)}\|l')(l'\|\mathbf{C}^{(k)}\|l)B_q^k e \int R_{nl}(r) r R_{n'l'}(r) \, dr. \tag{6-54}$$

This equation holds for a perturbing configuration of the type $nl^{N-1}n'l'$. Perturbing configurations of the type $n'l'^{4l'+1}nl^{N+1}$ will differ in the angular factors by not more than a phase factor. The summation index is limited to even values (that is, 2, 4, and 6 for f-electrons).

Several selection rules follow on application of the triangular conditions to the 3-j and 6-j symbols contained in Eqs. 6-53 and 6-54. These are as follows:

$$\Delta l = \pm 1; \quad \Delta S = 0; \quad \Delta L \leq 2l; \quad \Delta J \leq 2l.$$

The $\Delta l = \pm 1$ selection rule means that for f^N configurations the perturbing configurations may differ only by the single substitution of $n'd$- or $n'g$-electrons. Spin-orbit interaction will usually lead to a breakdown of the

---

* Ofelt[439] has given a detailed account of the closure, which may be greatly simplified if we change his order of summation first to sum $J''J_z''$, then L'', and finally over the states of the core.

selection rules on S and L. The selection rule $\Delta J \leq 6$ will be valid as long as J is a "good" quantum number. An example of this selection rule is seen in the absence of the transition $^6H_{15/2} \to {}^6F_{1/2}$ in most Dy^{3+} salts and solutions, whereas the $^6H_{15/2} \to {}^6F_{3/2}$ transition is readily observable. If the initial or final state has $J = 0$, an additional selection rule $\Delta J = 2$, 4, or 6 arises since λ is limited to even values. This selection rule is seen in the usual absence of the transitions $^5D_0 \to {}^7F_3$ and $^7F_5$ in Eu^{3+} spectra and to a lesser extent in the transitions $^7F_0 \to {}^7F_3$ and $^7F_5$ in Am^{3+} spectra.

The oscillator strength f_e of a transition at a wave number σ in a medium of refractive index η may be written as[437]

$$f_e = \frac{8\pi^2 mc}{3he^2} \sigma (A|\mathscr{P}_\rho^{(1)}|B)^2 \frac{(\eta^2 + 2)^2}{9} \qquad (6\text{-}55)$$

$$= \sigma \sum_{\lambda,q} \zeta(\lambda, q, \rho)(l^N\alpha SLJJ_z| U_{q+\rho}^{(\lambda)} |l^N\alpha' SL'J'J_z')^2, \qquad (6\text{-}56)$$

where

$$\zeta(\lambda, q, \rho) = \frac{8\pi^2 mc}{3he^2} \frac{(\eta^2 + 2)^2}{9} Y^2(\lambda, q, \rho). \qquad (6\text{-}57)$$

For a uniaxial crystal the x- and y-directions are equivalent and the oscillator strength of the σ-component will be the sum of Eq. 6-55 for $\rho = +1$ and $\rho = -1$.

The *odd* potential terms of V are, for D_{3h} symmetry,

$$B_3^3(\mathbf{C}_3^{(3)} - \mathbf{C}_{-3}^{(3)}) + B_3^5(\mathbf{C}_3^{(5)} - \mathbf{C}_{-3}^{(5)}) + B_3^7(\mathbf{C}_3^{(7)} - \mathbf{C}_{-3}^{(7)}). \qquad (6\text{-}58)$$

Then for π-polarization ($\rho = 0$) we have the selection rule $\Delta J_z = \pm 3$, or in terms of crystal quantum numbers $\Delta\mu = \pm 3$, and for σ-polarization ($\rho = \pm 1$) we have

$$\Delta J_z = \pm 2, \pm 4, \quad \text{or} \quad \Delta\mu = \pm 2, \pm 4.$$

These selection rules, which are identical to those for C_{3h} symmetry, are shown in Table 6-22. Note that the transitions $\mu = \pm\frac{5}{2} \leftrightarrow \mu' = \pm\frac{1}{2}$

TABLE 6-22 Crystal quantum number electric-dipole selection rules for D_{3h} symmetry

	Even Number Electrons				Odd Number Electrons		
	0	±1	±2	3	±½	±³⁄₂	±⁵⁄₂
0			σ	π	±½		σ	$\sigma\pi$
±1		σ	π	σ	±³⁄₂	σ	π	σ
±2	σ	π	σ	σ	±⁵⁄₂	$\sigma\pi$	σ	
3	π	σ						

occur in *both* π- and σ-polarizations, or more strictly, are elliptically polarized. The selection rules as they stand make no distinction between C_{3h} and D_{3h} symmetry.

For D_{3h} symmetry the irreducible representations of the point group form a wider class of labels than do the crystal quantum numbers.[299] Levels with $\mu = 0$ may be divided according to whether they transform as $^1\Gamma_1$ or $^1\Gamma_2$, and those with $\mu = 3$ divided according to their reducible representations $^1\Gamma_3$ and $^1\Gamma_4$. Now, for this symmetry z transforms as $^1\Gamma_4$, and x and y both transform as $^2\Gamma_6$. Thus for an even number of electrons we have

$$^1\Gamma_1 \times {}^1\Gamma_4 = {}^1\Gamma_4 \qquad {}^1\Gamma_1 \times {}^2\Gamma_6 = {}^2\Gamma_6$$
$$^1\Gamma_2 \times {}^1\Gamma_4 = {}^1\Gamma_3 \qquad {}^1\Gamma_2 \times {}^2\Gamma_6 = {}^2\Gamma_6$$
$$^1\Gamma_3 \times {}^1\Gamma_4 = {}^1\Gamma_2 \qquad {}^1\Gamma_3 \times {}^2\Gamma_6 = {}^2\Gamma_5$$
$$^1\Gamma_4 \times {}^1\Gamma_4 = {}^1\Gamma_1 \qquad {}^1\Gamma_4 \times {}^2\Gamma_6 = {}^2\Gamma_6$$
$$^2\Gamma_5 \times {}^1\Gamma_4 = {}^2\Gamma_6 \qquad {}^2\Gamma_5 \times {}^2\Gamma_6 = {}^2\Gamma_5 + {}^1\Gamma_3 + {}^1\Gamma_4$$
$$^2\Gamma_6 \times {}^1\Gamma_4 = {}^2\Gamma_5 \qquad {}^2\Gamma_6 \times {}^2\Gamma_6 = {}^2\Gamma_6 + {}^1\Gamma_1 + {}^1\Gamma_2$$

from which we may deduce the selection rules shown in Table 6-23.

TABLE 6-23   Electric-dipole selection rules for D_{3h} symmetry
Even Number Electrons

		$\mu = 0$		$\mu = 3$		$\mu = \pm 1$	$\mu = \pm 2$
		$^1\Gamma_1$	$^1\Gamma_2$	$^1\Gamma_3$	$^1\Gamma_4$	$^2\Gamma_5$	$^2\Gamma_6$
$\mu = 0$	$^1\Gamma_1$				π		σ
	$^1\Gamma_2$			π			σ
$\mu = 3$	$^1\Gamma_3$		π			σ	
	$^1\Gamma_4$	π				σ	
$\mu = \pm 1$	$^2\Gamma_5$			σ	σ	σ	π
$\mu = \pm 2$	$^2\Gamma_6$	σ	σ			π	σ

Thus, although the D_{3h} and C_{3h} symmetries are usually indistinguishable on the basis of their crystal field splittings, they may be readily distinguished by their different behavior with respect to polarization. Again we see that for an even number of electrons the physical properties of the states are frequently better described by the irreducible representations of the point group rather than by the crystal quantum numbers. The irreducible representations of the point symmetry group form a set of good quantum numbers irrespective of the coupling of the electrons in the crystal field. Therefore the selection rules involving the irreducible representations should be rigorously obeyed provided there are no deviations from the assigned point symmetry.

Selection rules may also be developed for a crystal in an applied magnetic field. If the field is in a direction specified by $\mathbf{j}$ and $(\mathbf{L} + g_s\mathbf{S}) \cdot \mathbf{j}$ transforms by some other representation, the selection rules will correspond to those of the largest subgroup for which $(\mathbf{L} + g_s\mathbf{S}) \cdot \mathbf{j}$ is invariant. Thus for D_{3h} symmetry $(L_z + g_sS_z)$ transforms as $^1\Gamma_2$, but application of the field along the z-axis destroys the twofold axes of symmetry, reducing it to C_{3h}. The appropriate selection rules will then correspond to those of C_{3h} since $(L_z + g_sS_z)$ then transforms as $^1\Gamma_1$ of C_{3h}.

Let us now return to the calculation of oscillator strengths. In a solution the structure associated with the removal of the J_z degeneracy by the microfields surrounding the rare earth ions is usually smeared out to leave Gaussian-shaped bands. The measured oscillator strength of such a band will be the sum of the oscillator strengths of the various component lines weighted to allow for the differential occupancy of the compounds of the initial level. In the absence of a detailed knowledge of these weighting factors we shall assume that the components are equally populated. This assumption will not always be valid.[440] Then for a solution we may write

$$f = \sigma \sum_\lambda T_\lambda (l^N\alpha SLJ \| U^{(\lambda)} \| l^N\alpha' SL'J')^2/(2J + 1), \qquad (6\text{-}59)$$

where

$$T_\lambda = \sum_{q,\rho} \zeta(\lambda, q, \rho). \qquad (6\text{-}60)$$

The matrix elements of Eq. 6-69 may be readily transformed from the SLJ-basis to the physical scheme by use of the eigenvectors obtained from the diagonalization of the free ion energy matrices. For a crystal the transformation from the $SLJJ_z$ basis to the physical scheme may be made using the eigenvectors found in the calculation of the crystal field energy levels.

The odd terms in the crystal field expansion of Eq. 6-2 will vanish if the rare earth ion is at a center of inversion and there will be no pure electric-dipole transitions. However, transitions may be excited by the vibrational modes of the complex surrounding the rare earth ion. If we suppose the crystal field parameters B_q^k correspond to some equilibrium arrangement of the complex, then for small vibrations we may replace Eq. 6-2 by

$$V' = \sum_{kq} \left[B_q^k + \sum_i \frac{\partial B_q^k}{\partial Q_i} \right] C_q^{(k)}, \qquad (6\text{-}2a)$$

where the normal coordinates of the vibrating complex are designated by Q_i. Judd[438] has shown that the dynamic term in Eq. 6-2a leads to an additional contribution f' to the oscillator strength. For a crystal

$$f' = \sigma \sum_{\lambda,q} \zeta'(\lambda, q, \rho)(l^N\alpha SLJJ_z | U_{q+\rho}^{(\lambda)} | l^N\alpha' SL'J'J_z')^2, \qquad (6\text{-}61)$$

where the $\zeta'(\lambda, q, \rho)$'s are identical to those of Eq. 6-57 except that in $Y(\lambda, q, \rho)$ (see Eq. 6-54) the quantities B_q^{k2} are replaced by the quantities

$$\sum_{i,\tau,\tau'} \left|\frac{\partial B_q^k}{\partial Q_i}\right|^2 |(\tau|Q_i|\tau')^2 \rho(\tau). \tag{6-62}$$

In this equation τ and τ' stand for the totality of the vibrational quantum numbers, whereas $\rho(\tau)$ is the probability that the vibrating complex is in a state defined by the quantum numbers τ.

Vibronic transitions will occur only if there is a change in the vibrational quantum numbers τ, and thus they will occur at energies that differ from the pure electric-dipole transitions by one or more vibrational quanta. These two types of transitions may be frequently (although not always!) distinguishable in crystal spectra. However, in solution spectra no such distinction will be possible. In general, we do not yet know enough about the detailed energy structure of rare earth ions and their interaction with the environment to be able to make absolute calculations of the quantities like T_λ, although Judd[438] has made some preliminary estimates. Consequently, it is usual to treat these quantities as parameters to be derived from the data.

Magnetic-dipole and electric-quadrupole transitions may also contribute to the oscillator strengths. The theory of magnetic-dipole transitions in free ions has been developed by Pasternack[441] and Shortley[442] among others. For a magnetic-dipole transition we have[436,437]

$$f_m = \frac{8\pi^2 mc}{3he^2} \sigma \left|\frac{-e}{2mc} (\alpha SLJJ_z|\mathbf{L} + g_s\mathbf{S}|\alpha SLJJ_z')\right|^2 \eta$$

$$= 4.028 \times 10^{-11}\sigma(\alpha SLJJ_z|\mathbf{L} + g_s\mathbf{S}|\alpha SLJ'J_z')^2\eta, \tag{6-63}$$

where σ is in units of cm^{-1}. The matrix elements of $\mathbf{L} + g_s\mathbf{S}$ will be given by

$$(\alpha SLJJ_z|\mathbf{L} + g_s\mathbf{S}|\alpha SLJ'J_z') = (-1)^{J-J_z}\begin{pmatrix} J & 1 & J' \\ -J_z & \rho & J_z' \end{pmatrix}$$

$$\times (\alpha SLJ\|\mathbf{L} + g_s\mathbf{S}\|\alpha SLJ'), \tag{6-64}$$

where $\rho = 0$ gives the z-components of $\mathbf{S}$ and $\mathbf{L}$ which will correspond to the absorption or emission of σ-polarized light, and $\rho = \pm 1$ gives the $x \pm iy$-components corresponding to π-polarized light.*

The following selection rules may be readily established:

$$\Delta l = 0; \quad \Delta S = 0; \quad \Delta L = 0; \quad \Delta J = 0, \pm 1 \quad (\text{not } 0 \leftrightarrow 0),$$
$$\Delta J_z = 0 \qquad\qquad\qquad\qquad \Delta\mu = 0 \quad (\sigma\text{-polarization}),$$
$$\Delta J_z = \pm 1 \qquad\qquad\qquad\qquad \Delta\mu = \pm 1 \quad (\pi\text{-polarization}).$$

---

* The reader will recall that the magnetic vector is perpendicular to the electric vector.

We note that magnetic-dipole transitions are possible only between states of the same configuration. In the limit of LS coupling these transitions will occur only between two levels of the same term. In the presence of intermediate coupling the selection rules on S and L will be broken, and then transitions may occur between two levels if they contain admixtures of a common LS basis state. For example, in europium salts, magnetic-dipole transitions occur between the levels $^7F_0$ and $^5D_1$ as a result of spin-orbit interaction mixing into each level a small admixture of the other state. There are comparatively few possibilities of obtaining optical magnetic-dipole transitions in the lanthanides apart from observing transitions within their ground multiplets. However, magnetic-dipole transitions should be more favored in the actinides where there is considerable intermediate coupling.*

The magnetic-dipole selection rules on the crystal field states labeled by the irreducible representations of the point group may be found once the representations by which L_z, L_x, and L_y transform are determined. For D_{3h} symmetry L_z transforms as $^1\Gamma_2$, and L_x and L_y both transform as $^2\Gamma_5$. The selection rules for D_{3h} symmetry are shown in Table 6-24.

TABLE 6-24　　Magnetic dipole selection rules for D_{3h} symmetry

Even Number Electrons

	$\mu = 0$		$\mu = 3$		$\mu = \pm 1$	$\mu = \pm 2$
	$^1\Gamma_1$	$^1\Gamma_2$	$^1\Gamma_3$	$^1\Gamma_4$	$^2\Gamma_5$	$^2\Gamma_6$
$\mu = 0\ \{^1\Gamma_1$		σ			π	
$\phantom{\mu = 0\ \{}^1\Gamma_2$	σ				π	
$\mu = 3\ \{^1\Gamma_3$				σ		σ
$\phantom{\mu = 3\ \{}^1\Gamma_4$			σ		π	
$\mu = \pm 1\ ^2\Gamma_5$	π	π		π	σ	
$\mu = \pm 2\ ^2\Gamma_6$			π			σ

Odd Number Electrons

	$\mu = \pm\tfrac{1}{2}$	$\mu = \pm\tfrac{5}{2}$	$\mu = \pm\tfrac{3}{2}$
	$^2\Gamma_7$	$^2\Gamma_8$	$^2\Gamma_9$
$\mu = \pm\tfrac{1}{2}\ ^2\Gamma_7$	σ		π
$\mu = \pm\tfrac{5}{2}\ ^2\Gamma_8$		σ	π
$\mu = \pm\tfrac{3}{2}\ ^2\Gamma_9$	π	π	σ

---

* An interesting exception is found in the absorption spectrum of Am^{3+} where the computed magnetic dipole oscillator strength of the $^7F_0 \rightarrow {}^5D_1$ transition is very much *less* than for the analogous transition in Eu^{3+}. See W. T. Carnall, P. R. Fields, and B. G. Wybourne, *J. Chem. Phys.*, **41**, 2195 (1964).

Sayre et al.[443] have given a simple, and unambiguous, method of distinguishing between electric- and magnetic-dipole transitions in uniaxial crystals. Essentially their method consists of observing both the isotropic *axial* spectrum and the *transverse* spectrum. The transverse spectrum is separated into its two components by polarizing the incident light (in the case of absorption spectra) so that its electric vector is oriented parallel with or perpendicular to the optic axis. During the observation of the axial spectrum both the electric and magnetic vectors of the incident light are orientated perpendicular to the optic axis. In the observation of the σ-polarized transverse spectrum only the electric vector of the incident light is perpendicular to the optic axis, and during the observation of the π-polarized transverse spectrum only the magnetic vector is perpendicular to the axis. Therefore, if the axial- and the σ-spectra coincide, the transition must be electric dipole, whereas if the π-spectrum coincides with the axial spectrum, the transition must be magnetic dipole.

The oscillator strength for a magnetic-dipole transition in a solution may be found by summing over the J_z quantum numbers and the polarizations in Eq. 6-63 to yield

$$f_m = 4.028 \times 10^{-11}\sigma|(\alpha SLJ|\mathbf{L} + g_s\mathbf{S}|\alpha SLJ')|^2 \frac{\eta}{(2J + 1)}, \quad (6\text{-}65)$$

where

$$(\alpha SLJ|\mathbf{L} + g_s\mathbf{S}|\alpha SLJ) = [J(J + 1)(2J + 1)]^{1/2}g \quad (6\text{-}66)$$

and

$$(\alpha SLJ|\mathbf{L} + g_s\mathbf{S}|\alpha SLJ - 1) = (g_s - 1)$$
$$\times \left[\frac{(S + L + J + 1)(J + L - S)(J + S - L)(S + L - J + 1)}{4J}\right]^{1/2}.$$
$$(6\text{-}67)$$

Pure electric-quadrupole transitions are unlikely to be observed in rare earth ion spectra, for their computed oscillator strengths fall several magnitudes below the observed oscillator strengths.[437,444] The oscillator strength for an electric-quadrupole transition in a free ion or solution is given by [437]

$$f_q = \frac{4\pi^4 mc}{5he^2}\sigma^3\frac{\mathscr{S}_q(\alpha SLJ; \alpha'SL'J')}{2J + 1}\frac{\eta(\eta^2 + 2)^2}{9}, \quad (6\text{-}68)$$

where [445]

$$\mathscr{S}_q^{1/2}(\alpha SLJ; \alpha'SL'J') = \frac{-2e}{3}\left(l^N\alpha SLJ\|\sum_i r_i^2\mathbf{C}_i^{(2)}\|l^N\alpha'SL'J'\right). \quad (6\text{-}69)$$

On evaluating the matrix element in Eq. 6-69, we have for a configuration l^N

$$f_q = T_2'\sigma^3\frac{(l^N\alpha SLJ\|\mathbf{U}^{(2)}\|l^N\alpha'SL'J')^2}{2J + 1}, \quad (6\text{-}70)$$

where

$$T_2' = \frac{16\pi^4 mc}{45h} (l\|\mathbf{C}^{(2)}\|l)^2 s_q{}^2(nl; nl) \frac{\eta(\eta^2 + 2)^2}{9} \tag{6-71}$$

and

$$s_q(nl; nl) = \int R_{nl}(r) r^2 R_{nl}(r) \, dr. \tag{6-72}$$

The electric-dipole oscillator strengths given by Eq. 6-52 have exactly the same angular dependence for $\lambda = 2$ as does Eq. 6-70 for the electric-quadrupole oscillator strengths. Judd[438] has noted that certain transitions of the lanthanide solution spectra are hypersensitive to changes in their environment. Furthermore, these transitions all have $\Delta J \leq 2$ and are associated with unusually large matrix elements of $\mathbf{U}^{(2)}$. Thus they appear to be extremely sensitive to the parameter T_2. Jørgensen and Judd[444] have cogently reasoned that the hypersensitive nature of the transitions is most unlikely to be associated with changes in their electric-dipole or vibronic character. Instead they have suggested that there is an asymmetrical distribution of the dipoles induced by the electro-magnetic field in the medium surrounding the lanthanide ion and consequently, the variation of the electric vector across the ion is very much greater than for a homogeneous dielectric. Thus the intensities of electric quadrupole transitions may be enormously enhanced and will be critically dependent on the environment. These transitions are said to be pseudoelectric quadrupole. The angular and frequency dependences of the pseudoelectric quadrupole and $\lambda = 2$ terms of the electric-dipole oscillator strengths are identical.

The theory of the intensities of rare earth crystal and solution spectra is still very much at a developmental stage, although the calculations of Judd[438] and Axe[440] give support to the theory as it stands. Further development should depend largely on gaining a deeper understanding of the interaction of rare earth ions with their environment.

6-11   Crystal Field Models

We have seen in the preceding sections how the simple expansion of the crystal field into a series of spherical harmonics or tensor operators that transform like spherical harmonics, as in Eq. 6-2, leads to a surprisingly successful phenomenological description of the properties of rare earth ions in crystals. The terms in the infinite series have been limited by the application of symmetry restrictions, whereas the coefficients of the expansion have been treated as crystal field parameters. The success of the phenomenological treatment of crystal field theory is largely attributable to the correct description of the symmetry properties of the crystal field.

To discover properties of the crystal field other than its symmetry it is necessary to construct a model that will give a rational explanation of the crystal field parameters.

Crystal field theory as it was first developed[270] was conceived as a purely electrostatic field perturbing the wave function of the central ion, the surrounding ions having been replaced by point changes. More generally, the environment may be represented by a classical electrostatic charge distribution $\rho(\mathbf{R})$ which is a function of position. The potential energy $V(\mathbf{r})$ for an electron of the central ion will be given by

$$V(\mathbf{r}) = -\int \frac{e\rho(\mathbf{R})\,d\tau}{|\mathbf{R} - \mathbf{r}|},\qquad(6\text{-}73)$$

where $\mathbf{r}$ is the position of the electron, $\mathbf{R}$ a general point in the environment, and the integration is over the variables $\mathbf{R}(R,\ \Theta,\ \Phi)$. This potential may be expanded in terms of Legendre polynomials and then the spherical harmonic addition theorem applied to yield

$$V(r) = \sum_{k,q} B_q^k \mathbf{C}_q^{(k)},$$

where

$$B_q^k = -e\int \rho(R)\,\frac{r_<^k}{r_>^{k+1}}\,(-1)^q \mathbf{C}_{-q}^{(k)}(\Theta,\ \Phi)\,d\tau.$$

If we consider the environment to be entirely external to the central ion (that is, $R > r$), the potential will then satisfy Laplace's equation and we may write

$$B_q^k = A_q^k \langle r^k \rangle,\qquad(6\text{-}74)$$

where

$$A_q^k = -e\int \frac{\rho(R)}{R^{k+1}}\,(-1)^q \mathbf{C}_q^{(k)}(\Theta,\ \Phi)\,d\tau.\qquad(6\text{-}75)$$

The detailed calculation of the crystal field parameters of the type $A_q^k\langle r^k\rangle$ for an electrostatic model has been considered by Hutchison and Wong,[446] Burns,[447] and Hutchings and Ray.[448] These calculations are fraught with serious difficulties. Burns[447] has shown that the structural parameters A_q^k are extremely sensitive to the positions of the ions. Furthermore, it is not at all clear how much charge should be assigned to each ion or how to estimate correctly the dipole (and higher) moments of molecules such as H_2O. In a perfect cubic crystal this latter problem should not arise since there can be no induced moments if all the ions have the normal valency.[449] The expectation values $\langle r^k\rangle$ for the f-electron have usually been taken directly from the Hartree-Fock wave functions of the free ion.[120]

Hutchings and Ray[448] have made a quite sophisticated calculation of the B_q^k parameters for $PrCl_3$ and $PrBr_3$ assuming the electrostatic model and using the lattice constants determined from x-ray crystallographic studies.[450,451] The calculated value of B_0^2 was twenty to thirty times the experimental value, that of B_0^4 showed quite reasonable agreement, and both B_0^6 and B_6^6 were about four to ten times smaller. The ratios of B_6^6/B_0^6 were in very good agreement with experiment; however, this result has more to do with the symmetry and structure of the crystal than with the validity of the electrostatic model.

Several attempts have been made to explain the discrepancies of the electrostatic model in terms of the shielding, or polarization, produced by the closed shells.[452-454] These calculations attempt to give a more realistic account of the wave function of the central ion by recognizing that the lower states of the rare earth ion should not be visualized as being derived solely from the f^N configuration, but rather as also containing admixtures of states from many excited configurations. These admixtures will result from two distinct mechanisms: (1) crystal field mixing of the states of f^N with excited states of both parities to yield admixed states as in Eq. 6-50; (2) electrostatic configuration interactions of the states of f^N with excited states of the same parity to yield admixed states of the type given in Eq. 6-50, except V is replaced by the corresponding electrostatic operators. Rajnak and Wybourne[112] have studied the effects of both mechanisms and shown that first mechanism results in a simple shielding (or antishielding) of crystal field parameters.* This mechanism is, however, incapable of ameliorating the discrepancies.†

The second mechanism involves electrostatically correlated crystal field interactions and gives rise to both *linear* and *nonlinear* shielding terms. The linear shielding is dominant[452-454] and its inclusion overcomes a large part of the discrepancies between the calculated and experimental B_q^k values. The nonlinear shielding arises from single electron substitutions into or from the f^N shell and results in the appearance of angular dependent terms of the type

$$\left(l^N \psi J J_z \left| \sum_{i>j} \{ \mathbf{C}_i^{(\varkappa)} \mathbf{C}_j^{(\varkappa')} \}^{(k)} \right| l^N \psi' J' J_z' \right). \tag{6-76}$$

These new angular quantities have the same JJ_z dependence as the $C_q^{(k)}$'s of the crystal field expansion of Eq. 6-2; however, they do differ in their

---

* This substantiates the idea that although the *odd* terms in the crystal field expansion are important in giving rise to induced electric-dipole transitions, they do not appear to be at all important in calculating crystal field splittings.

† This mechanism does, however, give rise to very large electric-quadrupole antishielding factors in the rare earths.[455-461]

dependence on the αSL quantum numbers. In a phenomenological treatment this amounts to associating different sets of B_q^k parameters with each multiplet. It is interesting to note that Eisenstein[340,392] has shown that in the rare earth crystal spectra it is not possible to find a single set of B^k parameters using Eq. 6-2 that will describe adequately the crystal field levels that are derived from different free ion states.

At this stage we might feel that the electrostatic model does indeed give a valid interpretation of the crystal field parameters if we are sufficiently careful in our treatment of shielding effects; thus the electrostatic model is physically significant. However, in many ways the shielding calculations are unrealistic in their use of free ion wave functions in what is basically a solid-state situation. The $\langle r^k \rangle$ values have been calculated without any recognition of the expansion of the wave function in the solid state. More seriously, the 4f-ionization energy in the solid state will be drastically reduced, with the result that the continuum states will assume far greater importance than in the free ion.

The pure electrostatic model is in direct conflict with a large body of experimental data. The model is completely unable to say anything about the role of f-electrons in chemical bonding.[278,279]* The commonly made assumption that there is no overlap of the central ion with its surroundings cannot be justified. The spatial extensions of the free ion wave functions indeed lead us to expect an appreciable overlapping.[448] The existence of the nephelauxetic effect cannot be explained on the basis of the electrostatic model without assuming an overlapping of the charge clouds of the central ion and its ligands.[112] The existence of vibronic transitions in rare earth crystals shows that the rare earth ions are not isolated from the lattice, but are, in fact, coupled to the vibrational modes. The observation of absorption and fluorescence involving rare earth ion pairs[462-467] is indicative of a coupling between the rare earth ions.[468] Studies by Van Uitert et al.[469] have shown that the fluorescence of rare earth salts undergo a concentration quenching, which they have suggested is a direct result of the mixing of f-orbital wave functions of different rare earth ions via the lattice. Selective excitation experiments[470] have shown that only some of the excited states of rare earth salt fluoresce, whereas for many of the salts fluorescence is entirely absent. Katzin and Barnett[471] have marshalled considerable evidence for the participation of f-orbitals in the chemical bonding of rare earth complexes. Finally, Baker and Hurrell[472] have observed interaction between Eu^{2+} ions and fluorine nuclei in CaF_2 by means of an electron nuclear, double resonance experiment. Thus it

---

* We note from Earnshaw's theorem of electrostatics that this model cannot lead to a stable crystal structure.

is apparent that the electrostatic model is lacking in the physical content needed to encompass a wide range of experimental data.

The crystal field expansion used in Eq. 6-2 has been quite successful in describing the observed crystal field splittings as long as the coefficients of the expansion are treated as phenomenological parameters. In developing a more sophisticated model we expect the symmetry properties used in applications of Eq. 6-2 to continue to play a vital role. We seek a theory that will not only give a realistic interpretation of the parameters but will also have sufficient physical content to encompass those properties that are clearly outside the domain of the electrostatic model.

As a first step we might regard the spherically symmetric field of the isolated rare earth ion as being replaced by a core field due to the ion itself and its overlapping ligands. This field will have the symmetry of the complex formed by the rare earth ion and its associated ligands rather than the point symmetry of the lattice site or the lattice space group.* For example, in praseodymium ethylsulfate, $Pr(C_2H_5SO_4)_3 \cdot 9H_2O$, the complex will be $Pr(H_2O)_9^{3+}$ and the relevant symmetry is D_{3h} rather than the lower C_{3h} symmetry of the lattice site or the C_{6h} symmetry of the lattice space group.†

The core field may be regarded as possessing components of descending symmetry as discussed in Sec. 6-4. The largest component will have spherical symmetry and will have the effect of *expanding* the wave function of the rare earth ion, giving rise to the well-known nephelauxetic effect. This expansion will preserve the angular properties of the atomic orbitals of the rare earth ion. The components of lower symmetry will contribute to the removal of the degeneracy of the states of the gaseous ion. Jørgensen[278,279,473-475] has emphasized that this model leads to the recognition that the radial integrals associated with the gaseous ion are *not* equivalent to those of the ion in a solid-state or liquid-state environment.

To obtain quantitative results it is necessary to further develop the model. The most obvious extension is to treat the rare earth ion complex from the point of view of molecular orbital (abbreviated as MO) theory. In the most general case, MO theory includes the interaction of all the nuclei and electrons of the solid, and hence should contain sufficient physical content to explain most of the experimental observations. The electrostatic model is obtained from MO theory as the special case where there is no overlapping of the ligands with the atomic orbitals of the

---

* Jørgensen[473] has given a fascinating discussion of relevant and irrelevant symmetry components.

† Experimentally, we find that the selection rules for optical transitions are frequently those associated with the higher symmetry of the complex rather than the lower symmetry of the lattice site.

central ion.   For practical purposes the MO description must be severely restricted in its development.

The simplest treatment is to construct linear combinations of the atomic orbitals (LCAO) of both the central rare earth ions and its associated ligands.   The orbitals constructed for the rare earth ion complex by the LCAO method will be of the form [476,477]

$$\Psi = \psi(\Gamma) + \sum_i a_i \psi_i, \qquad (6\text{-}77)$$

where $\psi(\Gamma)$ is a wave function of the rare earth ion which transforms according to the representation of the symmetry group of the complex and $\sum_i a_i \psi_i$ is a linear combination of the ligand wave functions.   Cross terms between the wave function of the rare earth ion and those of its ligands will only occur if $\sum_i a_i \psi_i$ also transforms invariantly under the same irreducible representation as $\psi(\Gamma)$.   Thus, if we know the irreducible representations under which the atomic orbitals of the rare earth ion transform for a particular complex, we may immediately decide on the orbitals of the ligands that are available for bonding.   Furthermore, we may then determine the basic functions for forming the linear combinations of ψ_i. Eisenstein [478] has given an extensive tabulation of basis functions for most of the groups of interest.

It is apparent from the preceding discussion that both MO theory and the electrostatic crystal field theory have a common group-theoretical basis and hence yield equivalent descriptions of properties that depend solely on symmetry.   The two descriptions will, of course, have different quantitative properties.   These two points were first expounded by Van Vleck.[476,477]   Thus the success of the crystal field expansion in Eq. 6-2 is simply due to its correct description of the symmetry aspects of the distortions of the atomic orbitals of the rare earth ion by its associated ligands.   The amalgamation of MO theory and the electrostatic crystal field theory has become known as *ligand field theory*.   A generalized treatment of the MO theory, with the inclusion of exchange, has been developed by Jarrett.[479]   He has shown that the effects of exchange lead to the association of different B_q^k parameters with each irreducible representation.   As yet no quantitative estimates have been made, but it would appear that these effects are relatively small because otherwise it is difficult to see how the usual ligand field theory could have obtained its present status.

At the present time no molecular orbital calculations are available for any rare earth complex.   Jørgensen et al.[480] have made a preliminary attack on the problem using the Wolfsberg-Helmholz [481] approximation to estimate the overlap integrals of the rare earth ion with its ligands. Their calculation is of great interest and shows that the crystal field parameters can be interpreted in terms of a relatively weak covalent bonding involving the f-orbitals. In essence they regard the B_q^k parameters as simply keeping track of the seven one-electron energies of the f-orbitals in the presence of σ-antibonding. This approach has particular emphasis on the energy contributions that arise from the overlapping of the atomic orbitals.

Experience in the transition ions[481-487] has shown all too often that calculations of crystal field parameters frequently yield the right order of magnitude only to result in a deterioration in agreement on further refinement or to lead to agreement simply as a result of a fortuitous cancellation of neglected interactions. Nevertheless, it would seem that future developments in the understanding of rare earth crystal spectra will draw heavily on the concepts of molecular orbital theory. The qualitative features of MO theory are already present in ligand field theory. The development of the quantitative features of MO theory will not be easy. We can anticipate many surprises and perhaps not a few false starts.

References

1. M. G. Mayer, *Phys. Rev.*, **60**, 184 (1941).
2. R. Latter, *Phys. Rev.*, **99**, 510 (1955).
3. C. A. Coulson and C. S. Sharma, *Proc. Phys. Soc. (London)*, **79**, 920 (1962).
4. C. K. Jørgensen, *J. Inorg. Nuclear Chem.*, **1**, 301 (1955).
5. W. F. Meggers, *Science*, **105**, 514 (1947).
6. H. N. Russell and W. F. Meggers, *J. Research Natl. Bur. Standards*, **9**, 625 (1932).
7. W. C. Martin, *J. Opt. Soc. Am.*, **53**, 1047 (1963).
8. C. E. Moore, Atomic Energy Levels, *Natl. Bur. Standards Circ.* 467 (1958).
9. W. F. Meggers, *J. Opt. Soc. Am.*, **31**, 157 (1941).
10. Marrus, Nierenberg, and Winocur, *Nuclear Phys.*, **23**, 90 (1961).
11. P. F. A. Klinkenberg and R. J. Lang, *Physica*, **15**, 774 (1949).
12. Bleaney, Llewellyn, and Jones, *Proc. Phys. Soc. (London)*, **B69**, 858 (1956).
13. Diamond, Street, and Seaborg, *J. Am. Chem. Soc.*, **76**, 1461 (1954).
14. R. J. Elliott, *Phys. Rev.*, **89**, 659 (1953).
15. J. C. Eisenstein and M. H. L. Pryce, *Proc. Roy. Soc. (London)*, **A229**, 20 (1955).
16. *Ibid.*, **A238**, 31 (1956).
17. *Ibid.*, **A255**, 181 (1960).
18. S. P. McGlynn and J. K. Smith, *J. Mol. Spectroscopy*, **6**, 164 (1961).
19. L. B. Asprey and B. B. Cunningham, *Prog. Inorg. Chem.*, **2**, 267 (1960).
20. B. B. Cunningham, *Int. Congr. Pure Appl. Chem.*, **17**, 64 (1959).
21. N. V. Sidgwick, *The Chemical Elements and Their Compounds*, Vol. 1, Clarendon Press, Oxford (1950).
22. W. Hayes and J. W. Twidell, *J. Chem. Phys.*, **35**, 1521 (1961).
23. Z. J. Kiss in *Lasers and Applications*, W. S. C. Chang, Ed., Ohio State University Press, Columbus (1963).
24. D. S. McClure and Z. J. Kiss, *J. Chem. Phys.*, **39**, 3251 (1963).
25. R. A. Marrus and W. A. Nierenberg, *Rendiconti S.I.F.*, **17**, 118 (1962).
26. I. Eastermann, *Recent Research in Molecular Beams*, Academic Press, New York (1959).
27. W. Low, *Paramagnetic Resonance in Solids*, Academic Press, New York (1960).
28. G. E. Pake, *Paramagnetic Resonance*, W. A. Benjamin, New York (1962).

29. M. A. El'yashevich, *Spectra of the Rare Earths*, State Publishing House of Technical-Theoretical Literature, Moscow (1953). Also available as U.S. Atomic Energy Commission Translation, AEC-tr 4403, Office of Technical Information, Department of Commerce, Washington, D.C. (1961).

30. H. G. Kuhn, *Atomic Spectra*, Academic Press, New York (1962).

31. H. N. Russell, *J. Opt. Soc. Am.*, **40**, 550 (1950).

32. J. Sugar, *J. Opt. Soc. Am.*, **53**, 831 (1963).

33. E. U. Condon and G. H. Shortley, *The Theory of Atomic Spectra*, Cambridge University Press, Cambridge (1935).

34. J. S. Griffiths, *Theory of Transition-Metal Ions*, Cambridge University Press, Cambridge (1961).

35. J. C. Slater, *The Quantum Theory of Atomic Structure*, Vols. I and II, McGraw-Hill Book Company, New York (1960).

36. D. R. Hartree, *The Calculation of Atomic Structures*, John Wiley and Sons, New York (1957).

37. G. Racah, *Phys. Rev.*, **76**, 1352 (1949).

38. G. Racah, *Group Theory and Spectroscopy*, mimeographed notes, Princeton (1951). These notes are available as a CERN (Geneva) reprint.

39. B. R. Judd, *Operator Techniques in Atomic Spectroscopy*, McGraw-Hill Book Company, New York (1963).

40. G. Racah, *Phys. Rev.*, **62**, 438 (1942).

41. *Ibid.*, **63**, 367 (1943).

42. B. G. Wybourne, *J. Chem. Phys.*, **36**, 2295 (1962).

43. C. W. Nielson and G. F. Koster, *Spectroscopic Coefficients for p^n, d^n and f^n Configurations*, M.I.T. Press, Cambridge, Mass. (1964).

44. A. R. Edmonds, *Angular Momentum in Quantum Mechanics*, Princeton University Press, Princeton (1960).

45. U. Fano and G. Racah, *Irreducible Tensorial Sets*, Academic Press, New York (1959).

46. Rotenberg, Bivins, Metropolis, and Wooten, *The 3-j and 6-j Symbols*, M.I.T. Press, Cambridge, Mass. (1959).

47. W. T. Sharp, *Racah Algebra and the Contraction of Groups*, A.E.C.L. Report No. 1098, Chalk River, Ontario (1960).

48. Yutsis, Levinson, and Vanagas, "Theory of Angular Momentum," *Akad. Nauk Lit. SSR Institut Fiziki i Matematiki*, Publication No. 3 (1960). Also available as U.S. National Aeronautic and Space Administration Translation, TT F-98, Office of Technical Information, Department of Commerce, Washington, D.C. (1961).

49. K. Rajnak and B. G. Wybourne, *Phys. Rev.*, **132**, 280 (1963).

50. N. Rosenzweig, *Phys. Rev.*, **88**, 580 (1952).

51. B. G. Wybourne, *J. Math. Phys.*, **4**, 354 (1963).

52. Fano, Prats, and Goldschmidt, *Phys. Rev.*, **129**, 2643 (1963).

53. B. R. Judd, *Phys. Rev.*, **125**, 613 (1962).

54. F. R. Innes and C. W. Ufford, *Phys. Rev.*, **111**, 194 (1958).

55. Arima, Horie, and Tanabe, *Progr. Theoret. Phys. (Japan)*, **11**, 143 (1954).

56. B. G. Wybourne, *J. Chem. Phys.*, **34**, 279 (1961).

57. B. G. Wybourne, *J. Chem. Phys.*, **36**, 2301 (1962).

58. Elliott, Judd, and Runciman, *Proc. Roy. Soc. (London)*, **A240**, 509 (1957).

59. B. R. Judd and R. Loudon, *Proc. Roy. Soc. (London)*, **A251**, 127 (1959).

60. M. H. Crozier and W. A. Runciman, *J. Chem. Phys.*, **35**, 1392 (1961); *ibid.*, **36**, 1088 (1962).

61. F. H. Spedding, *Phys. Rev.*, **58**, 255 (1940).
62. A. G. McLellan, *Proc. Phys. Soc. (London)*, **76**, 419 (1960).
63. B. G. Wybourne, *J. Chem. Phys.*, **35**, 334 (1961).
64. B. R. Judd, *J. Math. Phys.*, **3**, 557 (1962).
65. Trees, Cahill, and Rabinowitz, *J. Research Natl. Bur. Standards*, **55**, 335 (1955).
66. G. Racah, *Bull. Res. Council Israel*, **8F**, 1 (1959).
67. B. R. Judd, *Proc. Roy. Soc. (London)*, **A228**, 120 (1955).
68. D. Kessler, *Physica*, **17**, 913 (1951).
69. R. Lang, *Can. J. Research.*, **A13**, 1 (1935); **A14**, 127 (1936).
70. B. W. Bryant, *Johns Hopkins University Spectroscopic Report* No. 21 (1961).
71. de Bruin, Schuurmans, and Klinkenberg, *Z. Phys.*, **121**, 667 (1943).
72. J. R. McNally, *J. Opt. Soc. Am.*, **35**, 390 (1945).
73. G. E. M. A. Hassan, Doctoral Dissertation, University of Amsterdam (1962).
74. G. E. M. A. Hassan, *Physica*, **29**, 1119 (1963).
75. G. E. M. A. Hassan and P. F. A. Klinkenberg, *Physica*, **29**, 1133 (1963).
76. P. Schuurmans, *Physica*, **11**, 419 (1946).
77. W. Albertson, *Phys. Rev.*, **52**, 644 (1937).
78. B. R. Judd, *Proc. Phys. Soc. (London)*, **A69**, 157 (1956).
79. J. G. Conway and B. G. Wybourne, *Phys. Rev.*, **130**, 2325 (1963).
80. J. Sugar, *Johns Hopkins University Spectroscopic Report* No. 22 (1961).
81. R. E. Trees, *J. Opt. Soc. Am.*, **54**, 651 (1964).
82. N. Rosenzweig and C. E. Porter, *Phys. Rev.*, **120**, 1698 (1960).
83. E. P. Wigner, *Oak Ridge Natl. Lab. Report* ORNL-2309 (1956).
84. Hellwege, Hüfner, and Schmidt, *Z. Physik*, **172**, 460 (1963).
85. W. A. Runciman, *J. Chem. Phys.*, **30**, 1632 (1959).
86. W. T. Carnall and B. G. Wybourne, *J. Chem. Phys.*, **40**, 3428 (1964).
87. Blaise, Fred, Gerstenkorn, and Judd, *Compt. rend.*, **255**, 2403 (1962).
88. Bauche, Blaise, and Fred, *Compt. rend.*, **257**, 2260 (1963).
89. J. G. Conway, *J. Chem. Phys.*, **40**, 2504 (1964).
90. P. F. A. Klinkenberg, *Physica*, **16**, 618 (1950).
91. G. Racah, *Physica*, **16**, 651 (1950).
92. Bauche, Blaise, and Fred, *Compt. rend.*, **256**, 5091 (1963).
93. B. G. Wybourne (Unpublished, 1962).
94. Russell, Albertson, and Davis, *Phys. Rev.*, **60**, 641 (1941).
95. W. R. Callahan, *J. Opt. Soc. Am.*, **53**, 695 (1963).
96. W. F. Meggers, *J. Opt. Soc. Am.*, **31**, 157 (1941).
97. B. R. Judd and L. C. Marquet, *J. Opt. Soc. Am.*, **52**, 504 (1962).
98. Z. B. Goldschmidt, *J. Opt. Soc. Am.*, **53**, 594 (1963).
99. M. Fred and F. S. Tomkins, *J. Opt. Soc. Am.*, **47**, 1076 (1957).
100. Schuurmans, Van der Bosch, and Dijkwel, *Physica*, **13**, 117 (1947).
101. Russell, King, and Lang, *Phys. Rev.*, **52**, 456 (1937).
102. N. Spector (Unpublished, 1963).
102a. Kiess, Humphreys, and Laun, *J. Research Natl. Bur. Standards*, **37**, 57 (1946).
103. J. Sugar, *J. Opt. Soc. Am.* (In press).
103a. J. Blaise (Unpublished. See Reference 53).
104. G. Racah, *Phys. Rev.*, **61**, 537 (1942).
105. L. Minnhagen, *Ark. Fys.*, **18**, 97 (1961).
106. N. H. Möller, *Ark. Fys.*, **18**, 135 (1961).
107. G. H. Shortley and B. Fried, *Phys. Rev.*, **54**, 739 (1938).
108. G. Racah, *Lunds Univ. Arsskr.*, **50**, 31 (1954).

109. G. Racah, *J. Opt. Soc. Am.*, **50**, 408 (1960).
110. W. F. Meggers (Unpublished).
111. B. R. Judd, *Proc. Phys. Soc. (London)*, **82**, 874 (1963).
112. K. Rajnak and B. G. Wybourne, *J. Chem. Phys.*, **41**, 565 (1964).
113. J. P. Elliott, *Proc. Roy. Soc. (London)*, **A254**, 128 (1958).
114. *Ibid.*, **A254**, 562 (1958).
115. K. Rajnak and B. G. Wybourne, *Phys. Rev.*, **134**, A596 (1964).
116. H. Horie, *Progr. Theoret. Phys. (Japan)*, **10**, 296 (1953).
117. R. K. Nesbet, *Rev. Mod. Phys.*, **33**, 28 (1961).
118. I. P. Grant, *Proc. Roy. Soc. (London)*, **A262**, 555 (1961).
119. M. E. Rose, *Relativistic Electron Theory*, John Wiley and Sons, New York (1961).
120. A. J. Freeman and R. E. Watson, *Phys. Rev.*, **127**, 2058 (1962).
121. E. C. Ridley, *Proc. Cambridge Phil. Soc.*, **56**, 41 (1960).
122. F. Herman and S. Skillman, *Atomic Structure Calculations*, Prentice-Hall, Englewood Cliffs, New Jersey (1963).
123. J. C. Slater, *Phys. Rev.*, **81**, 385 (1951).
124. S. Cohen, *University of California Lawrence Radiation Laboratory Report* UCRL-8633 (1959).
125. Boyd, Larson, and Waber, *Phys. Rev.*, **129**, 1639 (1963).
126. H. A. Bethe and E. E. Salpeter, *Quantum Mechanics of One- and Two-Electron Atoms*, Academic Press, New York (1957).
127. C. G. Darwin, *Phil. Mag.*, **39**, 537 (1920).
128. S. Yanagawa, *J. Phys. Soc. (Japan)*, **10**, 1029 (1955).
129. B. G. Wybourne *J. Chem. Phys.*, **40**, 1457 (1964).
130. H. Marvin, *Phys. Rev.*, **71**, 102 (1947).
131. F. R. Innes, *Phys. Rev.*, **91**, 31 (1953).
132. G. Araki, *Progr. Theoret. Phys. (Japan)*, **3**, 152 (1948).
133. Aller, Ufford, and Van Vleck, *Astrophys. J.*, **109**, 42 (1949).
134. R. E. Trees, *Phys. Rev.*, **82**, 683 (1951).
135. B. R. Judd, *Proc. Phys. Soc. (London)*, **A69**, 157 (1956).
136. M. Blume and R. E. Watson, *Proc. Roy. Soc. (London)*, **A270**, 127 (1962).
137. *Ibid.*, **A271**, 565 (1962).
138. B. Bleaney, page 595, *Quantum Electronics III*, P. Grivet and N. Bloembergen, Eds., Columbia University Press (1964).
139. Meggers, Corliss, and Scribner, "Tables of Spectral-Line Intensities," *Natl. Bur. Standards, Mono.*, **32**, Pts. I and II, U.S. Government Printing Office, Washington 25, D.C. (1961).
140. C. H. Corliss and W. R. Bozman, "Experimental Transition Probabilities for Spectral-Lines of Seventy Elements," *Natl. Bur. Standards Mono.*, **53**, U.S. Government Printing Office, Washington 25, D.C. (1962).
141. B. M. Glennon and W. L. Wiese, *Natl. Bur. Standards, Mono.*, **50**, U.S. Government Printing Office, Washington 25, D.C. (1962).
142. G. H. Shortley, *Phys. Rev.*, **47**, 295 (1935).
143. C. E. Moore, *J. Appl. Opts.*, **2**, 665 (1963).
144. D. R. Bates and A. Damgaard, *Phil. Trans. Roy. Soc. (London)*, **A242**, 101 (1949).
145. J. Schwinger, *Phys. Rev.*, **73**, 416 (1947).
146. C. M. Sommerfield, *Phys. Rev.*, **107**, 328 (1957).
147. M. Catalan, *J. Research Natl. Bur. Standards*, **47**, 502 (1951).
148. B. G. Wybourne, *J. Opt. Soc. Am.*, **54**, 267 (1964).

149. Hubbs, Marrus, Nierenberg, and Worcester, *Phys. Rev.*, **109**, 390 (1958).
150. Rosen, Harrison, and McNalley, *Phys. Rev.*, **60**, 722 (1941).
151. B. R. Judd and I. Lindgren, *Phys. Rev.*, **122**, 1802 (1961).
152. A. Abragam and J. H. Van Vleck, *Phys. Rev.*, **92**, 1448 (1953).
153. G. Breit, *Phys. Rev.*, **34**, 553 (1929).
154. F. M. J. Pichanick and G. K. Woodgate, *Proc. Roy. Soc. (London)*, **A263**, 89 (1961).
155. R. J. Blin-Stoyle, *Theories of Nuclear Moments*, Oxford University Press, Oxford (1957).
156. C. Schwartz, *Phys. Rev.*, **97**, 380 (1955).
157. A. de-Shalit and I. Talmi, *Nuclear Shell Theory*, Academic Press, New York (1963).
158. N. F. Ramsey, *Nuclear Moments*, John Wiley and Sons, New York (1953).
159. N. F. Ramsey, *Molecular Beams*, Oxford University Press, Oxford (1956).
160. H. Kopfermann, *Nuclear Moments*, 2nd Edition, Academic Press, New York (1958).
161. R. H. Garstang, *J. Opt. Soc. Am.*, **52**, 845 (1962).
162. B. G. Wybourne, *J. Chem. Phys.*, **37**, 1807 (1962).
163. Goodman, Kopfermann, and Schlüpmann, *Naturwissenschaften*, **49**, 101 (1962).
164. B. Bleaney, *Proc. Phys. Soc. (London)*, **A68**, 937 (1955).
165. M. E. Foglio and M. H. L. Pryce, *Mol. Phys.*, **4**, 287 (1961).
166. I. Lindgren, *Nuclear Phys.*, **32**, 151 (1962).
167. R. E. Trees, *Phys. Rev.*, **92**, 308 (1953).
168. H. B. G. Casimir, *On the Interaction between Atomic Nuclei and Electrons*, Teyler's Tweede Genootschap, Haarlem (1936), and W. H. Freeman, San Francisco (1963).
169. H. E. White, *Introduction to Atomic Spectra*, McGraw-Hill Book Company, New York (1934).
170. E. Fermi, *Z. Physik*, **60**, 320 (1930).
171. W. A. Nierenberg, *Ann. Rev. Nuclear Sci.*, **7**, 349 (1957).
172. B. Budick and R. Marrus, *Phys. Rev.*, **132**, 723 (1963).
173. J. Reader and S. P. Davis, *J. Am. Opt. Soc.*, **53**, 431 (1963).
174. P. A. M. Dirac, *The Principles of Quantum Mechanics*, Clarendon Press, Oxford (1930).
175. M. E. Rose, *Relativistic Electron Theory*, John Wiley and Sons, New York (1961).
176. G. Breit and L. A. Wills, *Phys. Rev.*, **44**, 470 (1933).
177. E. Fermi and E. Segre, *Z. Physik*, **82**, 729 (1933).
178. G. Breit, *Phys. Rev.*, **37**, 51 (1931).
179. *Ibid.*, **38**, 463 (1931).
180. G. Racah, *Z. Physik*, **71**, 431 (1931).
181. C. Schwartz, *Phys. Rev.*, **105**, 173 (1957).
182. A. P. Stone, *Proc. Phys. Soc. (London)*, **77**, 786 (1961).
183. *Ibid.*, **81**, 868 (1963).
184. I. N. Sneddon, *Special Functions of Mathematical Physics and Chemistry*, Interscience Publishers, New York (1956).
185. G. N. Watson, *Theory of Bessel Functions*, Cambridge University Press, New York (1952).
186. G. Racah, *Nuovo Cimento*, **8**, 178 (1931).
187. W. R. S. Garton, *J. Quant. Spectroscopy Radiation Transfer*, **2**, 335 (1963).

188. R. F. Christy and J. M. Keller, *Phys. Rev.*, **61**, 147 (1942).

189. M. F. Crawford and A. L. Schawlow, *Phys. Rev.*, **76**, 1310 (1949).

190. J. E. Rosenthal and G. Breit, *Phys. Rev.*, **41**, 459 (1932).

191. G. Racah, *Nature*, **129**, 723 (1932).

192. H. T. Davis, *Tables of the Higher Mathematical Functions*, The Principia Press, Bloomington, Indiana (1933).

193. A. H. Wapstra, *Handbuch der Physik*, **XXXVIII/I**, 1 (1958).

194. L. R. B. Elton, *Nuclear Sizes*, Oxford University Press, Oxford (1961).

195. A. Bohr and V. F. Weisskopf, *Phys. Rev.*, **77**, 94 (1950).

196. A. Bohr, *Phys. Rev.*, **81**, 331 (1951).

197. D. S. Hughes and C. Eckart, *Phys. Rev.*, **36**, 694 (1930).

198. E. W. Foster, *Rept. Progr. Phys.* (*London*), **14**, 228 (1951).

199. J. E. Mack and O. H. Arroe, *Ann. Rev. Nuclear Sci.*, **6**, 117 (1956).

200. L. Wilets, *Handbuch der Physik*, **XXXVII/I**, 96 (1958).

201. G. Breit, *Rev. Mod. Phys.*, **30**, 507 (1958).

202. W. Pauli and R. Peierls, *Z. Physik*, **32**, 670 (1931).

203. J. H. Bartlett, *Nature*, **128**, 408 (1931).

204. L. Wilets and L. C. Bradley, *Phys. Rev.*, **87**, 1018 (1952).

205. L. C. Marquet and S. P. Davis (Unpublished, 1963).

206. A. R. Bodmer, *Proc. Phys. Soc.* (*London*), **A66**, 1041 (1953).

207. *Ibid.*, **A67**, 622 (1954).

208. A. R. Bodmer, *Nuclear Phys.*, **21**, 347 (1960).

209. E. K. Broch, *Arch. Math. Naturvidenskab.*, **48**, 25 (1945).

210. A. S. Meligy, *Nuclear Phys.*, **16**, 99 (1960).

211. Hahn, Ravenhall, and Hofstader, *Phys. Rev.*, **101**, 1131 (1956).

212. R. Hofstader, *Rev. Mod. Phys.*, **28**, 214 (1949).

213. P. Brix and H. Kopfermann, *Z. Physik*, **126**, 344 (1949).

214. *Ibid.*, *Festschr. Akad. Wiss. Göttingen, Math-Phys. Kl.*, **17** (1951).

215. A. Bohr and B. R. Mottelson, *Mat. Fys. Medd. Dan. Vid. Selsk.*, **27**, No. 16 (1953).

216. B. R. Mottelson and S. G. Nilsson, *ibid.*, **L**, No. 8 (1959).

217. Wilets, Hill and Ford, *Phys. Rev.*, **91**, 1488 (1953).

218. P. G. H. Sandars and G. K. Woodgate, *Proc. Roy. Soc.* (*London*), **A257**, 269 (1960).

219. Meligy, Tadros, and El-Wahab, *Nuclear Phys.*, **16**, 99 (1960).

220. N. J. Ionesco-Pallas, *Ann. Physik*, **7**, 9 (1960).

221. Breit, Arfken, and Clendenin, *Phys. Rev.*, **78**, 390 (1950).

222. Pichanick, Sandars, and Woodgate, *Proc. Roy. Soc.* (*London*), **A257**, 277 (1960).

223. J. M. Baker and F. J. B. Williams, *Proc. Roy. Soc.* (*London*), **A267**, 283 (1962).

224. Abraham, Kedzie, and Jefferies, *Phys. Rev.*, **108**, 58 (1957).

225. S. S. Alpert, *Phys. Rev.*, **129**, 1344 (1963).

226. Abragam, Horowitz, and Pryce, *Proc. Roy. Soc.* (*London*), **A230**, 169 (1955).

227. V. Heine, *Phys. Rev.*, **107**, 1002 (1957).

228. Judd, Lovejoy, and Shirley, *Phys. Rev.*, **128**, 1733 (1962).

229. R. M. Sternheimer, *Phys. Rev.*, **80**, 102 (1950).

230. *Ibid.*, **84**, 244 (1951).

231. *Ibid.*, **86**, 316 (1952).

232. *Ibid.*, **95**, 736 (1954).

233. *Ibid.*, **105**, 158 (1957).

234. G. J. Ritter, *Phys. Rev.*, **126**, 240 (1962).

235. F. R. Petersen, *University of California Lawrence Radiation Laboratory Report* UCRL-9480 (1960).
236. I. J. Spalding, *Proc. Phys. Soc. (London)*, **81**, 156 (1963).
237. Woodgate, Pichanick, and Sandars, *Brookhaven Molecular Beams Conference* (Unpublished, 1962).
238. Marrus, Nierenberg, and Winocur, *Phys. Rev.*, **120**, 1429 (1960).
239. J. Bauche and B. R. Judd, *Proc. Phys. Soc. (London)*, **83**, 145 (1964).
240. R. E. Watson and A. J. Freeman, *Phys. Rev.*, **131**, 250 (1962).
241. A. J. Freeman and R. E. Watson, *Phys. Rev.*, **131**, 2566 (1963).
242. *Ibid.*, **132**, 706 (1963).
243. J. R. Zacharias, *Phys. Rev.*, **61**, 270 (1942).
244. I. Lindgren, "Tables of Nuclear Spins and Moments" in *Perturbed Angular Correlations*, page 379, Karlsson, Matthias and Siegbahn, Eds., North-Holland Publishing Company, Amsterdam (1964).
245. W. A. Runciman, *Rept. Progr. Phys.*, **21**, 30 (1958).
246. D. S. McClure, *Solid State Physics*, **9**, 399 (1959).
247. G. H. Dieke, *Quantum Electronics*, page 164, S. F. Singer, Ed., Columbia University Press, New York (1960).
248. G. H. Dieke and H. M. Crosswhite, *J. Appl. Opt.*, **2**, 675 (1963).
249. H. A. Kramers, *Proc. Amsterdam Acad.*, **33**, 959 (1930).
250. M. G. Klein, *Am. J. Phys.*, **20**, 65 (1952).
251. K. W. H. Stevens, *Proc. Phys. Soc. (London)*, **A65**, 209 (1952).
252. R. J. Elliott and K. W. H. Stevens, *Proc. Roy. Soc. (London)*, **A219**, 387 (1953).
253. R. J. Elliott and K. W. H. Stevens, *Proc. Roy. Soc. (London)*, **A218**, 553 (1953).
254. B. R. Judd, *Proc. Roy. Soc. (London)*, **A227**, 552 (1955).
255. R. J. Elliott and K. W. H. Stevens, *Proc. Roy. Soc. (London)*, **A219**, 387 (1953).
256. W. Moffitt and C. J. Ballhausen, *Ann. Rev. Phys. Chem.*, **7**, 107 (1950).
257. P. George and D. S. McClure, *Progr. Inorg. Chem.*, **1**, 381 (1959).
258. C. J. Ballhausen, *Introduction to Ligand Field Theory*, McGraw-Hill Book Company, New York (1962).
259. B. R. Judd, *Proc. Roy. Soc. (London)*, **A250**, 562 (1959).
260. B. R. Judd, *Proc. Phys. Soc. (London)*, **74**, 330 (1959).
261. B. R. Judd, *Mol. Phys.*, **2**, 407 (1959).
262. B. R. Judd, *Proc. Roy. Soc. (London)*, **A241**, 122 (1957).
263. Templeton, Zalkin, and Forrester, *J. Chem. Phys.*, **39**, 2881 (1963).
264. K. H. Hellwege, *Ann. Physik*, **4**, 95 (1949).
265. H. Weyl, *Gruppentheorie und Quantenmechanik*, S. Hirzel Verlag, Leipzig (1931); translated by H. P. Robertson, *The Theory of Groups and Quantum Mechanics*, reprinted by Dover Publication, New York.
266. E. P. Wigner, *Group Theory and Its Applications to the Quantum Mechanics of Atomic Spectra*, Academic Press, New York (1959).
267. V. Heine, *Group Theory in Quantum Mechanics*, Pergamon Press, New York (1960).
268. M. Hamermesh, *Group Theory*, Addison-Wesley Publishing Company, Reading, Mass. (1962).
269. C. M. Herzfeld and P. H. E. Meijer, "Group Theory and Crystal Field Theory," *Solid State Physics*, **12**, 1 (1961).
270. H. A. Bethe, *Ann. Physik*, **3**, 133 (1929); translated as *Splitting of Terms in Crystals*, Consultants Bureau, New York (1958).

271. Eyring, Walter and Kimball, *Quantum Chemistry*, John Wiley and Sons, New York (1954).

272. Koster, Dimmock, Wheeler, and Statz, *Properties of the Thirty-Two Point Groups*, M.I.T. Press, Cambridge, Mass. (1963).

273. F. A. Cotton, *Chemical Applications of Group Theory*, John Wiley and Sons, New York (1963).

274. J. L. Prather, "Atomic Energy Levels in Crystals," *Natl. Bur. Standards Mono.*, **19**, U.S. Government Printing Office, Washington, D.C. (1961).

275. W. Opechowski, *Physica*, **7**, 552 (1940).

276. W. A. Runciman, *Phil. Mag.* (8), **1**, 1075 (1956).

277. Oshima, Hayakawa, Nagano, and Nagusa, *J. Chem. Phys.*, **24**, 903 (1956).

278. C. K. Jørgensen, *Absorption Spectra and Chemical Bonding in Complexes*, Addison-Wesley Publishing Company, Reading, Mass. (1962).

279. C. K. Jørgensen, *Orbitals in Atoms and Molecules*, Academic Press, New York (1962).

280. B. R. Judd, *Proc. Roy. Soc. (London)*, **A232**, 458 (1955).

281. A. Speiser, *Die Theorie der Gruppen von Endlicher Ordnung*, Birkhauser Verlag Base (1956).

282. H. S. M. Coxeter, *Regular Polytopes*, Pitman, New York (1948).

283. F. Klein, *The Icosahedron*, Dover Publications, New York (1956).

284. B. R. Judd and E. Y. Wong, *J. Chem. Phys.*, **28**, 1097 (1958).

285. A. G. McLellan, *J. Chem. Phys.*, **34**, 1350 (1961).

286. J. Brochard and K. H. Hellwege, *Z. Physik*, **135**, 620 (1953).

287. G. H. Dieke and L. Heroux, *Phys. Rev.*, **103**, 1227 (1956).

288. G. H. Dieke and L. Heroux, *U.S. Atomic Energy Commission Report*, NYO-3977 (1955).

289. B. M. Tinsley, *J. Chem. Phys.*, **39**, 3503 (1963).

290. Wilson, Decius, and Cross, *Molecular Vibrations*, McGraw-Hill Book Company, (1955).

291. R. L. White and J. P. Andelin, *Phys. Rev.*, **115**, 1435 (1959).

292. K. A. Wickersheim and R. L. White, *Phys. Rev. Letters*, **4**, 123 (1960).

293. R. Pappalardo and D. L. Wood, *J. Chem. Phys.*, **33**, 1734 (1960).

294. R. Pappalardo, *Il Nuovo Cimento* (X), **26**, 748 (1963).

295. R. Pappalardo, *Z. Physik*, **173**, 374 (1963).

296. J. A. A. Ketelaar, *Physica*, **4**, 619 (1937).

297. E. V. Sayre and S. Freed, *J. Chem. Phys.*, **24**, 1213 (1956).

298. K. H. Hellwege, *Nachr. Akad. Wiss. Göttingen Math. Physik*, **K1**, 58 (1947).

299. J. S. Margolis, *J. Chem. Phys.*, **35**, 1367 (1961).

300. P. H. E. Meijer, *Phys. Rev.*, **95**, 1443 (1954).

301. S. Hüfner, *Z. Physik*, **172**, 512 (1963).

302. J. M. Baker and B. Bleaney, *Proc. Roy. Soc. (London)*, **A245**, 156 (1958).

303. G. J. Koster and H. Statz, *Phys. Rev.*, **113**, 445 (1959).

304. H. Statz and G. F. Koster, *Phys. Rev.*, **115**, 1568 (1959).

305. J. D. Axe and G. H. Dieke, *J. Chem. Phys.*, **37**, 2364 (1962).

306. Z. K. Chow, *Z. Physik*, **124**, 62 (1947).

307. G. H. Dieke and H. M. Crosswhite, *J. Opt. Soc. Am.*, **46**, 885 (1956).

308. G. H. Dieke and L. Leopold, *J. Opt. Soc. Am.*, **47**, 944 (1957).

309. Sayre, Sancier, and Freed, *J. Chem. Phys.*, **23**, 2060 (1955).

310. *Ibid.*, **29**, 242 (1958).

311. G. H. Dieke and R. Sarup, *J. Chem. Phys.*, **29**, 741 (1958).

312. J. C. Eisenstein, *J. Chem. Phys.*, **39**, 2134 (1963).
313. E. H. Carlson, *Johns Hopkins Spectroscopic Report* No. **18**, (1960).
314. E. H. Carlson and G. H. Dieke, *J. Chem. Phys.*, **34**, 1602 (1961).
315. F. Varsanyi and G. H. Dieke, *J. Chem. Phys.*, **33**, 1616 (1960).
316. J. G. Conway and J. B. Gruber, *J. Chem. Phys.*, **32**, 1586 (1960).
317. J. B. Gruber and J. G. Conway, *J. Inorg. Nuclear Chem.*, **14**, 303 (1960).
318. G. W. Parker and P. M. Lantz, *J. Am. Chem. Soc.*, **72**, 2834 (1950).
319. Meggers, Scribner, and Bozman, *J. Research Natl. Bur. Standards*, **46**, 85 (1951).
320. D. S. Stewart, *Argonne National Laboratory Report*, ANL-4812 (1956).
321. H. Lämmermann, *Z. Physik*, **150**, 551 (1958).
322. *Ibid.*, **160**, 355 (1960).
323. Friederich, Hellwege, and Lämmermann, *Z. Physik*, **158**, 251 (1960).
324. *Ibid.*, **159**, 524 (1960).
325. M. S. Magno and G. H. Dieke, *J. Chem. Phys.*, **37**, 2354 (1962).
326. G. S. Ofelt, *J. Chem. Phys.*, **38**, 2171 (1963).
327. L. G. De Shazer and G. H. Dieke, *J. Chem. Phys.*, **38**, 2190 (1963).
328. B. G. Wybourne (Unpublished, 1963).
329. Hellwege, Hüfner, and Schmidt, *Z. Physik*, **172**, 460 (1963).
330. Thomas, Singh, and Dieke, *J. Chem. Phys.*, **38**, 2180 (1963).
331. A. M. Rosa, *Ann. Physik*, **43**, 161 (1943).
332. G. H. Dieke and S. Singh, *J. Opt. Soc. Am.*, **46**, 495 (1956).
333. H. M. Crosswhite and G. H. Dieke, *J. Chem. Phys.*, **35**, 1535 (1961).
334. G. Gramberg, *Z. Physik*, **159**, 125 (1960).
335. H. Gobrecht, *Ann. Physik*, (5) **28**, 673 (1937).
336. G. Rosenthal, *Phys. Z.*, **40**, 5 (1959).
337. H. Severin, *Z. Physik*, **125**, 455 (1949).
338. H. G. Kahle, *Z. Physik*, **145**, 347 (1956).
339. C. K. Jørgensen, *Acta. Chem. Scand.*, **11**, 981 (1957).
340. J. C. Eisenstein, *J. Chem. Phys.*, **39**, 2128 (1963).
341. G. H. Dieke and S. Singh, *J. Chem. Phys.*, **35**, 555 (1961).
342. F. Varsanyi and G. H. Dieke, *J. Chem. Phys.*, **36**, 2951 (1962).
343. J. S. Margolis, *University of California, Los Angeles, Department of Physics Technical Report* No. **1**, (1960).
344. H. Gobrecht, *Ann. Physik*, **7**, 88 (1950).
345. H. A. Bethe and F. H. Spedding, *Phys. Rev.*, **52**, 454 (1937).
347. W. A. Runciman and B. G. Wybourne, *J. Chem. Phys.*, **31**, 149 (1959).
348. W. Marshall and R. Stuart, *Phys. Rev.*, **123**, 2048 (1961).
349. E. Y. Wong and I. Richman, *J. Chem. Phys.*, **36**, 1889 (1961).
350. *Ibid.*, **37**, 2498 (1962).
351. I. Richman and E. Y. Wong, *J. Chem. Phys.*, **37**, 2270 (1962).
352. Wong, Stafsudd and Johnson, *ibid.*, **39**, 786 (1963).
353. R. D. McLaughlin and J. G. Conway, *ibid.*, **38**, 1037 (1963).
354. K. M. Sancier and S. Freed, *ibid.*, **20**, 349 (1962).
355. H. Lämmermann and J. G. Conway, *ibid.*, **38**, 259 (1963).
356. J. G. Conway, *ibid.*, **40**, 2504 (1964).
357. J. B. Gruber, *ibid.*, **35**, 2186 (1961).
358. J. B. Gruber and J. G. Conway, *ibid.*, **36**, 191 (1962).
359. J. B. Gruber, *J. Inorg. Nuclear Chem.*, **25**, 1093 (1963).
360. B. G. Wybourne, *J. Chem. Phys.*, **40**, 1456 (1964).
361. W. T. Carnall and P. R. Fields, *J. Am. Chem. Soc.*, **81**, 4445 (1959).

362. Yost, Russell, and Garner, *The Rare-Earth Elements and Their Compounds*, John Wiley and Sons, New York (1947).
363. Z. Kiss, *Phys. Rev.*, **127**, 718 (1962).
364. W. Hayes and J. W. Twidell, *Proc. Phys. Soc.* (*London*), **79**, 1295 (1962).
365. Hayes, Jones and Twidell, *ibid.*, **81**, 371 (1963).
366. F. D. S. Butement, *Trans. Far. Soc.*, **44**, 667 (1948).
367. J. Sugar, *J. Opt. Soc., Am.* (in press, 1964).
368. J. D. Axe and P. P. Sorokin, *Phys. Rev.*, **130**, 945 (1963).
369. P. P. Feofilov, *Optika i Spectroskopiya*, **1**, 992 (1956).
370. *Ibid.*, *Zapiski Usesoyuy Mineral Obachestra*, **85**, 569 (1956).
371. P. P. Sorokin and M. J. Stevenson, *I.B.M. J. Research and Devlp.*, **5**, 56 (1961).
372. Garrett, Kaiser, and Wood, *Phys. Rev.*, **123**, 766 (1961).
373. Sorokin, Stevenson, Linkard, and Pettit, *ibid.*, **127**, 503 (1962).
374. W. A. Runciman and C. V. Stager, *J. Chem. Phys.*, **37**, 196 (1962).
375. G. H. Dieke and R. Sarup, *ibid.*, **36**, 371 (1962).
376. D. L. Wood and W. Kaiser, *Phys. Rev.*, **126**, 2079 (1962).
377. N. Rabbiner, *Phys. Rev.*, **132**, 224 (1963).
378. P. P. Feofilov and A. A. Kaplyanskii, *Optics and Spectroscopy*, **12**, 272 (1962).
379. A. A. Kaplyanskii and A. K. Przhevuskii, *ibid.*, **13**, 508 (1962).
380. B. P. Zakharchenya and A. Y. Ryskin, *ibid.*, **13**, 501 (1962).
381. S. Freed and S. Katcoff, *Physica*, **14**, 17 (1948).
382. W. A. Runciman and C. V. Stager, *J. Chem. Phys.*, **38**, 279 (1963).
383. B. P. Zakharchenya and A. Y. Ryskin, *Optics and Spectroscopy*, **13**, 162 (1962).
384. A. A. Kaplyanskii and P. P. Feofilov, *ibid.*, **13**, 129 (1962).
385. P. P. Feofilov, *ibid.*, **12**, 296 (1962).
386. Kiss, Lewis, and Duncan, *Appl. Phys. Letters*, **2**, 93 (1963).
387. Agrawal, Asundi, Naik, Ramakrishnan, and Singh, *Proc. Indian Acad. Sci.*, **55**, 106 (1962).
388. J. T. Hougen and S. Singh, *Phys. Rev. Letters*, **10**, 406 (1963).
389. *Ibid.*, *Proc. Roy. Soc.* (*London*), **A277**, 193 (1964).
390. Makovsky, Low, and Yatsiv, *Phys. Letters*, **2**, 186 (1962).
391. B. R. Judd, *Proc. Roy. Soc.* (*London*), **A241**, 414 (1957).
392. J. C. Eisenstein in *Symposium on Paramagnetic Resonance*, Vol. I, page 253, W. Low, Ed., Academic Press, New York (1963).
393. J. B. Gruber, *J. Chem. Phys.*, **38**, 946 (1963).
394. E. Y. Wong (Unpublished). See Reference 352.
395. Hellwege, Hess, and Kahle, *Z. Physik*, **159**, 333 (1960).
396. J. B. Gruber and R. A. Satten, *J. Chem. Phys.*, **39**, 1455 (1963).
397. M. J. D. Powell and R. Orbach, *Proc. Phys. Soc.* (*London*), **78**, 753 (1961).
398. E. V. Sayre and S. Freed, *J. Chem. Phys.*, **24**, 1213 (1956).
399. S. Hüfner, *Z. Physik*, **169**, 417 (1962).
400. H. G. Kahle and H. Kalbfleisch, *ibid.*, **166**, 184 (1962).
401. Grohmann, Hellwege, and Kahle, *ibid.*, **164**, 243 (1961).
402. S. Hüfner, *ibid.*, **169**, 427 (1962).
403. E. H. Erath, *J. Chem. Phys.*, **34**, 1985 (1961).
404. Hellwege, Hüfner, and Kahle, *Z. Physik*, **160**, 149 (1960).
405. E. Y. Wong, *J. Chem. Phys.*, **39**, 2781 (1963).
406. E. Y. Wong and I. Richman, *ibid.*, **34**, 1182 (1961).
407. J. B. Gruber and J. G. Conway, *ibid.*, **32**, 1178 (1960).
408. J. B. Gruber and J. G. Conway, *ibid.*, **32**, 1531 (1960).

409. Axe, Stapelton, and Jeffries, *Phys. Rev.* **121**, 1630 (1961).
410. J. D. Axe, *University California Radiation Laboratory Report*, UCRL-9293 (1960).
411. J. G. Conway, *J. Chem. Phys.*, **31**, 1002 (1959).
412. Satten, Young, and Gruen, *ibid.*, **33**, 1140 (1960).
413. S. A. Pollack and R. A. Satten, *ibid.*, **36**, 804 (1962).
414. R. McLaughlin, *ibid.*, **36**, 2699 (1962).
415. Title, Sorokin, Stevenson, Pettit, Scarfield, and Lankard, *Phys. Rev.*, **128**, 62 (1962).
416. R. C. L. Mooney, *Acta Cryst.*, **2**, 189 (1949).
417. L. E. Orgel, *An Introduction to Transition-Metal Chemistry*, John Wiley and Sons, New York (1960).
418. L. Pauling, *The Nature of the Chemical Bond*, 2nd edition, Oxford University Press, Oxford (1940).
419. J. C. Eisenstein, *J. Chem. Phys.*, **25**, 142 (1956).
420. E. Y. Wong and E. H. Erath, *ibid.*, **39**, 1629 (1963).
421. Richman, Satten, and Wong, *ibid.*, **39**, 1833 (1963).
422. R. A. Satten, *ibid.*, **40**, 1200 (1964).
423. Murphy, Caspers, and Buchanan, *ibid.*, **40**, 743 (1964).
424. N. Krishnamurthy and R. S. Krishnan, *Proc. Indian Acad. Sci.*, **A57**, 352 (1963).
425. Bleaney, Elliott, Scovil, and Trenan, *Phil. Mag.*, **42**, 1062 (1951).
426. G. S. Bogle and V. Heine, *Proc. Phys. Soc. (London)*, **A67**, 734 (1954).
427. M. Weger and W. Low, *Phys. Rev.*, **111**, 1526 (1958).
428. Hutchison, Judd, and Pope, *Proc. Roy. Soc. (London)*, **B70**, 541 (1957).
429. W. Low and D. Shaltiel, *J. Phys. Chem. Solids*, **6**, 315 (1958).
430. Jones, Baker, and Pope, *Proc. Phys. Soc. (London)*, **74**, 249 (1959).
431. J. H. Van Vleck and W. G. Penney, *Phil. Mag.*, **17**, 961 (1934).
432. M. H. L. Pryce, *Phys. Rev.*, **80**, 1106 (1950).
433. A. Abragam and M. H. L. Pryce, *Proc. Roy. Soc. (London)*, **A205**, 135 (1951).
434. R. J. Elliott and K. W. H. Stevens, *ibid.*, **A219**, 387 (1953).
435. Abraham, Judd, and Wickman, *Phys. Rev.*, **130**, 611 (1963).
436. J. H. Van Vleck, *J. Phys. Chem.*, **41**, 67 (1937).
437. Broer, Gorter, and Hoogschagen, *Physica*, **11**, 231 (1945).
438. B. R. Judd, *Phys. Rev.*, **127**, 750 (1962).
439. G. S. Ofelt, *J. Chem. Phys.*, **37**, 511 (1962).
440. J. D. Axe, *ibid.*, **39**, 1154 (1963).
441. S. Pasternack, *Astrophys. J.*, **92**, 129 (1940).
442. G. H. Shortley, *Phys. Rev.*, **57**, 225 (1940).
443. Sayre, Sancier, and Freed, *J. Chem. Phys.*, **23**, 2060 (1955).
444. C. K. Jørgensen and B. R. Judd, *Mol. Phys.* (In press).
445. R. H. Garstang, *Proc. Camb. Phil. Soc.*, **53**, 214 (1957).
446. C. A. Hutchison and E. Y. Wong, *J. Chem. Phys.*, **29**, 754 (1958).
447. G. Burns, *Phys. Rev.*, **128**, 2121 (1962).
448. M. T. Hutchings and D. K. Ray, *Proc. Phys. Soc. (London)*, **81**, 663 (1963).
449. B. Bleaney, *Proc. Roy. Soc. (London)*, **A277**, 289 (1964).
450. D. H. Templeton and C. H. Dauber, *J. Amer. Chem. Soc.*, **76**, 5237 (1954).
451. W. H. Zachariasen, *J. Chem. Phys.*, **16**, 254 (1948).
452. C. J. Lenander and E. Y. Wong, *ibid.*, **38**, 2750 (1963).
453. D. K. Ray, *Proc. Phys. Soc. (London)*, **82**, 47 (1963).
454. R. E. Watson and A. J. Freeman, *Phys. Rev.*, **133**, A1571 (1964).

455. Judd, Lovejoy, and Shirley, *Phys. Rev.*, **128**, 1733 (1962).
456. D. T. Edmonds, *Phys. Rev. Letters*, **10**, 129 (1963).
457. J. Blok and D. A. Shirley, *J. Chem. Phys.*, **39**, 1128 (1963).
458. A. J. Freeman and R. E. Watson, *Phys. Rev.*, **132**, 706 (1963).
459. Barnes, Kankeleit, Mossbauer, and Pointdexter, *Phys. Rev. Letters*, **11**, 253 (1963).
460. Hüfner, Kalvius, Kienle, Wiedmann, and Eicher, *Z. Physik*, **175**, 416 (1963).
461. R. L. Mossbauer, *Rev. Mod. Phys.*, **36**, 362 (1964).
462. F. Varsanyi and G. H. Dieke, *Phys. Rev. Letters*, **7**, 442 (1962).
463. G. H. Dieke and E. Dorman, *ibid.*, **11**, 17 (1963).
464. F. Varsanyi, *ibid.*, **11**, 314 (1963).
465. Holloway, Kestigian, and Newman, *ibid.*, **11**, 458 (1963).
467. A. Y. Cabezas and L. G. De Shazer, *Appl. Phys. Letters*, **4**, 37 (1964).
468. D. L. Dexter, *Phys. Rev.*, **126**, 1962 (1963).
469. Van Uitert, Linares, Soden, and Ballman, *J. Chem. Phys.*, **36**, 702 (1962).
470. F. Varsanyi and G. H. Dieke, *ibid.*, **31**, 1066 (1957).
471. L. Katzin and L. Barnett, *J. Phys. Chem.* (To be published 1964).
472. J. M. Baker and J. P. Hurrell, *Proc. Phys. Soc. (London)*, **82**, 742 (1963).
473. C. K. Jørgensen, *Phys. Stat. Solids*, **2**, 1146 (1962).
474. *Ibid., Progr. Inorg. Chem.*, **4**, 73 (1962).
475. *Ibid., Faraday Soc. Disc.*, **26**, 110 (1958).
476. J. H. Van Vleck, *J. Chem. Phys.*, **3**, 803 (1935).
477. *Ibid.*, **3**, 807 (1935).
478. J. C. Eisenstein, *J. Chem. Phys.*, **25**, 142 (1956).
479. H. S. Jarrett, *ibid.*, **31**, 1579 (1959).
480. Jørgensen, Pappalardo, and Schmidtke, *ibid.*, **39**, 1422 (1963).
481. M. Wolfsberg and L. Helmholz, *ibid.*, **20**, 837 (1952).
482. J. C. Phillips, *J. Phys. Chem. Solids*, **11**, 226 (1959).
483. W. H. Kleiner, *J. Chem. Phys.*, **20**, 1784 (1952).
484. L. E. Orgel, *ibid.*, **23**, 1819 (1955).
485. L. L. Lohr and W. N. Lipscomb, *ibid.*, **38**, 1607 (1963).
486. S. Sugano and R. G. Shulman, *Phys. Rev.*, **130**, 517 (1963).
487. R. E. Watson and A. J. Freeman, *Phys. Rev.*, **134**, A1526 (1964).

Index